Mrs Farmon Foote

a block 1 ft long 1 ft wide 1 ft thick = 1 cu ft

" " 6 " " " " " " = 6 " "

" " 6 " " 1 " " " " = 6×3 = 18 " "

" " 6 " " 3 " " " " 3 " " = 18×3 = 54 " "

Miss Barbra Cullar
Walkerton
Ind.

Mr L1arren or Foote
South Bend
Ind

PREFACE.

It is now thirteen years since the first issue of the author's Complete Arithmetic, which has been used from that time to the present with increasing satisfaction in thousands of American schools. In all this time there has been little demand for its revision, and the changes suggested from time to time have been comparatively unimportant. It is believed that few text-books have more satisfactorily met the test of wide and continued use—the best possible test of a school book.

But the demand for a **two-book series,** which called for a new first book (the "Elementary"), has afforded an opportunity for a revision of the Complete Arithmetic, and this has been improved, not only with a view of better adapting it to its place as the second book in the new series, but also of bringing it fully up to the present condition of school instruction and of business. In this revision neither author nor publishers have spared expense or labor required to make the **New Complete Arithmetic** worthy of general use in the most progressive schools of the country.

The most important change made in the revision is a large increase in the number of **practical problems,** and this has been done without any reduction in the aggregate number of purely drill problems. This increase in practical problems is most marked in Mensuration and the applications of Percentage, including stock investments. There is an increase in the number of review problems in all parts of the book, and there is no reduction in the number and variety of the oral problems. A few of the more difficult problems, oral and written, have been omitted. It has been the aim to eliminate all obsolete terms

(iii)

and measures, and to present the current values, forms, and usages of business. To this end, the author has gone to science and to the most recent statistics for data for problems, and to business men for present business usages.

Special attention is called to the new treatment of the Metric System. The omission of formal tables and the presentation of the metric denominations on the decimal scale will meet the hearty approval of teachers.

The characteristics that have given the author's arithmetics wide and successful use, are preserved in the new two-book series. These include:

1. A special adaptation, in matter and method, to the grades of pupils for which each book is designed.

2. A practical union of oral and written exercises in a natural and philosophic system of instruction.

3. A true and practical embodiment of the inductive method, in which definitions, principles, and rules follow processes and problems.

4. The great number and variety and the practical character of the problems, a feature in which the new series is believed to be without an equal.

The author acknowledges his indebtedness to Prof. J. C. GREENOUGH, Principal of the State Normal School of Rhode Island, and to other eminent teachers, for valuable assistance in the work of revision.

PURDUE UNIVERSITY,
Lafayette, Ind., June 12, 1883.

CONTENTS.

INTEGERS.

FRACTIONS.

DECIMAL FRACTIONS.

UNITED STATES MONEY.

DENOMINATE NUMBERS.

MENSURATION.

PERCENTAGE.

ANALYSIS.

RATIO AND PROPORTION.

INVOLUTION AND EVOLUTION.

GENERAL REVIEW.

APPENDIX.

WHITE'S

NEW COMPLETE ARITHMETIC

ARTICLE 1. A **Unit** is one.

ART. 2. A **Number** is a unit or a collection of units.

ART. 3. **Arithmetic** is the science and the art of numbers.

As a *science*, arithmetic treats of the properties, relations, and principles of numbers; as an *art*, it treats of numerical computation.

ART. 4. An **Integer** is a number composed of whole or entire units; as, 5, 12, 20. It is also called a *Whole Number*.

An integer is composed of integral units, and a fraction is composed of fractional units (Art. 72.)

ART. 5. Numbers are either *Concrete* or *Abstract*.

A **Concrete Number** is applied to a particular thing or quantity; as, 4 stars, 6 hours.

(7)

An **Abstract Number** is not applied to a particular thing or quantity; as, 4, 6, 20.

A concrete number is composed of concrete units; and an abstract number, of abstract units.

ART. 6. A **Problem** is a question proposed for solution.

ART. 7. An **Example** is a problem used to illustrate a process or a principle.

ART. 8. A **Rule** is a general description of a process.

ART. 9. In the **Written Solution** of a problem, the results of the successive steps are written.

In the **Mental Solution** of a problem, the results of the successive steps are not written.

NUMERATION AND NOTATION.

ORAL EXERCISES.

1. How many tens and how many units in 37? 65? 84? 90? 75? 18? 60? 80?

2. Read 29; 47; 85; 70; 77; 90.

3. How many hundreds, tens, and units in 368? 427? 549? 608? 680? 600? 806? 860? 800?

4. Read 452; 506; 560; 600; 784; 690; 900; 909.

5. How many ten-thousands and how many thousands in 48500? 83250? 50400? 60070? 82405?

6. Read 37500; 84250; 70840; 92080; 90900.

7. How many hundred-thousands, ten-thousands, and thousands in 456048? 707803? 680435? 700450? 650048? 805347? 170480?

8. Read the thousands' period in 3045; 40607; 150482; 405360; 920400; 600060; 508320.

9. Read first the thousands' period and then the units' period in 65671; 120408; 400750; 650400; 80008.

10. Read 45037406; 520600480; 138405050.

11. Read 50008140; 600650508; 805000030.

12. Read 5308008450; 35006060600; 120500408080.

13. Read 7008360004; 302000860060; 500080800008.

WRITTEN EXERCISES.

14. Express in figures the number composed of 5 thousands, 7 tens, and 3 units.

15. Express in figures the number composed of 4 ten-thousands, 6 hundreds, and 5 units.

16. Express in figures 50 thousands and 40 units; 406 thousands and 30 units; 700 thousands and 7 units; 650 thousands and 13 units.

Express the following numbers in figures:

17. Five million five thousand five hundred.

18. Sixty million sixty thousand and sixty.

19. Seven hundred million seven hundred thousand seven hundred.

20. Five hundred sixty million sixty-eight thousand.

21. Four billion fourteen million forty-five thousand.

22. Sixty-five billion six thousand and fifty.

23. Three hundred fifty billion forty-nine million.

24. Seventeen trillion seventy billion seven hundred thousand four hundred.

25. Fifty-six trillion sixteen million and ninety.

26. Seven quadrillion eighty-five billion two hundred and four.

27. Eighty-five billion fifteen thousand.

28. Ninety million nine hundred fifty.

DEFINITIONS, PRINCIPLES, AND RULES.

ART. 10. There are three methods of expressing numbers, viz:

1. By *words;* as, five, fifty, etc.
2. By *letters*, called the *Roman* method.
3. By *figures*, called the *Arabic* method.

ART. 11. In the Roman Notation, numbers are expressed by means of the seven *capital letters*, I, V, X, L, C, D, M.

I denotes one; V, five; X, ten; L, fifty; C, one hundred; D, five hundred; M, one thousand. All other numbers are expressed by repeating or combining these letters.

A bar placed over a letter, as $\overline{D}$, $\overline{M}$, multiplies its value by one thousand.

ART. 12. In the Arabic Notation, numbers are expressed by means of characters called *figures*. There are ten figures; viz, 0, 1, 2, 3, 4, 5, 6, 7, 8, 9.

The first (0) is called *Naught, Cipher,* or *Zero,* and is used to fill vacant orders. The other nine figures are called *Significant Figures*, and each denotes one or more units. They are also called *Digits*.

ART. 13. Notation is the art of expressing numbers by figures or letters.

ART. 14. Numeration is the art of reading numbers expressed by figures or letters.

The term Notation is commonly used to denote the writing of numbers by figures; and Numeration, the reading of numbers expressed by figures.

ART. 15. The successive figures which express a number denote successive *Orders of Units*. These orders are numbered from the right, as *first, second, third, fourth,* and so on.

ART. 16. A figure standing in the first order denotes ones or *units;* in the second order, *tens;* in the third order, *hundreds;* in the fourth order, *thousands;* in the fifth order, *ten-thousands;* in the sixth order, *hundred-thousands,* etc.

ART. 17. The successive orders of units are divided into groups of three orders each, called *Periods,* as shown in the following table:

Hundred-trillions.	Ten-trillions.	Trillions.	Hundred-billions.	Ten-billions.	Billions.	Hundred-millions.	Ten-millions.	Millions.	Hundred-thousands.	Ten-thousands.	Thousands.	Hundreds.	Tens.	Units.
5	5	5,	4	4	4,	3	3	3,	2	2	2,	1	1	1

5th Period.	4th Period.	3d Period.	2d Period.	1st Period.
Trillions.	Billions.	Millions.	Thousands.	Units.

NOTE.—The name of the sixth period is *Quadrillions;* the seventh, *Quintillions;* the eighth, *Sextillions;* the ninth, *Septillions;* the tenth, *Octillions,* etc.

ART. 18. The three orders of any period, counting from the right, denote respectively *units, tens,* and *hundreds* of that period. The first three orders express units, tens, and hundreds of *units;* the second three orders, units, tens, and hundreds of *thousands;* the third three orders, units, tens, and hundreds of *millions,* etc.

ART. 19. The **Value** of a figure is the number which it expresses; and this depends on the order in which the figure stands.

The value of each of the successive figures which express a number is a *Term.* The terms of 325 are 3 *hundreds,* 2 *tens,* and 5 *ones.*

ART. 20. **Principles.**—1. Ten units of the first order equal one unit of the second order; ten units of the second order equal one unit of the third; and, generally, *ten units of any order equal one unit of the next higher order.* Hence,

2. *The removal of a figure one order to the left multiplies its value by ten, and the removal of a figure one order to the right divides its value by ten.*

The successive figures which express a number are written on a *scale of ten.*

ART. 21. **Rule for Notation.**—*Begin at the left, and write the figures of each period in their proper orders, filling all vacant orders and periods with ciphers.*

ART. 22. **Rule for Numeration.**—1. *Begin at the right, and separate the number into periods of three figures each.*

2. *Begin at the left, and read each period containing one or more figures as if it stood alone, adding its name.*

NOTES.—1. The name of the units' period is usually omitted.

2. In reading numbers, it is not necessary to connect the terms of a period or the successive periods with "and." 405,020 may be read *four hundred five thousand twenty.* The use of "and" is not, however, incorrect. 405,020 may be read *four hundred and five thousand and twenty;* and this reading is in accordance with general usage. (Art. 116, note 3.)

ADDITION.

ORAL EXERCISES.

1. Add by 3's from 1 to 100; thus: 1, 4, 7, 10, etc.

2. Add by 4's from 3 to 51; from 51 to 99.

3. Add by 5's from 2 to 52; from 52 to 102.

4. Add by 6's from 1 to 49; from 49 to 97.

5. Add by 6's from 2 to 50; from 50 to 98.

6. Add by 7's from 3 to 52; from 52 to 94.

7. Add by 7's from 4 to 53; from 53 to 95.

8. Add by 8's from 5 to 53; from 53 to 93.

9. Add by 8's from 2 to 50; from 50 to 98.

10. Add by 9's from 1 to 55; from 55 to 100.

WRITTEN EXERCISES.

11. Add 347, 4086, 7080, 29408, and 67736.

12. $667 + 3804 + 45608 + 304867 + 87609 =$ what?

13. Add four thousand fifty-six; sixty-three thousand seven hundred; seven million nine thousand ninety-nine; and fifty-six million nine hundred seventy-eight.

14. Add eight million eighty thousand eight hundred; seven hundred thousand and seventy; five million eighty-six thousand seven hundred and eight; and sixty million six hundred thousand and seventy.

15. A grain dealer bought wheat as follows: Monday, 2480 bushels; Tuesday, 788 bushels; Wednesday, 1565 bushels; Thursday, 2684 bushels; Friday, 985 bushels; Saturday, 3867 bushels. How many bushels did he buy during the week?

16. The value of the property of a certain university is as follows: endowment fund, $340,000; land, $59,000; college building, $155,817; steam, water, and gas fixtures, $35,655; apparatus, cabinets, and other appliances, $22,562; other improvements, $39,624. What is the total value of the property?

17. Ohio contains 41060 square miles; Indiana, 36350; Illinois, 56650; Michigan, 58915; Wisconsin, 56040; Minnesota, 83365; Iowa, 56025; and Missouri, 69415. What is the total area of these eight states?

18. The population of these states, in 1880, was as follows: Ohio, 3198062; Indiana, 1978301; Illinois, 3077871; Michigan, 1636937; Wisconsin, 1315497; Minnesota, 780773; Iowa, 1624615; Missouri, 2168380. What was their total population?

19. The territory of the United States has been acquired as follows:

SQ. MILES.

Territory ceded by England, 1783, ...	866391
Louisiana, acquired from France, 1803, ...	862922
Florida, acquired from Spain, 1821, ...	58680
Texas, admitted to the Union, 1845, ...	365573
Oregon, settled by treaty, 1846, ...	298804
California, etc., conquered from Mexico, 1847, ...	515764
Arizona, acquired from Mexico by treaty, 1854, . . .	57466
Alaska, acquired from Russia by purchase, 1867, . . .	577390

What is the total area of the United States?

ADDITION OF TWO COLUMNS.

ART. 23. There is a practical advantage in adding two columns at one operation. Some accountants add three or more columns in this manner.

20. Add 67, 58, 43, 36, and 54.

PROCESS.

```
 67
 58
 43
 36
 54
────
258
```

Add thus: $54 + 30 = 84, + 6 = 90$; $90 + 40 = 130$, $+ 3 = 133$; $133 + 50 = 183, + 8 = 191$; $191 + 60 = 251, + 7 = 258$.

Or thus, naming only results: 54, 84, 90; 130, 133; 183, 191; 251, 258.

NOTE.—The process consists in first adding the tens of each couplet, and then the units. If preferred, the units may first be added, and then the tens. Sufficient practice will enable the accountant to add two columns without separating the numbers into tens and units.

21. Add 37, 40, 63, 84, 67, 22, and 70.
22. Add 95, 36, 77, 66, 88, 63, 33, and 44.
23. Add 67, 76, 45, 54, 38, 83, 27, and 72.
24. Add 68, 86, 97, 79, 86, 68, 78, and 87.

25. Add 45, 60, 57, 86, 83, 76, 49, 58, and 84.

26. Add 56, 75, 83, 96, 69, 37, 73, 38, and 205.

27. Add 27, 72, 33, 38, 69, 96, 75, 57, and 336.

28. Add 235, 88, 77, 66, 55, 44, 33, 22, and 11.

29. Add 405, 56, 43, 47, 74, 38, 63, 75, and 66.

30. Add 46, 67, 72, 38, 99, 87, 65, 74, and 88.

31. Add 73, 86, 47, 56, 69, 65, 58, 33, 52, and 94.

32. A drover bought 37 sheep of one farmer, 44 sheep of another, 48 sheep of another, and 27 sheep of another: how many sheep did he buy?

33. The Senior class of a college contains 27 students, the Junior class 34, the Sophomore class 38, and the Freshman class 46: how many students in the college?

34. A lady paid $36 for a carpet, $34 for a bureau, $16 for a washstand, $28 for a bedstead, and $42 for chairs: how much did she pay for all?

35. A man paid $85 for a horse, and $17 for his keeping; and then sold him so as to gain $15: for how much did he sell the horse?

DEFINITIONS, PRINCIPLES, AND RULE.

Art. 24. The **Sum** of two or more numbers contains as many units as all the numbers taken together. It is also called the *Amount.*

Art. 25. **Addition** is the process of finding the sum of two or more numbers.

Art. 26. An **Arithmetical Sign** is a character which denotes an operation with numbers, or a relation between them.

The **Sign of Addition** is a vertical cross [+]. It is read *plus*, which means *more.*

The **Sign of Equality** is two short horizontal parallel lines [=], and is read *equals* or *is equal to.* Thus, $7 + 8 = 15$ is read 7 *plus* 8 *equals* 15.

ART. 27. **Like Numbers** are composed of units of the same kind or order. Thus, 4 steps and 8 steps are like numbers; also 4 dimes and 8 dimes; 4 tens and 8 tens; 4 and 8.

ART. 28. **Principles.**—1. *Only like numbers can be added.*
2. *The sum is of the same kind or order as the numbers added.*

ART. 29. **Rule.**—1. *Write the numbers to be added so that figures denoting units of the same order shall be in the same column, and draw a line underneath.*
2. *Beginning with units, add each column, and write the sum, when less than ten, underneath.*
3. *When the sum of any column exceeds nine, write the right-hand figure under the column added, and add the number denoted by the left-hand figure or figures with the next column.*
4. *Write the entire sum of the left-hand column.*

NOTE.—See appendix for method of proof by "casting out the 9's."

SUBTRACTION.

ORAL PROBLEMS.

1. Count by 4's from 61 back to 1; thus: 57, 53, etc.
2. Count by 6's from 53 back to 5; from 74 back to 2.
3. Count by 7's from 66 back to 3; from 85 back to 1.
4. Count by 8's from 75 back to 3; from 94 back to 6.
5. Count by 9's from 73 back to 1; from 96 back to 6.
6. Count by 9's from 94 back to 58; from 58 back to 4.
7. A man sold a horse for $95, which was $28 more than the horse cost him: what was the cost of the horse?

8. Two men start at once from the same point, and travel in the same direction, one traveling 52 miles a day, and the other 39 miles: how far will they be apart at the close of the first day?

9. A man earns $85 a month, and pays $18 for house rent, and $35 for other expenses: how much does he save each month?

10. A gentleman being asked his age said, that if he should live 27 years longer, he should then be three score and ten: what was his age?

11. From a piece of carpeting containing 68 yards, a merchant sold 27 yards to one man and 18 yards to another: how many yards of the piece were left?

12. A man bought a carriage for $135, paid $21 for repairing it, and then sold it for $170; how much did he gain?

13. A boy earned 65 cents, and his father gave him 33 cents; he paid 45 cents for an arithmetic, 15 cents for a slate, and 12 cents for pencils: how much money had he left?

WRITTEN PROBLEMS.

14. A builder contracted to build a school-house for $25460, and the job cost him $21385: what were his profits?

15. The earth's mean distance from the sun (old value) is 95274000 miles, and that of Mars is 145168136: how much farther is Mars from the sun than the earth?

16. The population of Illinois, in 1880, was 3077871, and in 1865 its population was 2141510: what was the increase in fifteen years?

17. The population of Massachusetts, in 1880, was 1783085, and in 1865 it was 1267031: what was the increase in fifteen years?

N. C. A.—2.

18. The area of the Chinese Empire is 4553102 square miles, and the area of the United States is 3602990 square miles: how much greater is the Chinese Empire than the United States?

19. The area of Europe is 3928252 square miles: how much greater is Europe than the United States? The Chinese Empire than Europe?

20. In 1880, Ohio produced 112681046 bushels of corn, and Illinois 327796895 bushels: how many bushels did Illinois produce more than Ohio?

21. A man bought a farm for $5867, and built upon it a house at a cost of $1850, and then sold the farm for $7250: how much did he lose?

22. An estate of $13450 was divided between a widow and two children; the widow's share was $6340; the son's, $1560 less than the widow's; and the rest fell to the daughter: what was the daughter's share?

23. A man deposited in a bank at one time $850, at another, $367, and at another, $670; he then drew out $480, and $375: how much money had he still in bank?

24. A man bought a farm for $6450, giving in exchange a house worth $4500, a note for $1150, and paying the difference in money: how much money did he pay?

25. A grain dealer bought 15640 bushels of wheat, and sold at one time 3465 bushels, at another, 4205, and at another, 1080: how many bushels remained?

26. From the sum of 45003 and 13478, take their difference.

DEFINITIONS, PRINCIPLES, AND RULE.

Art. 30. **Subtraction** is the process of taking a less number from a greater.

The **Minuend** is the number from which the less number is taken.

The **Subtrahend** is the number taken from the minuend.

The **Difference** is the number obtained by subtracting.

The difference is the number of units in the minuend more than in the subtrahend. When the subtrahend is a part of the minuend, as in division, the difference is called the *Remainder*.

ART. 31. The **Sign of Subtraction** is a short horizontal line [—], and is read *minus* or *less*. Thus, 12 — 5 is read 12 *minus* 5 or 12 *less* 5.

ART. 32. Principles.—1. *A number can be subtracted only from a like number.*

2. *The minuend is the sum of the subtrahend and difference.*

3. *If the minuend and subtrahend be equally increased, the difference will not be changed.*

ART. 33. Rule.—1. *Write the subtrahend under the minuend, placing units under units, tens under tens, hundreds under hundreds, etc.*

2. *Begin at the right, and subtract each term of the subtrahend from the term above it, and write the difference underneath.*

3. *When any term of the subtrahend is greater than the term above it, add 10 to the upper term, and then subtract, and write the difference underneath.*

4. *When 10 has been added to the upper term, add 1 to the next higher term of the subtrahend before subtracting.*

Proof.—*Add the remainder and subtrahend; if their sum is equal to the minuend, the work is correct.*

NOTES.—1. The adding of 10 to a term of the minuend and 1 to the next higher term of the subtrahend, increases the minuend and subtrahend equally, and hence does not affect the difference (Prin. 2).

2. Instead of adding 1 to the next term of the subtrahend, 1 may be subtracted from the next term of the minuend.

MULTIPLICATION.

ORAL PROBLEMS.

1. There are 24 hours in a day: how many hours in 7 days? In 9 days? 11 days? 20 days?

2. There are 60 minutes in an hour: how many minutes in 8 hours? In 12 hours? 10 hours? 7 hours? 15 hours? 20 hours?

3. If a man earn $63 a month, and spend $48, how much will he save in 1 month? In 5 months? 6 months? 8 months? 12 months?

4. If 12 men can do a piece of work in 15 days, how long will it take one man to do it?

5. If 35 bushels of oats will feed 8 horses 25 days, how long will they feed one horse?

6. Two men start from the same place and travel in opposite directions, one at the rate of 28 miles a day, and the other at the rate of 32 miles a day: how far will they be apart at the end of 1 day? At the end of 5 days? At the end of 10 days?

7. A drover bought 15 sheep at $4 a head, and sold them at $6 a head: how much did he gain?

8. A merchant bought 12 suits of boys' clothes at $15 a suit, and sold them at $18 a suit: how much did he gain?

9. A cask has two pipes, one discharging into it 90 gallons of water an hour, and the other drawing from it 75 gallons an hour: how many gallons of water will there be in the cask at the end of 12 hours?

10. A farmer sold to a grocer 15 pounds of butter at 30 cents a pound, and bought 8 pounds of sugar at 15 cents a pound, and 9 pounds of coffee at 20 cents a pound: how much was still due him?

WRITTEN PROBLEMS.

11. Multiply 624 by 45; by 405; by 4005.

12. Multiply 38400 by 27; by 607; by 6007.

13. Multiply 7863 by 69; by 6900; by 64000.

14. Multiply 48000 by 760; by 7600000.

15. There are 5280 feet in a mile: how many feet in 608 miles? In 3300 miles?

16. The earth moves 1092 miles in a minute: how far does it move in 1440 minutes, or one day?

17. A square mile contains 640 acres, and the state of Ohio contains 41060 square miles: how many acres in the state?

18. If a garrison of 380 soldiers consume 56 barrels of flour in 75 days, how many soldiers will the same amount of flour supply one day?

19. A man bought a farm, containing 472 acres, at $24 an acre, and, after investing $3450 in buildings, he sold the farm at $33 an acre: did he gain or lose, and how much?

20. Two men start from the same point, and travel in opposite directions, the one at the rate of 54 miles a day, and the other at the rate of 48 miles a day: how far will they be apart at the end of 14 days?

21. Two men are 450 miles apart: if they approach each other, one traveling 30 miles a day, and the other 35 miles a day, how far apart will they be at the end of 6 days?

22. Multiply 648 by 10; by 100; by 1000.

SUGGESTION.—Since each removal of a figure one order to the left multiplies its value by 10 (Art. 20, Prin. 2), the annexing of one cipher to 648 multiplies it by 10, the annexing of two ciphers multiplies it by 100, and three ciphers by 1000.

23. Multiply 456 by 10; by 1000; by 10000.

24. Multiply 3050 by 100; by 1000; by 100000.

DEFINITIONS, PRINCIPLES, AND RULES.

ART. 34. **Multiplication** is a process of taking one number as many times as there are units in another.

The **Multiplicand** is the number taken or multiplied.

The **Multiplier** is the number denoting how many times the multiplicand is taken.

The **Product** is the number obtained by multiplying.

The multiplicand and multiplier are *Factors* of the product.

NOTE.—The product may be obtained by adding the multiplicand to itself as many times less one as there are units in the multiplier, and hence *Multiplication is a short method of finding the sum of several equal numbers.* The Multiplicand is one of the equal numbers; the Multiplier, the number of equal numbers; and the Product, the sum of the equal numbers.

ART. 35. The **Sign of Multiplication** is an oblique cross [×], and is read *multiplied by* or *times*. Thus, 8 × 6 is read 8 *multiplied by* 6 or 8 *times* 6.

When the sign [×] is placed between two numbers, it shows that they are to be multiplied together; and, since the order of the factors does not affect the product, either number may be made the multiplier. The multiplier is usually written after the sign, which is then read *multiplied by;* when the multiplier is written before the sign it is read *times.*

ART. 36. **Principles.**—1. *The multiplier must always be regarded as an abstract number.*

2. *The multiplicand and product are like numbers, and may be either concrete or abstract.* ▶

NOTE.—When one of the factors is concrete, the concrete number is the *true* multiplicand, but when it is the smaller number, it may be used *abstractly* as the multiplier.

3. *The product is not affected by changing the order of the factors.* Thus, 4 × 3 = 3 × 4.

4. *The product divided by either of its two factors will give the other factor.*

Art. 37. **Rule.**—1. *Write the multiplier under the multiplicand, placing units under units, tens under tens, etc.*

2. *When the multiplier consists of but one term, begin at the right and multiply successively each term of the multiplicand, writing the right-hand term of each result in the product, and adding the left-hand term to the next result.*

3. *When the multiplier consists of more than one term, multiply the multiplicand successively by each significant term of the multiplier, writing the first term of each partial product under the term of the multiplier which produces it.*

4. *Add the partial products thus obtained, and the sum will be the true product.*

NOTE.—When the multiplier or multiplicand, or both, end with one or more ciphers, *the ciphers may be omitted in forming the partial products, and annexed to the sum of the partial products.*

Art. 38. To multiply by 10, 100, 1000, etc.:

Rule.—*Annex to the multiplicand as many ciphers as there are ciphers in the multiplier.*

MULTIPLICATION TABLE.

1	2	3	4	5	6	7	8	9	10	11	12
2	4	6	8	10	12	14	16	18	20	22	24
3	6	9	12	15	18	21	24	27	30	33	36
4	8	12	16	20	24	28	32	36	40	44	48
5	10	15	20	25	30	35	40	45	50	55	60
6	12	18	24	30	36	42	48	54	60	66	72
7	14	21	28	35	42	49	56	63	70	77	84
8	16	24	32	40	48	56	64	72	80	88	96
9	18	27	36	45	54	63	72	81	90	99	108
10	20	30	40	50	60	70	80	90	100	110	120
11	22	33	44	55	66	77	88	99	110	121	132
12	24	36	48	60	72	84	96	108	120	132	144

ABBREVIATED PROCESSES.

THE MULTIPLIER AN ALIQUOT PART OF 10, 100, Etc.

ART. 39.   An **Aliquot Part** of a number is any integer or mixed number which will exactly divide it.

NOTE.—If the class be not sufficiently familiar with the subject of fractions, this case may be omitted until the review.

The following are the aliquot parts of 10, 100, and 1000 respectively, most frequently occurring in practice:

$2\frac{1}{2} = \frac{1}{4}$ of 10	$12\frac{1}{2} = \frac{1}{8}$ of 100	$125 = \frac{1}{8}$ of 1000
$3\frac{1}{3} = \frac{1}{3}$ of 10	$16\frac{2}{3} = \frac{1}{6}$ of 100	$166\frac{2}{3} = \frac{1}{6}$ of 1000
$5 = \frac{1}{2}$ of 10	$25 = \frac{1}{4}$ of 100	$200 = \frac{1}{5}$ of 1000
	$33\frac{1}{3} = \frac{1}{3}$ of 100	$250 = \frac{1}{4}$ of 1000
	$50 = \frac{1}{2}$ of 100	$333\frac{1}{3} = \frac{1}{3}$ of 1000

ORAL AND WRITTEN PROBLEMS.

1. There are 24 sheets of paper in a quire: how many sheets in $2\frac{1}{2}$ quires? In $3\frac{1}{3}$ quires? In 5 quires?

2. There are 60 minutes in an hour: how many minutes in $3\frac{1}{3}$ hours? In $12\frac{1}{2}$ hours? $16\frac{2}{3}$ hours?

3. If a workman earn $40 a month, how much will he earn in $2\frac{1}{2}$ months? In $3\frac{1}{3}$ months? $12\frac{1}{2}$ months?

4. At 36 cents a yard, what will 25 yards of cloth cost? 50 yards? $33\frac{1}{3}$ yards?

5. At 24 cents a dozen, what will $12\frac{1}{2}$ dozens of eggs cost? $16\frac{2}{3}$ dozens? $33\frac{1}{3}$ dozens? 25 dozens?

6. Multiply 486 by $3\frac{1}{3}$; by $33\frac{1}{3}$; by $333\frac{1}{3}$.

7. Multiply 5280 by $12\frac{1}{2}$; by 125; by $166\frac{2}{3}$.

8. Multiply 1688 by $16\frac{2}{3}$; by $166\frac{2}{3}$; by 250.

9. Multiply 40648 by $16\frac{2}{3}$; by $33\frac{1}{3}$; by $333\frac{1}{3}$.

ART. 40.   **Principle.**—*If the multiplier be multiplied by a given number, and the resulting product be divided by the same number, the quotient will be the true product.*

ART. 41. To multiply by an aliquot part of 10, 100, 1000, etc. :

Rule.—*Multiply by 10, 100, 1000, etc., and divide the product by the number of times the multiplier is contained in 10, 100, 1000, etc.*

THE MULTIPLIER A LITTLE LESS THAN 10, 100, Etc.

10. Multiply 467 by 98.

PROCESS.

    46700
      934
    ───────
    45766, *Prod.*

Since $98 = 100 - 2$, the product of 467 by $98 = 467 \times 100 - 467 \times 2$, or $46700 - 934$. In multiplying by 100, the multiplicand is taken two times more than it should be.

11. Multiply 5672 by 99; by 999; by 98; by 998.
12. Multiply 40863 by 97; by 997; by 99; by 999.
13. Multiply 8679 by 998; by 9998; by 99; by 997.
14. Multiply 618734 by 95; by 995; by 98; by 998.

ART. 42. To multiply by a number a little less than 10, 100, 1000, etc. :

Rule.—*Multiply by 10, 100, 1000, etc., and subtract from the product the multiplicand, multiplied by the difference between the multiplier and 10, 100, 1000, etc., as the case may be.*

THE MULTIPLIER 14, 15, Etc., OR 31, 51, Etc.

15. Multiply 7856 by 14; by 41.

FIRST PROCESS.	SECOND PROCESS.
7856×14	7856×41
31424	31424
109984, *Product.*	322096, *Product.*

NOTE.—An inspection of each process will suggest its explanation. The second partial product need not be written, as the successive terms can be added mentally to the proper terms of the first partial product.

N. C. A.—3.

16. Multiply 38407 by 13; by 15; by 17.
17. Multiply 4960 by 16; by 18; by 19.
18. Multiply 360978 by 31; by 51; by 71.
19. Multiply 48706 by 61; by 81; by 91.
20. Multiply 34087 by 17; by 71; by 18.

ART. 43. 1. To multiply by 13, 14, 15, etc.:

Rule.—*Multiply by the units' term, and add the successive products, after the first (which is units), to the successive terms of the multiplicand.*

2. To multiply by 31, 41, 51, etc.:

Rule.—*Multiply by the tens' term, and add the successive products to the successive terms of the multiplicand, beginning with tens.*

DIVISION.

ORAL PROBLEMS.

1. There are 7 days in a week: how many weeks in 63 days? 98 days? 126 days?

2. There are eight quarts in a peck: how many pecks in 72 quarts? 120 quarts? 144 quarts?

3. There are 60 minutes in an hour: how many hours in 480 minutes? 720 minutes? 1440 minutes?

4. A man paid $3600 for a farm, paying at the rate of $40 an acre: how many acres in the farm?

5. A grocer bought 12 barrels of flour for $90, and sold them so as to gain $18: how much did he receive per barrel?

6. Two men are 120 miles a part, and are traveling toward each other, one at the rate of 7 miles an hour, and the other at the rate of 8 miles an hour: in how many hours will they meet?

7. If a man can build a wall in 84 days, how long will it take 7 men to build it?

8. The large wheel of a boy's velocipede is 8 feet in circumference: how many times will the wheel rotate in running 560 feet?

9. How many acres will produce 750 bushels of wheat with an average yield of 25 bushels to the acre?

10. A man earns $16 while a boy earns $9: how much will the man earn while the boy earns $72?

WRITTEN PROBLEMS.

11. Divide 486 by 6; by 8; by 9.

12. Divide 8408 by 12; by 24; by 36.

13. Divide 255136 by 238; by 476.

14. Divide 197776 by 94; by 376.

15. Divide 600790 by 365; by 1646.

16. Divide 368600 by 485; by 760.

17. Divide 84600 by 900; by 12000; by 4500.

18. Divide 412304 by 3600; by 303000; by 7500.

19. The dividend is 1059984, and the divisor is 306: what is the quotient?

20. The dividend is 2185750, and the quotient is 250: what is the divisor?

21. The product is 1123482, and the multiplier is 246: what is the multiplicand?

22. How many passenger cars, costing $2450 each, can be bought for $100450?

23. Divide 4560 by 10; by 100.

Suggestion.—Since the removal of a figure one order to the right divides its value by 10 (Art. 21), the cutting off of one figure from the right of 4560 divides it by 10, and the cutting off of two figures divides it by 100. The figures cut off are the remainder.

24. Divide 356000 by 10; by 100; by 1000.

25. Divide 46035 by 100; by 1000; by 10000.

26. Divide 384602 by 100; by 1000; by 10000.

27. Divide 95000000 by 10000; by 1000000.

28. Divide 58864 by 4500.

PROCESS.

45|00)588|64(13
45
───
138
135
───
3

Remainder, 364

First divide both dividend and divisor by 100, which, in the case of the dividend, leaves a remainder of 64. Next divide 588 by 45, leaving a remainder of 3, which is 3 *hundreds* since the dividend (588) is hundreds. The first remainder is 64 *units*, which, annexed to the 3 hundreds, give 364, the true remainder.

29. Divide 63200 by 7900; by 7000.

30. Divide 116000 by 2500; by 4800.

31. Divide 172800 by 14400; by 18000.

32. Divide 129600 by 4800; by 64000.

33. There are 160 square rods in an acre: how many acres in 384000 square rods?

34. There are 320 rods in a mile: how many miles in 51200 rods?

35. There are 3600 seconds in an hour: how many hours in 738000 seconds? In 2952000 seconds?

DEFINITIONS, PRINCIPLES, AND RULES.

ART. 44. **Division** is the process of finding how many times one number is contained in another; or, it is the process of finding one of the equal parts of a number.

The **Dividend** is the number divided.

The **Divisor** is the number by which the dividend is divided.

The **Quotient** is the number of times the divisor is contained in the dividend; or, it is one of the equal parts of the dividend.

The **Remainder** is the part of the dividend which is left undivided.

One number is contained in another as many times as it must be taken to produce it, and hence *Division is the reverse of multiplication.*

One number is contained in another as many times as it can be taken from it, and hence *Division is a brief method of finding how many times one number can be subtracted from another.*

ART. 45. The **Sign of Division** is a short horizontal line between two dots [÷]. It is read *divided by.* Thus, $16 \div 4$ is read 16 *divided by* 4.

Division is also expressed by writing the dividend above and the divisor below a short horizontal line. Thus, $\frac{18}{3}$ is read 18 *divided by* 3.

ART. 46. There are two methods of division, called *Short Division* and *Long Division.*

In **Short Division** the partial products and partial dividends are not written, but are formed mentally.

In **Long Division** the partial products and partial dividends are written.

ART. 47. **Principles.**—1. *The divisor and quotient are factors of the dividend, which is their product.*

2. When division finds how many times one number is contained in another, *the divisor and dividend are* LIKE NUMBERS, *and the quotient is an abstract number.* Thus, 48 ft. ÷ 8 ft. = 6.

3. When division finds one of the equal parts of a number, *the divisor is an abstract number, and the dividend and quotient are* LIKE NUMBERS. Thus, 48 ft. ÷ 6, or $\frac{1}{6}$ of 48 ft., = 8 ft.

NOTE.—In this case, the quotient corresponds to the multiplicand; and the divisor, to the multiplier.

4. *The multiplying of both divisor and dividend by the*

same number does not change the quotient. Thus, $12 \div 4 = 12 \times 3 \div 4 \times 3$.

5. *The dividing of both dividend and divisor by the same number does not change the quotient.* Thus, $18 \div 9 = \frac{18}{3} \div \frac{9}{3} = 6 \div 3$.

ART. 48. **Rule for Long Division.**—1. *Write the divisor at the left of the dividend, draw a curved line between them, and also at the right of the dividend, to separate it from the quotient.*

2. *Take as many of the left-hand terms of the dividend as will contain the divisor, for a partial dividend; find how many times this will contain the divisor, and write the quotient at the right of the dividend for the left-hand term of the quotient.*

3. *Multiply the divisor by the quotient term found, write the product under the partial dividend used, and subtract.*

4. *To the remainder annex the next term of the dividend for a second partial dividend, and divide, multiply, and subtract, as before.*

5. *Proceed in this manner until all the terms of the dividend have been used.*

Proof.—*Multiply the divisor by the quotient, to the product add the remainder, if there be any, and if the result equals the dividend, the work is correct.*

ART. 49. **To divide any number by 10, 100, etc.:**

Rule.—*Cut off as many figures from the right of the number as there are ciphers in the divisor. The figures cut off express the remainder.*

NOTE.—When one or more of the right-hand figures of the divisor are ciphers, the process may be shortened by cutting off the ciphers from the right of the divisor and an equal number of figures from the right of the dividend, and *then dividing the new dividend thus formed by the new divisor.* The true remainder is found by prefixing the figures which express the remainder, if any, to the figures cut off from the dividend.

ABBREVIATED PROCESSES.

THE DIVISOR AN ALIQUOT PART OF 10, 100, Etc.

ORAL AND WRITTEN PROBLEMS.

1. At $3\frac{1}{3}$ cents apiece, how many lemons can be bought for 90 cents? For 240 cents?

SUGGESTION.—Since 10 is 3 times $3\frac{1}{3}$, multiply the dividend by 3, and divide the product by 10 by omitting the right-hand figure (Prin. 3).

2. At $12\frac{1}{2}$ cents a yard, how many yards of cloth can be bought for 75 cents? For 225 cents? 250 cents?

3. At $16\frac{2}{3}$ bushels per acre, how many acres will produce 150 bushels of wheat? 450 bushels? 700 bushels?

4. At $33\frac{1}{3}$ a head, how many cows can be bought for $200? For $1200? $500? $1500?

5. Divide 4375 by 125.　　**6.** Divide 13600 by $333\frac{1}{3}$.

PROCESS.	PROCESS.
4375	13600
8	3
35|000	40|800
35, *Quotient.*	40, *Quotient.*

$$800 \div 3 = 266\frac{2}{3}, \ Remainder.$$

7. Divide 6250 by $33\frac{1}{3}$; by 50; by 125.

8. Divide 4365 by 250; by $166\frac{2}{3}$; by $333\frac{1}{3}$.

9. Divide 15300 by $16\frac{2}{3}$; by $333\frac{1}{3}$; by 250.

ART. 50. **Principle.**—*The multiplying of both divisor and dividend by the same number does not change the quotient.*

ART. 51.   To divide by a convenient part of 10, 100, 1000, etc.:

Rule.—*Multiply the dividend by the number denoting how many times the divisor is contained in 10, 100, 1000, etc., and divide the product by 10, 100, 1000, etc.*

THE DIVISOR A COMPOSITE NUMBER.

10. Divide 18315 by 45.

PROCESS.

$$45 = 5 \times 9$$

$$5)\overline{18315}$$
$$9)\overline{3663}$$

407, *Quotient.*

ILLUSTRATIVE PROCESS.

$$5)\overline{18315 \div 45} = 3663 \div 9$$
$$9)\overline{3663 \div 9} =\ \ 407 \div 1$$
$$407 \div 1 = 407$$

Since $45 = 5 \times 9$, the quotient obtained by dividing 18315 by 5, is 9 *times too large*, and hence this quotient (3663) divided by 9, is the true quotient.

NOTE.—The process of dividing by the factors of the divisor successively is the same in principle as the division of both dividend and divisor by these factors successively, which (Prin. 5) does not change the quotient. See "Illustrative Process" above.

11. Divide 58636 by 28; by 56; by 77.

12. Divide 13328 by 49; by 56; by 70.

13. Divide 3687 by 63.

PROCESS.

$$7)\overline{3687} \qquad\qquad 63 = 7 \times 9$$
$$9)\overline{526}\ .\ .\ .\ 5,\ \textit{Rem. (1)} = \ .\ .\ .\ 5$$
$$58\ .\ .\ .\ 4,\ \textit{Rem. (2)} = 4 \times 7 = 28$$
$$\textit{True remainder} = 33$$

A unit of the first quotient (526) equals 7 units of the dividend, and hence the second remainder (4) equals 4 times 7 units of the dividend, or 28 units, which, added to 5 units (the first remainder), gives 33 as the true remainder. Hence, the true remainder is found *by multiplying the second remainder by the first divisor and adding to the product the first remainder, if any.*

14. Divide 31365 by 54; by 81.

15. Divide 34567 by 63; by 72.

16. Divide 120473 by 56; by 81.

17. Divide 400671 by 64; by 77.

18. Divide 346000 by 55; by 96.

19. Divide 47633 by 90; by 110.

ART. 52. **Principle.**—*The division of both divisor and dividend by the same number does not change the quotient.*

ART. 53. To divide by a composite number:

Rule.—1. *Resolve the divisor into convenient factors; divide the dividend by one of these factors, the quotient thus obtained by another, and so on until all the factors are used as divisors. The last quotient will be the true quotient.*

2. *Multiply each remainder, except the first, by all the divisors preceding its own. The sum of these products and the first remainder will be the true remainder.*

THE CANCELLATION OF FACTORS.

ART. 54. When the dividend and divisor are each the product of several given factors, the process may often be shortened by canceling equal factors in divisors and dividend.

20. Divide the product of 4, 7, 9, and 12 by the product of 4, 7, and 9.

PROCESS.

$$\text{Dividend,} \quad \frac{4 \times 7 \times 9 \times 12}{4 \times 7 \times 9} = 12 \quad \text{Divisor,}$$

Instead of forming the products, indicate the multiplication by the proper sign, and write the divisor underneath the dividend. Since dividing both dividend and divisor by the same number does not affect the value of the quotient (Art. 47), divide each by 4, 7, and 9. This may be done by canceling, as indicated in the process. The quotient is 12.

21. Divide $4 \times 7 \times 12$ by 4×12.

22. Divide $12 \times 3 \times 75$ by 25×6.

23. Divide $6 \times 8 \times 20$ by 4×20.

24. Divide $5 \times 7 \times 11 \times 13\frac{1}{2}$ by $7 \times 13\frac{1}{2}$.

25. Divide $12 \times 16 \times 28$ by $9 \times 24 \times 21$.

PROCESS.

$$\frac{\overset{8}{\cancel{12}} \times \overset{4}{\cancel{16}} \times \cancel{28}}{9 \times \underset{2}{\cancel{24}} \times \underset{3}{\cancel{21}}} = \frac{8 \times 4}{9 \times 3} = \frac{32}{27} = 1\frac{5}{27}.$$

Cancel 12 in the dividend and divide 24 in the divisor by 12, giving 2. Cancel the 2, and divide 16 in the dividend by 2, giving 8. Divide the 28 in the dividend and 21 in the divisor, each by 7, giving 4 and 3. The uncanceled factors of the divisor are 8 and 4, and those of the dividend are 9 and 3.

26. Divide $24 \times 27 \times 12\frac{1}{2}$ by $18 \times 54 \times 50$.

27. Divide $28 \times 30 \times 100$ by $21 \times 15 \times 33\frac{1}{3}$.

28. Divide $40 \times 22 \times 35 \times 16\frac{2}{3}$ by $20 \times 44 \times 50 \times 49$.

29. Divide $24 \times (10 - 7) \times 6$ by $12 \times 3 \times (4 + 2)$.

NOTE.—The power of the sign $\times$ does not extend, right or left, beyond a $+$ or $-$, without the aid of a parenthesis. Thus: $24 \times 10 - 7 \times 6 = 240 - 42$; but $24 \times (10 - 7) \times 6 = 24 \times 3 \times 6$. $12 \times 3 \times 4 + 2 \times 3 = 144 + 6$; but $12 \times 3 \times (4 + 2 \times 3) = 12 \times 3 \times 10$. The same is true of the power of the sign $\div$.

30. Divide $18 \times (24 - 6 \times 3) \times 5$ by $(24 - 18) \times (3 + 6)$.

31. Divide $(8 + 4) \times (8 - 4)$ by $(13 - 7) \times (6 + 2)$.

32. Divide $6 \times 7 \times (9 - 5)$ by $14 \times 3 \times (7 - 3)$.

33. $(9 \times 7 \times 8 \times 3) \div (12 \times 4 \times 18) =$ what?

34. $(15 \times 4 \times 21 \times 12) \div (20 \times 14 \times 9 \times 2) =$ what?

NOTE.—Arithmeticians are not agreed respecting the order in which the operations indicated by $\times$ and $\div$, are to be performed. $8 \times 6 \div 4 \times 3$ may equal 36 or 4, since the operations may be performed in their order from left to right, or 8×6 may be divided by 4×3. All ambiguity is removed by the use of the parenthesis, as in examples 31 and 32. See "Manual of Arithmetic."

ART. 55. **Cancellation** is the omission of one or more of the equal factors of divisor and dividend, to shorten the process of division.

ART. 56. **Principles.**—1. *The canceling of one of the factors of a number divides the number by the factor canceled.*

2. *Canceling equal factors of both dividend and divisor divides them by the same number, and hence does not change the value of the quotient.*

ART. 57. To divide the product of several numbers by the product of several other numbers by cancellation :

Rule.—*Indicate the multiplications by the proper sign, and write the divisor underneath the dividend. Cancel the factors common to both dividend and divisor, and divide the product of the factors left in the dividend by the product of those left in the divisor.*

NOTE.—When all the expressed factors of either dividend or divisor are canceled, 1 remains as a factor.

PROPERTIES OF INTEGERS.

ART. 58. Integral numbers are either *Even* or *Odd*.

An **Even Number** is exactly divisible by 2; as, 4, 8, 10, 14, 20.

An **Odd Number** is not exactly divisible by 2; as, 5, 9, 13, 17, 21.

1. Name all the even numbers from 1 to 20; from 30 to 50; from 50 to 70.

2. Name all the odd numbers from 0 to 20; from 20 to 40; from 50 to 70.

ART. 59. Integral numbers are either *Composite* or *Prime.*

A **Composite Number** is divisible by other integers besides itself and one; as, 6, 12, 21.

A **Prime Number** is divisible only by itself and one; as, 7, 13, 17.

A composite number is the product of two other integers; and a prime number is not the product of two other integers.

3. Name all the composite numbers from 0 to 20; from 20 to 50.

4. Name all the prime numbers from 0 to 20; from 20 to 50.

5. Is the number 21 prime or composite? The number 23? 27? 29? 41? 42? 47?

ART. 60. The following tests are useful in determining whether a number is prime or composite:

1. A number is divisible by 2 if its last digit is even.

2. A number is divisible by 5 if its last digit is either 5 or 0.

3. A number is divisible by 3 if the sum of its digits is divisible by 3.

4. If any prime number be divided by 6, the remainder will be either 1 or 5.

NOTE.—The best way to determine whether a number is divisible by 7, 13, 17, and other higher prime numbers, is to attempt to divide by them.

ART. 61. Two or more numbers are *prime to each other, or relatively prime,* when they have no common divisor except 1. Thus, 9 and 16 are prime to each other.

All prime numbers are prime to each other. Composite numbers may be relatively prime; as, 9 and 10; 16 and 25.

FACTORS.

Note.—The terms *number, factor, divisor,* and *multiple* used in the next ten pages denote *integers.*

ORAL EXERCISES.

1. What two numbers multiplied together will produce 15? 21? 33? 28? 35? 42? 56?

The numbers which, multiplied together, will produce a number, are its *Factors.*

2. What are the factors of 6? 10? 15? 14? 25? 39? 45? 55? 77? 63? 72? 77?

3. Give all the pairs of factors of 24.

Answer.—24 = 12 × 2, or 4 × 6, or 3 × 8.

4. Give all the prime factors of 12; 18; 27; 30; 36; 42; 45; 50; 60; 63; 72.

5. What are the prime factors of 24? 32? 48? 56? 60? 80? 84? 90?

6. Of what number are 2, 3, and 5 the prime factors? 2, 3, and 7? 3, 5, and 7? 2, 5, and 11?

WRITTEN EXERCISES.

7. What are the prime factors of 90?

PROCESS.

$$2)90$$
$$3)45$$
$$3)15$$
$$5$$

What are the prime factors of:

8. 100? 96? 120? 150?
9. 124? 256? 220? 320?
10. 112? 140? 168? 280?
11. 84? 126? 210? 420?
12. 126? 252? 125? 288?

2, 3, 3, 5, *Prime factors.*

13. What prime factors are common to 72 and 84?

PROCESS.

The common factors may be designated by drawing a line through them.

$$72 = 2 \times 2 \times 2 \times 3 \times 3$$
$$84 = 2 \times 2 \times 3 \times 7$$

2, 2, 3, *Common factors.*

14. What prime factors are common to 100 and 120? 124 and 180? 220 and 320? 126 and 210?

15. What is the greatest factor common to 84 and 108?

PROCESS.

Resolve 84 and 108 into their prime factors. The product of their common prime factors is their greatest common factor.

$$84 = 2 \times 2 \times 3 \times 7$$
$$108 = 2 \times 2 \times 3 \times 3 \times 3$$

2, 2, 3, *Common factors.*
$2 \times 2 \times 3 = 12$, *G. C. F.*

What is the greatest common factor of:

16. 84 and 210?	**21.** 225, 315, 420?
17. 96 and 240?	**22.** 192, 243, 405?
18. 115 and 210?	**23.** 210, 420, 245?
19. 189 and 378?	**24.** 189, 252, 315?
20. 275 and 550?	**25.** 42, 84, 105, 210?

DEFINITIONS, PRINCIPLES, AND RULES.

ART. 62. A **Factor** of a number is one of the two or more numbers which, multiplied together, will produce it.

When a number is a factor of each of two or more numbers, it is their *Common Factor.*

When a number is the greatest factor common to two or more numbers, it is their *Greatest Common Factor.*

ART. 63. **Principles.**—1. *A factor of a number is a factor of any number of times that number.*

2. *A composite number is the product of all its prime factors.*

3. *If a composite number, composed of two factors, be divided by one factor, the quotient will be the other factor.*

4. *If any composite number be divided by a factor, or by the product of any number of its factors, the quotient will be the product of the remaining factors.*

ART. 64. 1. To resolve a composite number into its prime factors:

Rule.—*Divide it by any prime factor, and the quotient by any prime factor, and so continue until a quotient is obtained which is a prime number. The several divisors and the last quotient are the prime factors.*

2. To find the greatest common factor of two or more numbers:

Rule.—*Resolve the given numbers into their prime factors and select the factors which are found in all the numbers. The product of the common prime factors, thus found, will be the greatest common factor.*

DIVISORS.

ORAL EXERCISES.

1. What are the divisors of 15? 28? 45? 23? 75? 90? 81? 96? 108? 121?

2. What are the prime divisors of 10? Of 18? 20? 30? 42? 50? 60? 63? 75? 81?

3. What is a common divisor of 15 and 35? 42 and 56? 63 and 72? 64 and 80? 36 and 72? 35 and 70? 42 and 77? 56 and 72?

4. What is a common divisor of 27 and 36? 18, 30, and 42? 36, 54, and 72? 35, 42, and 70? 36, 60, and 84? 40, 64, and 72? 56, 72, and 80?

5. What is the greatest number that will exactly divide 32 and 48? 45 and 90? 60 and 96? 36 and 90? 48 and 72? 36 and 108?

6. What is the greatest common divisor of 36 and 60? 45, 60, and 75? 18, 54, and 90? 24, 48, and 72?

7. What is the greatest common divisor of 24, 48, and 72? 16, 48, and 80? 20, 31, and 45? 16, 80, and 96? 24, 36, and 144? 50, 75, and 250?

8. Show that every common divisor of 16 and 28 is a divisor of their *sum.*

9. Show that every common divisor of 16 and 28 is a divisor of their *difference.*

SUGGESTION.—The common divisors of 16 and 28 are 2 and 4, and each is a divisor of 44, the sum of 16 and 28, and in like manner it may be shown that *a common divisor of any two numbers is a divisor of their sum.*

The common divisors of 16 and 28 are each a divisor of 12, their difference, and in like manner it may be shown that *a common divisor of any two numbers is a divisor of their difference.*

Any common divisor of 16 or 28 and 12, their difference, is a common divisor of 16 and 28, and in like manner it may be shown that *a common divisor of either of two numbers and their difference, is a common divisor of the two numbers.*

WRITTEN EXERCISES.

10. What is the greatest common divisor of 126 and 210?

PROCESS BY FACTORING.

$$126 = 2 \times 3 \times 3 \times 7$$
$$210 = 2 \times 3 \times 5 \times 7$$
$$\overline{2 \times 3 \times 7 = 42, \; G. \; C. \; D.}$$

Resolve 126 and 210 into their prime factors. The product of all the prime factors common to 126 and 210 will be their greatest common divisor.

What is the greatest common divisor of:

11. 60 and 84?

12. 63 and 126?

13. 144 and 192?

14. 112, 140, and 168?

15. 84, 126, and 210?

16. 128, 256, and 1280?

17. What is the greatest common divisor of 288 and 528?

288)528(1
288
240)288(1
240
48)240(5
240

48 = *G. C. D.* of 288 and 528.

Divide 528 by 288, and 288 by the first remainder, 240, and 240 by the second remainder, 48; and, there being no remainder, 48 is the greatest common divisor of 288 and 528. Since 48, the *greatest* divisor of itself, is a divisor of 240, it is the G. C. D. of 48 and 240.

Since 48 is a common divisor of 48 and 240, it is a divisor of 288, their *sum;* and since every common divisor of 240 and 288 is a divisor of 48, their *difference*, 48, the *greatest* divisor of itself, and a common divisor of 240 and 288, is the G. C. D. of 240 and 288.

Since 48 is a common divisor of 240 and 288, it is a divisor of 528, their *sum;* and since every common divisor of 288 and 528 is a divisor of 240, their *difference*, 48, the *greatest* common divisor of 240 and 288, is the G. C. D. of 288 and 528.

NOTE.—The explanation of this process is too difficult for young pupils. It may be given to advanced pupils, who should be required to show, in like manner, that the last divisor in the solution of other examples is the greatest common divisor.

What is the greatest common divisor of:

18. 196 and 1728?

19. 336 and 576?

20. 407 and 888?

21. 326 and 807?

22. 756 and 1764?

23. 1064 and 1274?

24. 768 and 5184?

25. 741 and 1938?

26. \$260 and \$416?

27. \$1815 and \$3465?

28. 2145 lb. and 3471 lb. ?

29. 175, 225, and 275?

30. 240, 360, and 480?

31. 144, 216, and 648?

32. 140, 308, and 819?

33. 240, 336, and 1768?

34. 156, 585, and 1287?

35. 2731 and 3120?

36. 2323 and 4242?

37. 320, 368, and 432?

33. 504, 672, and 1260?

39. 160, 240, and 960?

N. C. A.—4.

DEFINITIONS, PRINCIPLES, AND RULES.

ART. 65. A **Divisor** of a number is a number that will exactly divide it. It is also called a **Measure**.

Every divisor of a number is a factor, and conversely every factor is a divisor. The terms factor and divisor differ only in origin, the former implying *multiplication* and the latter *division*.

A **Common Divisor** of two or more numbers is a number that will exactly divide each of them.

The **Greatest Common Divisor** of two or more numbers is the greatest number that will exactly divide each of them.

ART. 66. **Principles.**—1. *Every divisor of a number is a prime factor, or the product of two or more of its prime factors.*

2. *The product of all the prime factors common to two or more numbers is their greatest common divisor.*

3. *A common divisor of two numbers is a divisor of their sum, or of their difference.*

4. *Any common divisor of either of two numbers and their difference is a common divisor of the two numbers.*

5. *The divisor of a number is a divisor of any multiple of it, and a common divisor of two or more numbers is a divisor of any multiple of either of them.*

ART. 67. 1. To find the greatest common divisor of two or more numbers by factoring:

Rule.—*Resolve the given numbers into their prime factors, and select the factors which are common. The product of the common factors will be the greatest common divisor.*

2. To find the greatest common divisor of two numbers by division:

Rule.—*Divide the greater number by the less, and the divisor by the remainder, and the second divisor by the second remainder, and so on, until there is no remainder. The last divisor will be the greatest common divisor.*

NOTE.—When there are three or more numbers, first find the greatest common divisor of two of them, and then the greatest common divisor of this G. C. D. and a third number, and so on.

MULTIPLES.

ORAL EXERCISES.

The product of two or more numbers is a multiple of each of them. 21 is a multiple of 3 and 7.

1. Of what number is 15 a multiple? 21? 42? 35? 63? 33? 56?

2. What number is a multiple of 7? 13? 10? 12?

3. How many multiples has 5? Any number?

4. What is a common multiple of 5 and 7? 8 and 12? 6 and 18? 10 and 15?

5. What is a common multiple of 6 and 7? 5 and 9?

6. How many common multiples have 3 and 5? Any two or more numbers?

7. What number is the least common multiple of 3 and 5? 4 and 7? 5 and 8? 6 and 10?

8. How many least common multiples have 3 and 5? Any two or more numbers?

9. Show that every multiple contains all the prime factors of the numbers of which it is a product.

SUGGESTION.—12 is a multiple of 2 and 6, or 3 and 4. The prime factors of 12 are 2, 2, and 3, and the prime factors of 2 and 6, or 3 and 4, are 2, 2, and 3. It may also be shown that *any number that contains all the prime factors of a given number is its multiple.*

WRITTEN EXERCISES.

10. What is the least common multiple of 12, 18, and 30?

PROCESS BY FACTORING.

$$12 = 2 \times 2 \times 3$$
$$18 = 2 \times 3 \times 3$$
$$30 = 2 \times 3 \times 5$$

$$2 \times 2 \times 3 \times 3 \times 5 = 180, \text{ L. C. M.}$$

Resolve the numbers into their prime factors, and select all the different factors, repeating each as many times as it is found in any one of the numbers. The factor 2 is found twice in 12; the factor 3, twice in 18; and the factor 5, once in 30. The product of $2 \times 2 \times 3 \times 3 \times 5$ is the least common multiple required, since it is the least number which contains all the prime factors of 12, 18, and 30.

What is the least common multiple of:

11. 8, 12, 20?

12. 9, 21, 42?

13. 32, 48, 80?

14. 27, 54, 108?

15. 18, 24, 72, 48?

16. 15, 35, 70, 105?

17. 25, 75, 100, 150?

18. $16, $40, $60, $72?

19. What is the least common multiple of 12, 15, 42, 70?

PROCESS BY DIVISION.

2)	12	15	42	70
3)	6	15	21	35
5)	2	5	7	35
7)	2	1	7	7
	2	1	1	1

$$2 \times 3 \times 5 \times 7 \times 2 = 420, \text{ L. C. M.}$$

Find all the prime factors by dividing the given numbers by any prime number that will exactly divide two or more of them, thus: Divide by 2, a prime factor of 12, 42, and 70, and write the quotients with the 15 underneath. Divide by 3, a prime factor of 6, 15, and 21, and hence a prime factor of 12, 15, and 42. Divide by 5, a prime factor of 5 and 35, and hence of 15 and 70. Divide by 7, a prime factor of 7 and 7, and hence of 42 and 70. The remaining quotient 2 is a prime factor of 12.

Hence, all the prime factors of 12, 15, 42, and 70 are 2, 3, 5, 7, and 2, and since the product of these several prime factors ($2 \times 3 \times 5 \times 7 \times 2 = 420$) is the least number that contains each of them, it is the least common multiple of 12, 15, 42, and 70.

What is the least common multiple of:

20. 12, 18, 30 ?

21. 8, 28, 70 ?

22. 9, 20, 15, 36 ?

23. 15, 24, 25, 30 ?

24. 18, 21, 27, 36 ?

25. 30, 45, 48, 80, 120 ?

26. 16, 30, 40, 50, 75 ?

27. 15, 27, 35, 42, 70 ?

28. 8, 28, 20, 24, 32, 48 ?

29. 2, 3, 4, 5, 6, 7, 8, 9 ?

30. 10, 12, 15, 20, 30 ?

31. 12, 18, 27, 36, 54 ?

32. 9, 15, 18, 30, 45 ?

33. 14, 21, 30, 35, 70 ?

34. 16, 30, 48, 56, 72 ?

35. 15, 16, 18, 20, 24 ?

36. 7, 14, 15, 21, 45 ?

37. 12, 18, 27, 28, 63 ?

38. A can walk round a mile course in 10 minutes, B in 12 minutes, and C in 15 minutes: how many minutes will each walk if they all start together and walk until they are all again together? How many miles will each walk?

DEFINITIONS, PRINCIPLES, AND RULES.

ART. 68. A **Multiple** of a number is any number of which it is a factor.

A product is the multiple of each of its factors. A multiple may be defined as the product arising from taking a number two or more times.

A **Common Multiple** of two or more numbers is a multiple of each of them.

The **Least Common Multiple** of two or more numbers is the least multiple of each of them.

Every number will exactly divide its multiple, and two or more numbers will each exactly divide their common multiple or least common multiple.

ART. 69. **Principles.**—1. *Every multiple of a number contains all its prime factors.*

2. *A common multiple of two or more numbers contains all their prime factors.*

3. *The least common multiple of two or more numbers contains all their prime factors, and no other factors.*

ART. 70. 1. To find the least common multiple of two or more numbers by factoring:

Rule.—*Resolve each of the numbers into its prime factors, and then select all the different factors, taking each the greatest number of times it is found in any number. The product of the different factors, thus selected, will be the least common multiple.*

2. To find the least common multiple of two or more numbers by division:

Rule.—*Write the numbers in a line, and divide by any prime divisor of two or more of them, writing the quotients and the undivided numbers underneath. Divide these resulting numbers by any prime divisor of two or more of them, and so proceed until no two of the resulting numbers have a common prime divisor. The product of the divisors and the last resulting numbers will be the least common multiple required.*

NOTE.—If no two of the given numbers have a common divisor, their product will be the least common multiple.

FRACTIONS.

NUMERATION AND NOTATION.

1. If a single thing be divided into two equal pieces, what part of the whole will one piece be?

2. If a single thing be divided into four equal pieces, what part of the whole will one piece be? Two pieces? Three pieces?

3. How many halves in a single thing or unit? How many fourths?

4. Which is the greater, one half or one fourth of a unit? How many fourths in one half?

5. What is meant by one third of a unit? Two thirds? One sixth? Three sixths? Two fifths? Four fifths? Two fourths? Three fourths?

ART. 71. Such parts of a unit as one half, two thirds, three fourths, etc., are called *Fractions*. A fraction may be expressed in figures by writing the figure denoting the number of equal parts into which the unit is divided below a short horizontal line $[\frac{}{6}]$, and the figure denoting the number of equal parts taken above the same line $[\frac{5}{}]$. Thus, $\frac{5}{6}$ expresses five sixths of a unit.

6. What does $\frac{5}{7}$ express? What does the figure 7, below the line, denote? The figure 5, above the line?

Read the following fractions, and tell, in each case, what each of the two numbers denotes:

7. $\frac{3}{5}$.	**10.** $\frac{5}{8}$.	**13.** $\frac{7}{10}$.	**16.** $\frac{9}{20}$.
8. $\frac{5}{6}$.	**11.** $\frac{6}{9}$.	**14.** $\frac{5}{12}$.	**17.** $1\frac{5}{24}$.
9. $\frac{6}{7}$.	**12.** $\frac{7}{6}$.	**15.** $\frac{8}{15}$.	**18.** $\frac{27}{40}$.

(17)

Write the following fractions in figures:

19.	20.	21.
Two fifths.	Seven twelfths.	Twenty-four fortieths.
Seven ninths.	Ten thirteenths.	Thirty-five fiftieths.
Ten ninths.	Twenty seventeenths.	Forty fifty-fifths.

22. Is the fraction $\frac{3}{4}$ greater or less than 1? Why?

23. Is $\frac{5}{4}$ greater or less than 1? Why?

Compare the value of each of the following fractions with 1:

24. $\frac{5}{7}$.	**26.** $\frac{10}{9}$.	**28.** $\frac{9}{9}$.	**30.** $\frac{41}{45}$.
25. $\frac{8}{5}$.	**27.** $\frac{7}{12}$.	**29.** $\frac{12}{12}$.	**31.** $\frac{33}{20}$.

32. When is the value of a fraction less than 1? When greater than 1?

DEFINITIONS AND PRINCIPLES.

ART. 72. A **Fraction** is one or more of the equal parts of a unit.

The unit divided is the *unit of the fraction*, and one of the equal parts into which it is divided is a *fractional unit*. An integer is composed of integral units, and a fraction of fractional units.

ART. 73. The **Denominator** of a fraction is the number of equal parts into which the unit is divided.

The **Numerator** of a fraction is the number of equal parts taken.

The numerator and denominator are called the **Terms** of the fraction.

ART. 74. A **Common Fraction** is a fraction that results from the division of a unit into *any number* of equal parts.

A common fraction results from the division of a unit into halves, thirds, fourths, fifths, sixths, sevenths, eighths, ninths, tenths, etc., called a *common* division; and a decimal fraction results from the division of a unit into *tenths, hundredths*, etc., called the *decimal* division (Art. 109).

A common fraction may be expressed by words or by figures. It is expressed by figures by two numbers written one above the other with a line between them. The number above the line denotes the *Numerator*, and the number below the line the *Denominator*.

NOTE.—The fraction $\frac{3}{5}$ may be considered as expressing 3 fifths of 1 unit, or 1 fifth of 3 units, or 3 *divided by* 5. Hence, a fraction may be considered an expressed division, the numerator being the dividend, the denominator the divisor, and the fraction itself the quotient.

ART. 75. Common Fractions are *Proper* or *Improper*.

A **Proper Fraction** is one whose numerator is less than its denominator; as, $\frac{5}{6}$, $\frac{3}{8}$.

An **Improper Fraction** is one whose numerator is equal to or greater than its denominator.

The value of a proper fraction is *less* than one; and the value of an improper fraction is *equal to* or *greater* than one, and hence it is regarded as *not properly* the fraction of a unit.

ART. 76. Common Fractions are *Simple, Compound,* or *Complex*.

A **Simple Fraction** is a fraction not united with another, and both of whose terms are integral; as, $\frac{5}{6}$.

A **Compound Fraction** is a fraction of a fraction; as, $\frac{2}{3}$ of $\frac{3}{5}$; $\frac{2}{5}$ of $3\frac{1}{3}$.

A **Complex Fraction** is one having a fraction in one or both of its terms; as, $\frac{\frac{2}{3}}{4}$, $\frac{5}{\frac{3}{5}}$, $\frac{\frac{5}{6}}{\frac{3}{8}}$, $\frac{5\frac{1}{2}}{3\frac{1}{3}}$.

A **Mixed Number** is an integer and a fraction united; as, $5\frac{1}{2}$, $16\frac{1}{2}$.

REDUCTION OF FRACTIONS.

CASE I.

WHOLE OR MIXED NUMBERS TO IMPROPER FRACTIONS.

1. How many thirds in an apple? In 4 apples? 7 apples? 10 apples? 20 apples?

2. How many fifths in 3 melons? In 5 melons? 8 melons? 6 melons? 10 melons?

3. How many sixths in 1? In 5? 8? 12? 20?

4. How many fourths of an inch in $2\frac{1}{4}$ inches? In $3\frac{1}{4}$ inches? $4\frac{1}{4}$ inches? $6\frac{1}{4}$ inches?

5. How many fifths in $3\frac{1}{5}$? $4\frac{2}{5}$? $12\frac{3}{5}$? $16\frac{4}{5}$?

6. How many tenths in $5\frac{1}{10}$? $8\frac{3}{10}$? $12\frac{7}{10}$? $15\frac{9}{10}$?

WRITTEN PROBLEMS.

7. Reduce 225 to sevenths; $225\frac{5}{7}$ to sevenths.

PROCESS.	PROCESS.
225	$225\frac{5}{7}$
7	7
$\dfrac{1575}{7}$, *Ans.*	$\dfrac{1580}{7}$, *Ans.*

8. Reduce 324 to ninths; $324\frac{7}{9}$ to ninths.

9. Reduce $48\frac{11}{15}$ to 15ths; $65\frac{3}{15}$ to 15ths.

10. Reduce $54\frac{7}{20}$ to 20ths; $135\frac{11}{30}$ to 30ths.

11. Reduce $63\frac{7}{12}$ to an improper fraction.

Reduce to an improper fraction:

12. $74\frac{11}{15}$.	**15.** $137\frac{8}{25}$.	**18.** $365\frac{7}{24}$.
13. $206\frac{7}{30}$.	**16.** $408\frac{9}{50}$.	**19.** $208\frac{11}{35}$.
14. $145\frac{3}{40}$.	**17.** $600\frac{13}{41}$.	**20.** $607\frac{5}{12}$.

ART. 77. 1. To reduce an integer to a fraction:

Rule.—*Multiply the integer by the given denominator, and write the denominator under the product.*

2. To reduce a mixed number to a fraction:

Rule.—*Multiply the integer by the denominator of the fraction, to the product add the numerator, and write the denominator under the result.*

CASE II.

IMPROPER FRACTIONS TO WHOLE OR MIXED NUMBERS

21. How many dollars in 8 half-dollars? 10 half-dollars? 12 half-dollars? 16 half-dollars?

22. How many pints in 9 thirds of a pint? 15 thirds of a pint? 33 thirds of a pint? 24 thirds of a pint?

23. How many units in 20 fifths? 35 fifths? 40 fifths? 45 fifths? 50 fifths? 60 fifths?

24. How many units in 36 ninths? 63 ninths? 72 ninths? 45 ninths? 47 ninths? 50 ninths?

25. How many units in $\frac{28}{7}$? $\frac{56}{7}$? $\frac{57}{7}$? $\frac{59}{7}$? $\frac{65}{7}$?

26. How many units in $\frac{93}{10}$? $\frac{37}{12}$? $\frac{80}{25}$? $\frac{104}{25}$? $\frac{203}{50}$?

WRITTEN PROBLEMS.

27. Reduce $\frac{256}{16}$ to a whole number.

PROCESS: $\frac{256}{16} = 256 \div 16 = 16$, *Ans.*

28. Reduce $\frac{263}{16}$ to a mixed number.

Reduce to a whole or a mixed number:

29. $\frac{324}{12}$. **32.** $\frac{636}{32}$. **35.** $\frac{1340}{35}$. **38.** $\frac{4000}{333}$.

30. $\frac{265}{15}$. **33.** $\frac{720}{80}$. **36.** $\frac{2304}{50}$. **39.** $\frac{2388}{45}$.

31. $\frac{705}{18}$. **34.** $\frac{1128}{64}$. **37.** $\frac{4260}{39}$. **40.** $\frac{42351}{21}$.

Art. 78. To reduce an improper fraction to an integer or mixed number:

Rule.—*Divide the numerator of the fraction by the denominator.*

CASE III.

SIMPLE FRACTIONS TO LOWEST TERMS.

41. How many fourths of an inch in 2 eighths of an inch? In 4 eighths? 6 eighths?

42. How many sixths in 2 twelfths? In 4 twelfths? 6 twelfths? 8 twelfths? 10 twelfths?

43. How many sevenths in $\frac{4}{14}$? $\frac{6}{14}$? $\frac{8}{14}$? $\frac{12}{14}$?

44. How many eighths in $\frac{6}{16}$? $\frac{10}{16}$? $\frac{14}{16}$? $\frac{20}{16}$? $\frac{24}{16}$?

45. How many tenths in $\frac{9}{30}$? $\frac{15}{30}$? $\frac{24}{30}$? $\frac{33}{30}$? $\frac{40}{30}$?

46. Reduce $\frac{9}{15}$, $\frac{12}{20}$, $\frac{18}{30}$, $\frac{20}{25}$, $\frac{14}{35}$, $\frac{16}{40}$ each to fifths.

47. Reduce $\frac{20}{30}$, $\frac{28}{24}$, $\frac{35}{42}$, and $\frac{30}{60}$ each to sixths.

48. Divide both terms of $\frac{9}{12}$ by 3, and show that the resulting fraction is equal to $\frac{9}{12}$.

49. Show that the division of both terms of any fraction by the same number gives a fraction equal to the given fraction, and hence does not change its value.

WRITTEN PROBLEMS.

50. Reduce $\frac{105}{140}$ to its lowest terms.

PROCESS.

$$\frac{105 \div 5}{140 \div 5} = \frac{21}{28} \qquad \frac{21 \div 7}{28 \div 7} = \frac{3}{4}.$$

Or: $\dfrac{105 \div 35}{140 \div 35} = \dfrac{3}{4}$, *Ans.*

Divide both terms of $\frac{105}{140}$ by 6, reducing it to $\frac{21}{28}$; then divide both terms of $\frac{21}{28}$ by 7, reducing it to $\frac{3}{4}$. Since $\frac{3}{4}$ can not be reduced to smaller or lower terms, it is in its *lowest* terms. Or, divide both terms of $\frac{105}{140}$ by 35, their greatest common divisor, thus reducing the fraction to $\frac{3}{4}$.

Reduce to lowest terms:

51. $\frac{81}{189}$.	59. $\frac{264}{480}$.	67. $\frac{693}{792}$.	75. $\frac{480}{1245}$.
52. $\frac{195}{210}$.	60. $\frac{360}{576}$.	68. $\frac{720}{1125}$.	76. $\frac{891}{1485}$.
53. $\frac{216}{414}$.	61. $\frac{567}{783}$.	69. $\frac{288}{1728}$.	77. $\frac{2700}{3780}$.
54. $\frac{126}{198}$.	62. $\frac{615}{915}$.	70. $\frac{928}{1320}$.	78. $\frac{777}{1998}$.
55. $\frac{182}{196}$.	63. $\frac{728}{784}$.	71. $\frac{924}{1092}$.	79. $\frac{1818}{2323}$.
56. $\frac{192}{224}$.	64. $\frac{391}{667}$.	72. $\frac{324}{2184}$.	80. $\frac{1170}{1287}$.
57. $\frac{300}{625}$.	65. $\frac{480}{560}$.	73. $\frac{924}{1232}$.	81. $\frac{2388}{4704}$.
58. $\frac{252}{396}$.	66. $\frac{378}{594}$.	74. $\frac{875}{1500}$.	82. $\frac{4444}{7777}$.

83. Express the quotient of 23 divided by 45 in its simplest form. *Ans.* $\frac{23}{45}$.

84. Express the quotient of 19 divided by 37 in its simplest form; also $128 \div 256$.

85. Divide 288 by 360, and express the quotient in its simplest form.

DEFINITIONS, PRINCIPLE, AND RULES.

ART. 79. A fraction is reduced to *lower terms* when it is changed to an equivalent fraction with smaller terms.

A fraction is in its *lowest terms* when its terms are prime to each other.

ART. 80. **Principle.**—*The division of both terms of a fraction by the same number gives a fraction equivalent to the given fraction.*

ART. 81. To reduce a fraction to its lowest terms:

Rules.—*1. Divide both terms of the fraction by any common divisor; then divide both terms of the resulting fraction by any common divisor; and so on, until the terms of the resulting fraction have no common divisor except 1. Or,*

2. Divide both terms of the fraction by their greatest common divisor.

CASE IV.

FRACTIONS TO HIGHER TERMS.

86. How many eighths of a foot in 1 fourth of a foot? In 2 fourths? 3 fourths? 5 fourths? 7 fourths?

87. How many twelfths in 3 sixths? 4 sixths? 5 sixths? 6 sixths? 7 sixths? 10 sixths?

88. How many fifteenths in $\frac{1}{5}$? $\frac{2}{5}$? $\frac{4}{5}$? $\frac{3}{5}$? $\frac{6}{5}$?

89. Change $\frac{2}{3}$, $\frac{3}{4}$, and $\frac{5}{6}$ each to twelfths.

90. Change $\frac{3}{4}$, $\frac{3}{5}$, $\frac{5}{8}$, and $\frac{7}{10}$ each to fortieths.

91. Change $\frac{3}{5}$, $\frac{5}{6}$, $\frac{3}{10}$, and $\frac{7}{15}$ each to sixtieths.

92. Change $\frac{2}{3}$, $\frac{5}{6}$, $\frac{7}{10}$, and $\frac{7}{15}$ each to thirtieths.

93. Change $\frac{4}{5}$, $\frac{5}{8}$, $\frac{7}{10}$, and $\frac{11}{20}$ each to fortieths.

94. Multiply both terms of $\frac{2}{3}$ by 4, and show that the value of the fraction is not changed.

95. Show that the multiplication of both terms of any fraction by the same number does not change its value.

WRITTEN PROBLEMS.

96. Reduce $\frac{5}{6}$, $\frac{7}{8}$, and $\frac{11}{12}$ to twenty-fourths.

97. Reduce $\frac{5}{6}$, $\frac{7}{9}$, $\frac{5}{12}$, and $\frac{11}{18}$ to thirty-sixths.

PROCESS.

$$\frac{5}{6} \quad \frac{7}{8} \quad \frac{11}{12}$$

$$\frac{20}{24} \quad \frac{21}{24} \quad \frac{22}{24}$$

98. Reduce $\frac{3}{10}$, $\frac{7}{15}$, $\frac{9}{20}$, and $\frac{7}{30}$ to sixtieths.

99. Reduce $\frac{2}{3}$, $\frac{3}{5}$, $\frac{5}{9}$, and $\frac{4}{15}$ to forty-fifths.

100. Reduce $\frac{7}{8}$, $\frac{5}{12}$, $\frac{9}{16}$, and $\frac{11}{24}$ to forty-eighths.

101. Reduce $\frac{3}{5}$, $\frac{5}{6}$, $\frac{7}{15}$, and $\frac{13}{30}$ to sixtieths.

102. Solve problems 88 to 93 above on slate or paper.

DEFINITION, PRINCIPLE, AND RULE.

ART. 82. A fraction is reduced to *higher terms* when it is changed to an equivalent fraction with greater terms.

Art. 83. **Principle.**—*The multiplication of both terms of a fraction by the same number gives a fraction equivalent to the given fraction.*

Art. 84. To reduce a fraction to given higher terms:

Rule.—*Divide the given denominator by the denominator of the fraction, and multiply both terms by the quotient.*

CASE V.

FRACTIONS TO EQUIVALENT FRACTIONS WITH A COMMON DENOMINATOR.

WRITTEN PROBLEMS.

103. Reduce $\frac{5}{8}$, $\frac{7}{16}$, $\frac{11}{24}$, and $\frac{21}{32}$ to equivalent fractions with the least common denominator.

PROCESS.

$$\frac{5}{8} \quad \frac{7}{16} \quad \frac{11}{24} \quad \frac{21}{32}$$
$$\frac{60}{96} \quad \frac{42}{96} \quad \frac{44}{96} \quad \frac{63}{96}$$

The least common multiple of 8, 16, 24, and 32 is 96, and hence 96 is the least common denominator. Change the fractions to 96ths, as follows: $\frac{5}{8} = \frac{60}{96}$; $\frac{7}{16} = \frac{42}{96}$; $\frac{11}{24} = \frac{44}{96}$; $\frac{21}{32} = \frac{63}{96}$.

Reduce to equivalent fractions with the least common denominator:

104. $\frac{3}{4}$, $\frac{5}{8}$, $\frac{7}{16}$, $\frac{7}{12}$.

105. $\frac{3}{4}$, $\frac{1}{8}$, $\frac{5}{6}$, $\frac{7}{9}$.

106. $\frac{1}{2}$, $\frac{3}{4}$, $\frac{5}{8}$, $\frac{5}{12}$.

107. $\frac{3}{5}$, $\frac{5}{6}$, $\frac{7}{15}$, $\frac{11}{30}$.

108. $\frac{4}{5}$, $\frac{9}{10}$, $\frac{13}{20}$, $\frac{11}{40}$.

109. $\frac{2}{3}$, $\frac{3}{7}$, $\frac{5}{6}$, $\frac{4}{21}$.

110. $\frac{4}{9}$, $\frac{11}{12}$, $\frac{17}{36}$, $\frac{23}{24}$.

111. $\frac{2}{3}$, $\frac{3}{5}$, $\frac{5}{6}$, $\frac{7}{8}$.

112. $\frac{7}{10}$, $\frac{8}{15}$, $\frac{11}{20}$, $\frac{13}{30}$.

113. $\frac{7}{12}$, $\frac{8}{21}$, $\frac{11}{28}$, $\frac{17}{42}$.

114. $\frac{2}{5}$, $\frac{11}{12}$, $\frac{11}{20}$, $\frac{29}{30}$, $\frac{31}{60}$.

115. $\frac{5}{9}$, $\frac{14}{35}$, $\frac{22}{45}$, $\frac{12}{63}$, $\frac{101}{115}$.

Art. 85. To reduce several fractions to equivalent fractions with the least common denominator:

Rule.—*Divide the least common multiple of the denominators by the denominator of each fraction, and multiply both of its terms by the quotient.*

CASE VI.

COMPOUND FRACTIONS TO SIMPLE FRACTIONS.

116. How much is 1 half of 1 third of a pear? 1 half of 1 fourth of a pear? $\frac{1}{2}$ of $\frac{1}{6}$ of a pear?

117. A father divided $\frac{1}{2}$ of a pine-apple equally among 3 boys: what part of the pine-apple did each boy receive?

118. What is $\frac{1}{3}$ of $\frac{1}{2}$? $\frac{1}{3}$ of $\frac{1}{5}$? $\frac{1}{3}$ of $\frac{1}{8}$? $\frac{1}{3}$ of $\frac{1}{7}$?

119. What is $\frac{1}{2}$ of $\frac{1}{8}$? $\frac{1}{2}$ of $\frac{3}{8}$? $\frac{1}{2}$ of $\frac{5}{8}$? $\frac{1}{2}$ of $\frac{6}{7}$?

120. What is $\frac{1}{5}$ of $\frac{1}{3}$? $\frac{1}{5}$ of $\frac{2}{3}$? $\frac{2}{5}$ of $\frac{2}{3}$? $\frac{3}{5}$ of $\frac{2}{3}$?

SOLUTION.—$\frac{1}{5}$ of $\frac{1}{3}$ is $\frac{1}{15}$; $\frac{1}{5}$ of $\frac{2}{3}$ is $\frac{2}{15}$; and $\frac{2}{5}$ of $\frac{2}{3}$ is 2 times $\frac{2}{15}$, which is $\frac{4}{15}$.

121. What is $\frac{1}{7}$ of $\frac{1}{9}$? $\frac{1}{7}$ of $\frac{5}{9}$? $\frac{3}{7}$ of $\frac{5}{9}$? $\frac{5}{7}$ of $\frac{7}{9}$?

122. What is $\frac{2}{3}$ of $\frac{3}{4}$? $\frac{2}{3}$ of $\frac{5}{6}$? $\frac{2}{3}$ of $\frac{7}{8}$? $\frac{3}{7}$ of $\frac{7}{8}$?

123. What is $\frac{3}{5}$ of $\frac{4}{5}$? $\frac{3}{7}$ of $\frac{5}{6}$? $\frac{5}{6}$ of $\frac{7}{12}$? $\frac{6}{7}$ of $\frac{5}{9}$?

NOTE.—$\frac{3}{5}$ of $\frac{4}{5} = \frac{3}{5} \times \frac{4}{5}$, and hence "of" between two fractions is equivalent to $\times$.

WRITTEN PROBLEMS.

124. Reduce $\frac{5}{9}$ of $\frac{3}{5}$ of $3\frac{1}{3}$ to a simple fraction.

PROCESS: $\frac{5}{9}$ of $\frac{3}{5}$ of $3\frac{1}{3} = \frac{5}{9} \times \frac{3}{5} \times \frac{10}{3} = \frac{150}{135} = \frac{10}{9} = 1\frac{1}{9}$, *Ans.*

Or: $\frac{5}{9}$ of $\frac{3}{5}$ of $3\frac{1}{3} = \frac{\cancel{5} \times \cancel{3} \times 10}{9 \times \cancel{5} \times \cancel{3}} = \frac{10}{9} = 1\frac{1}{9}$, *Ans.*

Reduce to a simple fraction:

125. $\frac{2}{3}$ of $\frac{3}{4}$ of $\frac{4}{5}$.

126. $\frac{2}{5}$ of $\frac{3}{7}$ of $2\frac{1}{2}$.

127. $\frac{5}{7}$ of $1\frac{4}{15}$ of $1\frac{7}{8}$.

128. $\frac{4}{5}$ of $\frac{6}{7}$ of $2\frac{1}{3}$.

129. $\frac{3}{5}$ of $\frac{5}{9}$ of $\frac{6}{7}$ of $3\frac{1}{3}$.

130. $\frac{3}{4}$ of $\frac{4}{15}$ of $\frac{6}{7}$ of $4\frac{2}{3}$.

131. $\frac{2}{5}$ of $\frac{4}{7}$ of $2\frac{5}{8}$ of $2\frac{1}{2}$.

132. $\frac{2}{3}$ of $\frac{9}{10}$ of $\frac{7}{12}$ of $3\frac{1}{2}$.

133. $\frac{7}{8}$ of $\frac{16}{21}$ of $1\frac{1}{5}$ of $3\frac{1}{3}$.

134. $\frac{6}{7}$ of $\frac{14}{15}$ of $1\frac{1}{12}$ of $2\frac{2}{5}$.

ART. 86. To reduce a compound fraction to a simple fraction :

Rules.—*1. Multiply the numerators together for a numerator, and the denominators together for a denominator. Or :*

2. Indicate the continued multiplication of the numerators, and also of the denominators, and reduce the resulting fraction to its lowest terms, by cancellation.

---

135. Reduce 16 to a fraction having 8 for a denominator.

136. How many 15ths of a gallon in $33\frac{1}{3}$ gallons?

137. Reduce $\frac{304}{24}$ to a mixed number with the fraction in its lowest terms.

138. Reduce $\$\frac{99}{15}$, $\$1\frac{37}{25}$, $\$\frac{485}{60}$, and $\$\frac{700}{11}$ each to whole or mixed numbers.

139. Reduce $12\frac{1}{2}$, $18\frac{3}{4}$, and $33\frac{1}{3}$ to improper fractions, and each to 12ths.

140. Reduce $\frac{2}{15}$ of $\frac{1}{12}$ of $2\frac{1}{13}$ of 24 to a simple fraction.

141. Reduce $\frac{3}{4}$ of $\frac{7}{9}$, $\frac{5}{6}$ of $2\frac{2}{5}$, and $\frac{3}{7}$ of $13\frac{1}{8}$ to equivalent simple fractions in their lowest terms.

142. Reduce $\frac{5}{8}$, $\frac{5}{6}$, and $\frac{7}{12}$ to equivalent fractions having the least common denominator.

143. Reduce $\frac{5}{6}$, $\frac{7}{9}$, $\frac{11}{12}$, and $2\frac{1}{3}$ to equivalent fractions having the least common denominator.

144. Reduce $\frac{5}{6}$, $5\frac{1}{2}$, and $\frac{3}{5}$ of $\frac{5}{9}$ to equivalent simple fractions having the least common denominator.

145. Reduce $\frac{4}{9}$, $\frac{2}{3}$ of $\frac{6}{7}$, and $\frac{4}{5}$ of $6\frac{2}{3}$ to equivalent simple fractions having the least common denominator.

146. Reduce $\frac{1}{2}$ of $2\frac{1}{2}$, $\frac{5}{6}$ of 3, and $\frac{3}{7}$ of $\frac{7}{9}$ of $6\frac{1}{4}$ to equivalent simple fractions having the least common denominator.

147. Reduce $\frac{2}{3}$ of $\frac{3}{4}$ of $\frac{2}{5}$, $\frac{3}{5}$ of $2\frac{1}{2}$, and $\frac{3}{7}$ of $2\frac{1}{3}$ of $\frac{7}{8}$ to equivalent simple fractions with the least common denominator.

ADDITION OF FRACTIONS.

1. What is the sum of $\frac{2}{9}$, $\frac{5}{9}$, and $\frac{1}{9}$?

2. What is the sum of $\frac{5}{12}$, $\frac{7}{12}$, and $\frac{11}{12}$?

3. What is the sum of $\frac{1}{3}$ and $\frac{1}{4}$? $\frac{2}{3}$ and $\frac{1}{2}$? $\frac{1}{4}$ and $\frac{1}{2}$? $\frac{1}{2}$ and $\frac{1}{5}$? $\frac{1}{2}$ and $\frac{1}{6}$? $\frac{1}{3}$ and $\frac{5}{6}$?

4. What is the sum of $\frac{2}{5}$ and $\frac{3}{8}$? $\frac{3}{5}$ and $\frac{5}{8}$? $\frac{3}{5}$ and $\frac{5}{6}$?

5. What is the sum of $\frac{3}{8}$ and $\frac{5}{22}$? $\frac{5}{6}$ and $\frac{7}{12}$? $\frac{2}{3}$ and $\frac{7}{8}$? $\frac{3}{4}$ and $\frac{5}{6}$? $\frac{6}{7}$ and $\frac{7}{14}$? $\frac{5}{6}$ and $\frac{5}{9}$?

6. What is the sum of $\frac{4}{5}$ and $\frac{4}{7}$? $\frac{3}{7}$ and $\frac{4}{9}$? $\frac{5}{7}$ and $\frac{9}{14}$? $\frac{5}{8}$ and $\frac{7}{10}$? $\frac{3}{5}$ and $\frac{3}{10}$? $\frac{4}{11}$ and $\frac{2}{3}$?

7. What is the sum of $\frac{2}{3}$ and $2\frac{2}{3}$? $\frac{3}{4}$ and $1\frac{1}{2}$? $\frac{5}{6}$ and $\frac{7}{9}$? $\frac{3}{5}$ and $1\frac{1}{3}$? $\frac{7}{8}$ and $\frac{5}{12}$? $\frac{6}{7}$ and $\frac{7}{10}$?

8. What is the sum of $\frac{1}{2}$, $\frac{1}{4}$, and $\frac{1}{8}$? $\frac{1}{3}$, $\frac{1}{6}$, and $\frac{1}{12}$? $\frac{1}{2}$, $\frac{3}{4}$, and $\frac{5}{8}$? $\frac{1}{6}$, $\frac{2}{3}$, and $\frac{5}{12}$?

9. What is the sum of $\frac{1}{2}$ of $\frac{2}{5}$ and $\frac{2}{3}$ of $\frac{3}{8}$?

10. Show that fractions having a common denominator express like fractional units, and hence can be added.

WRITTEN PROBLEMS.

11. What is the sum of $\frac{9}{23}$, $\frac{16}{23}$, and $\frac{10}{23}$?

PROCESS: $\frac{9}{23} + \frac{16}{23} + \frac{10}{23} = \frac{9 + 16 + 10}{23} = \frac{35}{23} = 1\frac{12}{23}$, *Ans.*

12. What is the sum of $\frac{11}{18}$, $\frac{13}{18}$, $\frac{17}{18}$, and $\frac{7}{18}$?

13. What is the sum of $\frac{13}{45}$, $\frac{23}{45}$, $\frac{31}{45}$, and $\frac{37}{45}$?

14. What is the sum of $\frac{141}{160}$, $\frac{97}{160}$, and $\frac{153}{160}$?

15. What is the sum of $\frac{5}{8}$, $\frac{7}{12}$, and $\frac{11}{16}$?

PROCESS.

$\frac{5}{8} + \frac{7}{12} + \frac{11}{16} =$

$\frac{30}{48} + \frac{28}{48} + \frac{33}{48} =$

$\frac{91}{48} = 1\frac{43}{48}$, *Ans.*

Since only like fractional units can be added, reduce the fractions $\frac{5}{8}$, $\frac{7}{12}$, and $\frac{11}{16}$ to equivalent fractions having a common denominator, and then add the resulting fractions.

Add the following fractions:

16. $\frac{4}{5}$ and $\frac{11}{14}$.

17. $\frac{3}{8}$, $\frac{7}{12}$, and $\frac{9}{16}$.

18. $\frac{5}{6}$, $\frac{11}{12}$, and $\frac{13}{18}$.

19. $\frac{3}{5}$, $\frac{7}{10}$, and $\frac{13}{15}$.

20. $\frac{9}{14}$, $\frac{20}{21}$, and $\frac{31}{42}$.

21. $\frac{9}{16}$, $\frac{9}{20}$, $\frac{23}{30}$, and $\frac{41}{60}$.

22. $\frac{5}{6}$, $\frac{5}{9}$, $\frac{11}{15}$, and $\frac{17}{30}$.

23. $\frac{13}{18}$, $\frac{15}{27}$, $\frac{50}{81}$, and $\frac{2}{3}$.

24. $\frac{7}{8}$, $\frac{7}{12}$, $\frac{7}{18}$, and $\frac{7}{24}$.

25. $\frac{1}{12}$, $\frac{1}{15}$, $\frac{1}{20}$, and $\frac{1}{30}$.

26. Add $\frac{3}{4}$, $\frac{2}{3}$ of $\frac{3}{5}$, and $\frac{3}{7}$ of $\frac{5}{8}$ of $2\frac{1}{3}$.

PROCESS.

$\frac{2}{3}$ of $\frac{3}{5} = \frac{2}{5}$; $\frac{3}{7}$ of $\frac{5}{8}$ of $\frac{7}{3} = \frac{5}{8}$;

$\frac{3}{4} + \frac{2}{5} + \frac{5}{8} = \frac{30}{40} + \frac{16}{40} + \frac{25}{40} = 1\frac{31}{40}$

Since $\frac{2}{3}$ of $\frac{3}{5} = \frac{2}{5}$, and $\frac{3}{7}$ of $\frac{5}{8}$ of $2\frac{1}{3} = \frac{5}{8}$, the sum of $\frac{3}{4} + \frac{2}{3}$ of $\frac{3}{5} + \frac{3}{7}$ of $\frac{5}{8}$ of $2\frac{1}{3} = \frac{3}{4} + \frac{2}{5} + \frac{5}{8}$.

27. Add $\frac{2}{3}$ of $\frac{3}{8}$, $\frac{3}{5}$ of $\frac{5}{13}$ of $2\frac{1}{6}$, and $\frac{7}{8}$.

28. Add $\frac{4}{5}$ of $2\frac{1}{2}$, $\frac{3}{4}$ of $\frac{4}{9}$, and $\frac{3}{8}$ of $\frac{2}{3}$ of 6.

29. Add $\frac{3}{14}$, $\frac{1}{7}$ of 5, and $\frac{6}{7}$ of $\frac{8}{9}$ of $\frac{5}{8}$.

30. Add $\frac{3}{15}$ of 2, $\frac{2}{3}$ of $\frac{3}{5}$, $\frac{1}{2}$ of $\frac{4}{5}$ of $\frac{5}{12}$, and $3\frac{1}{3}$.

31. Add $33\frac{1}{3}$, $37\frac{1}{2}$, $55\frac{3}{4}$, and $66\frac{2}{3}$.

PROCESS.

$33\frac{1}{3}$	$\frac{4}{12}$
$37\frac{1}{2}$	$\frac{6}{12}$
$55\frac{3}{4}$	$\frac{9}{12}$
$66\frac{2}{3}$	$\frac{8}{12}$
$193\frac{1}{4}$, *Ans.*	

The sum of $33\frac{1}{3}$, $37\frac{1}{2}$, $55\frac{3}{4}$, and $66\frac{2}{3}$, equals the sum of $\frac{1}{3} + \frac{1}{2} + \frac{3}{4} + \frac{2}{3}$ added to the sum of $33 + 37 + 55 + 66$. $\frac{1}{3} + \frac{1}{2} + \frac{3}{4} + \frac{2}{3} = 2\frac{3}{12}$ or $2\frac{1}{4}$. Write the $\frac{1}{4}$ under the fractions and add the 2 with the integers. The sum is $193\frac{1}{4}$.

32. Add $39\frac{1}{3}$, $56\frac{3}{4}$, $88\frac{1}{6}$, and $104\frac{5}{12}$.

33. Add 45, $87\frac{3}{4}$, $66\frac{2}{3}$, and $75\frac{1}{2}$.

34. Add $12\frac{1}{2}$, $16\frac{2}{3}$, $18\frac{3}{4}$, $30\frac{1}{4}$, $33\frac{1}{3}$. and $62\frac{1}{2}$.

35. Add $\frac{2}{3}$, $\frac{2}{3}$ of $\frac{3}{4}$, $16\frac{2}{3}$, and $48\frac{1}{4}$.

36. Add $512\frac{1}{2}$, $318\frac{3}{4}$, 825, and $381\frac{1}{4}$.

37. Add $\frac{5}{7}$, $\frac{9}{14}$, $\frac{3}{7}$ of $5\frac{1}{4}$, and $65\frac{5}{21}$.

38. Add $\frac{3}{4}$, $\frac{2}{5}$, $\frac{3}{8}$, $\frac{7}{10}$, and $\frac{5}{12}$ of $2\frac{2}{5}$.

ART. 87. **Principles.**—1. *Only like fractional units can be added.* Hence,

2. *Fractions must have a common denominator before they can be added.*

ART. 88. 1. To add fractions:

Rule.—*Reduce the fractions to equivalent fractions having a common denominator, add the numerators of the new fractions, and under the sum write the common denominator.*

2. To add mixed numbers:

Rule.—*Add the fractions and the integers separately, and combine the results.*

NOTES.—1. Compound fractions must be reduced to simple fractions before they can be added.

2. When mixed numbers are small they may be reduced to improper fractions and then added.

SUBTRACTION OF FRACTIONS.

1. How much is $\frac{5}{8}$ of an orange less $\frac{3}{8}$ of an orange?

2. How much is $\frac{8}{8}$ less $\frac{3}{8}$? $\frac{8}{8}$ less $\frac{5}{8}$? $\frac{8}{8}$ less $\frac{7}{8}$?

3. How much is $\frac{11}{12}$ less $\frac{3}{12}$? $\frac{11}{12}$ less $\frac{5}{12}$? $\frac{11}{12}$ less $\frac{9}{12}$?

4. How much is $\frac{3}{4}$ of an apple less $\frac{1}{3}$ of an apple?

SUGGESTION.—Change $\frac{3}{4}$ and $\frac{1}{3}$ to twelfths.

5. How much is $\frac{3}{4}$ less $\frac{1}{3}$? $\frac{3}{4}$ less $\frac{2}{3}$? $\frac{2}{3}$ less $\frac{1}{4}$?

6. How much is $\frac{5}{6}$ less $\frac{3}{4}$? $\frac{3}{4}$ less $\frac{2}{6}$? $\frac{4}{5}$ less $\frac{3}{4}$?

7. How much is $\frac{5}{7}$ less $\frac{3}{5}$? $\frac{2}{5}$ less $\frac{2}{7}$? $\frac{6}{7}$ less $\frac{3}{4}$?

8. How much is $\frac{5}{8}$ less $\frac{1}{2}$? $\frac{7}{8}$ less $\frac{3}{5}$? $\frac{4}{7}$ less $\frac{3}{8}$?

9. How much is $\frac{7}{12}$ less $\frac{1}{3}$? $\frac{11}{12}$ less $\frac{3}{4}$? $\frac{5}{8}$ less $\frac{1}{12}$?

10. How much is $\frac{2}{5}$ less $\frac{1}{3}$? $\frac{2}{5}$ less $\frac{1}{7}$? $\frac{5}{7}$ less $\frac{1}{2}$?

11. Why can not $\frac{2}{3}$ be subtracted from $\frac{3}{4}$ without first reducing the fractions to equivalent fractions with a common denominator?

WRITTEN PROBLEMS.

12. Subtract $\frac{19}{35}$ from $\frac{27}{35}$.

PROCESS : $\frac{27}{35} - \frac{19}{35} = \frac{27-19}{35} = \frac{8}{35}$, *Ans.*

13. Subtract $\frac{37}{90}$ from $\frac{56}{90}$; $\frac{37}{85}$ from $\frac{75}{85}$; $\frac{49}{88}$ from $\frac{73}{88}$.

14. Subtract $\frac{7}{15}$ from $\frac{17}{18}$.

PROCESS : $\frac{17}{18} - \frac{7}{15} = \frac{85}{90} - \frac{42}{90} = \frac{43}{90}$, *Ans.*

How much is:

15. $\frac{14}{15} - \frac{5}{9}$?

16. $\frac{13}{18} - \frac{7}{12}$?

17. $\frac{16}{27} - \frac{5}{18}$?

18. $\frac{33}{50} - \frac{11}{20}$?

19. $\frac{19}{21} - \frac{11}{14}$?

20. $\frac{7}{12} - \frac{4}{15}$?

21. $\frac{10}{33} - \frac{9}{44}$?

22. $\frac{23}{36} - \frac{17}{54}$?

23. $\frac{29}{60} - \frac{13}{45}$?

24. From $\frac{1}{2}$ of $\frac{4}{5}$ take $\frac{2}{7}$ of $\frac{7}{8}$ of $\frac{2}{3}$.

PROCESS : $\frac{1}{2}$ of $\frac{4}{5} = \frac{2}{5}$; $\frac{2}{7}$ of $\frac{7}{8}$ of $\frac{2}{3} = \frac{1}{6}$; $\frac{2}{5} - \frac{1}{6} = \frac{7}{30}$, *Ans.*

25. From $\frac{3}{4}$ of $\frac{5}{9}$ take $\frac{3}{5}$ of $\frac{2}{3}$ of $\frac{5}{9}$.

26. From $\frac{4}{5}$ of 7 take $\frac{1}{2}$ of $\frac{3}{4}$ of 7.

27. From $\frac{2}{3}$ of $\frac{5}{6}$ of $\frac{3}{4}$ take $\frac{5}{6}$ of $\frac{2}{3}$ of $\frac{5}{8}$.

28. From $\frac{3}{5}$ of $\frac{2}{7}$ of $2\frac{1}{2}$ take $\frac{3}{11}$.

29. From $342\frac{2}{5}$ take $247\frac{3}{4}$.

PROCESS.

$342\frac{2}{5}$ $\frac{8}{20}$

$247\frac{3}{4}$ $\frac{15}{20}$

$94\frac{13}{20}$, *Ans.*

First subtract the fractions and then the integers. Since $\frac{15}{20}$ is greater than $\frac{8}{20}$, add $\frac{20}{20}$ to $\frac{8}{20}$, making $\frac{28}{20}$, and then subtract $\frac{15}{20}$ from $\frac{28}{20}$, writing the difference, $\frac{13}{20}$, under the fractions, and adding 1 ($\frac{20}{20}$) to the 7 units before subtracting the integers.

NOTE.—Instead of adding 1 to the 7 units, 1 may be taken from the 2 units in the minuend.

How much is:

30. $5\frac{1}{2} - 3\frac{1}{4}$?   **33.** $93\frac{3}{4} - 46\frac{7}{8}$?   **36.** $241\frac{7}{8} - 153\frac{5}{12}$?

31. $6\frac{2}{3} - 4\frac{1}{2}$?   **34.** $56\frac{3}{5} - 37\frac{1}{2}$?   **37.** $233\frac{1}{3} - 162\frac{1}{2}$?

32. $9\frac{3}{4} - 7\frac{1}{3}$?   **35.** $108\frac{2}{7} - 90\frac{2}{3}$?   **38.** $312\frac{1}{2} - 248\frac{3}{4}$?

39. What fraction added to $\frac{3}{8}$ will make $\frac{11}{12}$?

40. What number added to $6\frac{3}{4}$ will make $16\frac{2}{3}$?

41. From $\frac{2}{3}$ of $\frac{3}{4}$ of $\frac{4}{5}$ take $\frac{3}{5}$ of $\frac{5}{9}$ of $\frac{6}{7}$.

42. From $\frac{2}{5}$ of $\frac{3}{7}$ of $2\frac{1}{2}$ take $\frac{3}{4}$ of $\frac{4}{15}$ of $\frac{6}{7}$.

43. From $66\frac{2}{3}$ take $\frac{3}{4}$ of 75.

PRINCIPLES AND RULES.

ART. 89. **Principles.**—1. *Only like fractional units can be subtracted.* Hence,

2. *Fractions must have a common denominator before their difference can be found.*

ART. 90. 1. To subtract fractions:

Rule.—*Reduce the fractions to equivalent fractions having a common denominator, subtract the numerator of the subtrahend from the numerator of the minuend, and under the difference write the common denominator.*

2. To subtract mixed numbers:

Rule.—*Subtract the fractions and the integers separately, and unite the results.*

NOTES.—1. Compound fractions must be reduced to simple fractions before they can be subtracted.

2. When mixed numbers are small, they may be reduced to improper fractions and then subtracted.

---

44. From the sum of $\frac{5}{6}$ and $\frac{3}{4}$ take their difference.

45. From $\frac{5}{8} + \frac{3}{5}$ take $\frac{5}{6} - \frac{3}{5}$.

46. From $\frac{3}{5} + \frac{2}{3} + \frac{7}{10}$ take $\frac{3}{7}$ of $1\frac{1}{6}$.

47. From $\frac{7}{9} + \frac{3}{4}$ take $\frac{7}{12} - \frac{2}{3}$ of $\frac{5}{8}$.

48. From $\frac{5}{6} + \frac{3}{5}$ of $2\frac{1}{2} + 3\frac{1}{4}$ take $\frac{5}{12} + \frac{3}{5}$.

49. From $\frac{7}{12}$ of 14 take $\frac{7}{11}$ of $\frac{2}{3} + \frac{3}{11}$.

50. From a cask containing $45\frac{1}{2}$ gallons of sirup, a grocer sold one customer $16\frac{3}{4}$ gallons and another $21\frac{3}{8}$ gallons: how many gallons remained unsold?

51. A man bequeathed $\frac{3}{10}$ of his property to his wife, $\frac{5}{12}$ of it to his children, and the remainder to a college for its better endowment: what part of his property did the college receive?

52. A man owning $\frac{2}{3}$ of a factory, sold $\frac{2}{5}$ of his share: what part of the factory did he sell? What part did he still own?

53. Two ninths of a pole is in the mud, $\frac{2}{7}$ of it in the water, and the rest of it in the air: what part of the pole is in the air?

MULTIPLICATION OF FRACTIONS.

CASE I.

FRACTIONS MULTIPLIED BY INTEGERS.

1. How much is twice 2 ninths of an inch? 4 times 2 ninths of an inch?

2. If a basket hold $\frac{3}{4}$ of a bushel, how many bushels will 8 baskets hold? 10 baskets?

3. How much is 8 times $\frac{3}{4}$? 10 times $\frac{3}{4}$? 20 times $\frac{3}{4}$?

4. How much is 6 times $\frac{5}{7}$? 8 times $\frac{7}{9}$? 9 times $\frac{7}{11}$?

5. How much is 7 times $1\frac{1}{12}$? 9 times $\frac{4}{15}$? 8 times $1\frac{2}{20}$? 6 times $1\frac{1}{15}$? 10 times $\frac{5}{21}$?

6. How much is 12 times $\frac{7}{8}$? 11 times $\frac{8}{8}$? 10 times $\frac{7}{11}$? 9 times $\frac{10}{11}$? 8 times $\frac{5}{12}$? 7 times $\frac{8}{11}$?

7. How much is 6 times $5\frac{1}{2}$? 9 times $6\frac{2}{3}$? 7 times $10\frac{1}{2}$? 8 times $3\frac{3}{4}$? 10 times $5\frac{1}{2}$? 10 times $3\frac{1}{3}$?

8. How much is 7 times $4\frac{1}{4}$? 8 times $6\frac{1}{4}$? 12 times $3\frac{1}{3}$? 11 times $5\frac{1}{2}$? 9 times $6\frac{2}{3}$? 6 times $3\frac{1}{3}$?

9. Why does multiplying the numerator of $\frac{4}{15}$ by 3 multiply the fraction by 3?

10. Why does dividing the denominator of $\frac{4}{15}$ by 3 multiply the fraction by 3?

11. In how many ways may a fraction be multiplied by an integer?

WRITTEN PROBLEMS.

Multiply:

12. $\frac{8}{15}$ by 9.	**17.** $\frac{25}{144}$ by 12.	**22.** $62\frac{1}{2}$ by 36.
13. $\frac{13}{24}$ by 10.	**18.** $\frac{47}{256}$ by 16.	**23.** $45\frac{3}{4}$ by 80.
14. $\frac{5}{21}$ by 24.	**19.** $\frac{31}{360}$ by 60.	**24.** $518\frac{3}{4}$ by 32.
15. $\frac{11}{63}$ by 45.	**20.** $\frac{111}{625}$ by 25.	**25.** $66\frac{2}{3}$ by 52.
16. $\frac{16}{25}$ by 30.	**21.** $\frac{108}{133}$ by 50.	**26.** $37\frac{1}{2}$ ft. by 112.

PRINCIPLE AND RULES.

ART. 91. **Principle.**—*A fraction is multiplied by multiplying its numerator or dividing its denominator.*

ART. 92. 1. To multiply a fraction by an integer:

Rule.—*Multiply the numerator or divide the denominator.*

2. To multiply a mixed number by an integer:

Rule.—*Multiply the fraction and the integer separately, and add the products.*

CASE II.

INTEGERS MULTIPLIED BY FRACTIONS.

27. If a ton of hay cost \$16, what will $\frac{1}{4}$ of a ton cost? $\frac{3}{4}$ of a ton? $\frac{5}{8}$ of a ton?

28. If an acre of land is worth $50, what is $\frac{1}{5}$ of an acre worth? $\frac{4}{5}$ of an acre? $\frac{3}{5}$ of an acre?

29. What is $\frac{1}{6}$ of 42? $\frac{5}{6}$ of 42? $\frac{7}{6}$ of 42? $\frac{10}{6}$ of 42?

30. What is $\frac{3}{7}$ of 56? $\frac{5}{7}$ of 56? $\frac{4}{7}$ of 56? $\frac{8}{7}$ of 56?

31. What is $\frac{5}{9}$ of 63? $\frac{7}{11}$ of 99? $\frac{5}{12}$ of 72? $\frac{7}{9}$ of 56?

SOLUTION.—$\frac{1}{9}$ of $56 = 6\frac{2}{9}$, and $\frac{7}{9}$ of $56 = 7$ times $6\frac{2}{9} = 43\frac{5}{9}$.

32. What is $\frac{5}{8}$ of 66? $\frac{7}{9}$ of 66? $\frac{5}{12}$ of 66? $\frac{6}{7}$ of 74?

33. What is $16 \times \frac{3}{4}$? $50 \times \frac{4}{5}$? $42 \times \frac{5}{6}$?

SUGGESTION.—Since $\frac{3}{4}$ is $\frac{3}{4}$ of 1, $16 \times \frac{3}{4} = \frac{3}{4}$ of $16 \times 1 = \frac{3}{4}$ of 16.

34. $57 \times \frac{5}{8}$? $75 \times \frac{5}{9}$? $87 \times \frac{7}{12}$? $95 \times \frac{7}{10}$? $76 \times \frac{6}{7}$?

35. $47 \times \frac{5}{9}$? $68 \times \frac{7}{8}$? $75 \times \frac{5}{6}$? $83 \times \frac{9}{10}$? $100 \times \frac{5}{12}$?

36. Show that the product of an integer by a fraction equals the fraction of the integer.

WRITTEN PROBLEMS.

37. Multiply 654 by $\frac{7}{12}$.

PROCESS.

$12)\overline{654}$
$\quad 54\frac{1}{2}$
$\quad 7$
$\overline{381\frac{1}{2}}$, *Ans.*

Or:
$\quad 654$
$\quad 7$
$12)\overline{4578}$
$\quad 381\frac{1}{2}$

Since $\frac{7}{12} = 7$ times $\frac{1}{12}$ or $\frac{1}{12}$ of 7, the product of $654 \times \frac{7}{12} = 7$ times $\frac{1}{12}$ of 654, or $\frac{1}{12}$ of 7 times 654.

Multiply:

38. 66 by $\frac{7}{9}$.

39. 58 by $\frac{13}{15}$.

40. 92 by $\frac{7}{22}$.

41. 80 by $\frac{7}{11}$.

42. 784 by $\frac{13}{40}$.

43. 648 by $\frac{25}{26}$.

44. 564 by $\frac{33}{40}$.

45. 384 by $\frac{31}{48}$.

46. 757 by $\frac{2}{3}$ of $\frac{6}{7}$.

47. 908 by $\frac{3}{4}$ of $2\frac{1}{2}$.

48. 588 by $\frac{4}{15}$ of $3\frac{1}{3}$.

49. 560 by $\frac{3}{5}$ of $7\frac{1}{2}$.

50. Multiply 256 by $27\frac{5}{8}$.

SUGGESTION.—Since $256 \times 27\frac{5}{8} = 256 \times 27 + 256 \times \frac{5}{8}$, first multiply by the integer and then by the fraction, or first by the fraction and then by the integer, and add the products.

Multiply:

51. 66 by $8\frac{2}{3}$.

52. 72 by $9\frac{5}{8}$.

53. 96 by $8\frac{5}{12}$.

54. 645 by $12\frac{3}{4}$.

55. 465 by $18\frac{3}{5}$.

56. 406 by $33\frac{1}{3}$.

57. 745 by $60\frac{2}{3}$.

58. 385 by $45\frac{4}{15}$.

59. 708 by $60\frac{3}{8}$.

60. 625 by $46\frac{2}{5}$.

61. $405\frac{7}{8}$ by 48.

62. $676\frac{5}{12}$ by 72.

63. $964\frac{5}{7}$ by 50.

64. $709\frac{3}{11}$ by 67.

65. $907\frac{3}{15}$ by 90.

PRINCIPLE AND RULES.

ART. 93. **Principle.**—*The product of an integer by a fraction equals the fraction of the integer.* Thus, $5 \times \frac{2}{3} = \frac{2}{3}$ of 5.

ART. 94. 1. To multiply an integer by a fraction:

Rules.—*1. Divide the integer by the denominator, and multiply the quotient by the numerator.* Or,

2. Multiply the integer by the numerator, and divide the product by the denominator.

2. To multiply an integer by a mixed number:

Rule.—*Multiply by the integer and the fraction separately, and add the products.*

CASE III.

FRACTIONS MULTIPLIED BY FRACTIONS.

66. What is $\frac{1}{3}$ of $\frac{1}{4}$? $\frac{1}{3}$ of $\frac{3}{4}$? $\frac{2}{3}$ of $\frac{3}{4}$?

67. What is $\frac{3}{4}$ of $\frac{5}{6}$? $\frac{2}{3}$ of $\frac{5}{8}$? $\frac{5}{6}$ of $\frac{7}{8}$? $\frac{3}{8}$ of $\frac{5}{9}$?

68. What is $\frac{3}{4} \times \frac{5}{6}$? $\frac{5}{8} \times \frac{3}{7}$? $\frac{7}{9} \times \frac{5}{7}$? $\frac{7}{10} \times \frac{3}{14}$?

SUGGESTION.—$\frac{3}{4} \times \frac{5}{6} = \frac{3}{4}$ of $\frac{5}{6}$; $\frac{5}{8} \times \frac{3}{7} = \frac{5}{8}$ of $\frac{3}{7}$, etc.

69. What is $\frac{5}{9} \times \frac{9}{11}$? $\frac{6}{7} \times \frac{14}{15}$? $\frac{7}{12} \times \frac{5}{7}$? $\frac{4}{5} \times \frac{10}{11}$?

70. What is $\frac{1}{3}$ of $13\frac{1}{4}$? $\frac{2}{3}$ of $13\frac{1}{4}$?

SOLUTION.—$\frac{1}{3}$ of $13\frac{1}{4} = \frac{1}{3}$ of 12, which is 4, $+ \frac{1}{3}$ of $1\frac{1}{4}$, which is $\frac{5}{12}$, and $4 + \frac{5}{12} = 4\frac{5}{12}$; $\frac{2}{3}$ of $13\frac{1}{4} = 2$ times $4\frac{5}{12} = 8\frac{5}{6}$.

71. What is $\frac{3}{4}$ of $16\frac{2}{3}$? $\frac{4}{5}$ of $22\frac{1}{2}$? $\frac{5}{8}$ of $42\frac{1}{4}$?

72. What is $\frac{7}{6}$ of $37\frac{1}{6}$? $\frac{5}{6}$ of $42\frac{2}{3}$? $\frac{7}{9}$ of $65\frac{1}{4}$?

73. Show that $\frac{3}{4} \times \frac{5}{6} = \frac{5}{6}$ of $\frac{3}{4}$.

WRITTEN PROBLEMS.

74. Multiply $\frac{13}{15}$ by $\frac{3}{4}$.

PROCESS.

Since $\frac{3}{4} = \frac{1}{4}$ of 3, the product of $\frac{13}{15} \times \frac{3}{4} = \frac{1}{4}$ of 3 times $\frac{13}{15} = \frac{1}{4}$ of $\frac{13 \times 3}{15} = \frac{13 \times 3}{15 \times 4} = \frac{13}{20}$.

$$\frac{13}{15} \times \frac{3}{4} = \frac{13 \times 3}{15 \times 4} = \frac{13}{20}, \; Ans.$$

Multiply :

75. $\frac{13}{16}$ by $\frac{11}{13}$.

76. $\frac{10}{11}$ by $\frac{22}{27}$.

77. $\frac{19}{25}$ by $\frac{15}{38}$.

78. $\frac{10}{13}$ by $\frac{39}{40}$.

79. $\frac{3}{7}$ by $\frac{4}{5}$ of $\frac{5}{6}$.

80. $\frac{7}{8}$ of $\frac{4}{21}$ by $\frac{3}{10}$.

81. $\frac{3}{4}$ by $\frac{5}{6}$ of $\frac{7}{8}$.

82. $2\frac{1}{3}$ by $\frac{3}{10}$ of $\frac{15}{21}$.

83. $2\frac{1}{2}$ by $3\frac{1}{3}$.

84. $4\frac{1}{2}$ by $5\frac{1}{2}$.

85. $6\frac{1}{4}$ by $3\frac{2}{3}$.

86. $10\frac{1}{2}$ by $2\frac{2}{3}$.

87. Multiply the multiplicand in each of the above problems from 75 to 86 by $\frac{3}{5}$.

88. Multiply the multiplier in each of the above problems from 75 to 86 by $\frac{5}{6}$.

NOTE.—It is not necessary for the teacher to solve these problems to determine the correctness of the answers obtained by the pupils. See "Elementary Arithmetic," p. 268.

PRINCIPLE AND RULES.

ART. 95. **Principle.**—*The product of a fraction by a fraction equals the fraction of the fraction.* Thus, $\frac{2}{3} \times \frac{3}{4} = \frac{3}{4}$ of $\frac{2}{3}$.

ART. 96. 1. To multiply a fraction by a fraction:

Rule.—*Multiply the numerators together, and also the denominators.*

2. To multiply a mixed number by a mixed number:

Rule.—*Reduce the mixed numbers to improper fractions, and proceed as above.*

NOTES.—1. Mixed numbers may be multiplied together by *first multiplying the integers; next multiplying each integer by the fraction united with the other integer; next multiplying the two fractions; and then adding the four products.* Thus, $18\frac{3}{4} \times 12\frac{1}{2} = 18 \times 12 + 18 \times \frac{1}{2} + 12 \times \frac{3}{4} + \frac{3}{4} \times \frac{1}{2}$. But in most cases it is shorter to reduce the mixed numbers to improper fractions.

2. Cases I and II may be included in Case III, by changing the integer to the form of a fraction. Thus, $\frac{3}{8} \times 5 = \frac{3}{8} \times \frac{5}{1}$, and $8 \times \frac{3}{5} = \frac{8}{1} \times \frac{3}{5}$.

3. The process of multiplying fractions may be shortened by cancellation. Compound fractions need not be reduced to simple fractions, since $\frac{2}{3} \times \frac{4}{5}$ of $\frac{10}{11} = \frac{2}{3} \times \frac{4}{5} \times \frac{10}{11}$.

---

89. What is the product of $\frac{7}{10}$, $\frac{2}{3}$ of $\frac{6}{7}$, and $2\frac{1}{3}$?

90. What is the product of $\frac{2}{5}$ of $2\frac{1}{2}$ of $\frac{2}{7}$, and $1\frac{1}{3}$ of $\frac{7}{12}$?

91. Multiply $2\frac{1}{2} - 1\frac{3}{24}$ by $7\frac{2}{5} - 4\frac{3}{4}$.

92. Multiply $3\frac{1}{8} - \frac{3}{4}$ of $2\frac{2}{3}$ of $\frac{5}{6}$ by $\frac{4}{15} - \frac{1}{10}$.

93. How many acres in 9 village lots each containing $\frac{5}{8}$ of an acre?

94. What will $\frac{7}{8}$ of a yard of ribbon cost at 35 cents a yard? At 40 cents a yard?

95. What will $\frac{7}{8}$ of a yard of cloth cost at $\$\frac{5}{6}$ a yard?

96. What will $5\frac{1}{2}$ pounds of flour cost at $4\frac{1}{2}$ cents a pound? At $5\frac{1}{2}$ cts. a pound? At $6\frac{1}{4}$ cts. a pound?

97. What will $2\frac{1}{2}$ pounds of tea cost at $\$1\frac{1}{3}$ a pound?

98. What is the cost of 35 barrels of flour at $\$6\frac{1}{3}$ a barrel? At $\$7\frac{1}{4}$ a barrel? At $\$7\frac{2}{5}$ a barrel?

99. What will $12\frac{1}{2}$ pounds of butter cost at $18\frac{3}{4}$ cents a pound? At $22\frac{1}{2}$ cts. a pound? At $33\frac{1}{3}$ cts. a pound?

100. What will $27\frac{1}{2}$ yards of muslin cost at $6\frac{1}{4}$ cts. a yard? At $7\frac{1}{2}$ cts.? At $12\frac{1}{2}$ cts.?

101. What will $\frac{7}{8}$ of an acre of land cost at \$245 an acre? At \$163 an acre?

102. A man owned $\frac{7}{12}$ of a ship which was sold for \$13250: what was his share of the money?

DIVISION OF FRACTIONS.

CASE I.

FRACTIONS DIVIDED BY INTEGERS.

1. If a man can do $\frac{6}{7}$ of a piece of work in 3 days, how much can he do in 1 day?

2. A man divided $\frac{8}{9}$ of a farm equally between four sons: what part of the farm did each receive?

3. How much is $\frac{6}{7}$ of a week divided by 2? By 3?

4. How much is $\frac{3}{8}$ of a peck divided by 2? By 4?

SOLUTION.—$\frac{1}{8}$ peck divided by 2 is $\frac{1}{16}$ peck, and $\frac{3}{8}$ peck divided by 2 is $\frac{3}{16}$ peck. Or, $\frac{3}{8}$ peck $\div$ 2 is $\frac{1}{2}$ of $\frac{3}{8}$ peck, or $\frac{3}{16}$ peck.

NOTE.—In the first three problems, the fraction is divided by *dividing the numerator;* in the 4th problem, the fraction is divided by *multiplying the denominator.*

5. Divide $\frac{8}{9}$ by 2; by 3; by 4; by 5.

6. Divide $\frac{9}{10}$ by 3; by 4; by 5; by 6.

7. Divide $\frac{8}{15}$ by 4; by 8; by 3; by 5.

8. Divide $\frac{4}{5}$ by 8; $\frac{6}{7}$ by 5; $\frac{5}{9}$ by 6; $\frac{7}{12}$ by 5.

9. Divide $\frac{6}{11}$ by 6; $\frac{7}{10}$ by 8; $\frac{9}{10}$ by 5; $\frac{15}{16}$ by 5.

10. Why does dividing the numerator of $\frac{8}{9}$ by 4 divide the fraction by 4?

11. Why does multiplying the denominator of $\frac{8}{9}$ by 3 divide the fraction by 3?

12. In how many ways may a fraction be divided by an integer?

WRITTEN PROBLEMS.

13. Divide $\frac{12}{25}$ by 6.

PROCESS.

$\frac{12}{25} \div 6 = \frac{12 \div 6}{25} = \frac{2}{25}$, *Ans.*

Or: $\frac{12}{25} \div 6 = \frac{12}{25 \times 6} = \frac{2}{25}$.

Since to divide a number by 6 is to find $\frac{1}{6}$ of it, $\frac{12}{25} \div 6 =$ $\frac{1}{6}$ of $\frac{12}{25} = \frac{12 \div 6}{25}$ or $\frac{12}{25 \times 6}$.

Divide:

14. $\frac{16}{21}$ by 8.   **18.** $\frac{45}{47}$ by 15.   **22.** $2\frac{1}{3}$ by 8.

15. $\frac{14}{23}$ by 7.   **19.** $\frac{60}{61}$ by 20.   **23.** $5\frac{1}{2}$ by 12.

16. $\frac{33}{40}$ by 11.   **20.** $\frac{75}{77}$ by 25.   **24.** $6\frac{2}{3}$ by 10.

17. $\frac{28}{35}$ by 7.   **21.** $\frac{60}{81}$ by 20.   **25.** $12\frac{1}{2}$ by 15.

26. Divide the dividend in each of the above problems from 14 to 25 by 5; by 4; by 6.

27. Divide $265\frac{1}{2}$ by 8.

SUGGESTION.—$\frac{1}{8}$ of $265\frac{1}{2} = \frac{1}{8}$ of 264, which is 33, $+\frac{1}{8}$ of $1\frac{1}{2}$, which is $\frac{3}{15}$; $33 + \frac{3}{15} = 33\frac{3}{15}$, the quotient.

28. Divide $365\frac{1}{4}$ by 8; by 12; by 10; by 25.
29. Divide $746\frac{2}{3}$ by 8; by 9; by 12; by 20.

PRINCIPLE AND RULES.

ART. 97. **Principle.**—*A fraction is divided by dividing its numerator or multiplying its denominator.*

ART. 98. 1. To divide a fraction by an integer:

Rule.—*Divide the numerator or multiply the denominator.*

2. To Divide a mixed number by an integer:

Rules.—*1. Reduce the mixed number to an improper fraction and divide as above. Or,*
2. Divide the integral part and then the fractional including the remainder, if any, and unite the quotients.

CASE II.

INTEGERS DIVIDED BY FRACTIONS.

30. How many times is $\frac{2}{5}$ of a cent contained in 4 cents?

SOLUTION.—In 4 cents there are 20 fifths of a cent, and 2 fifths of a cent are contained in 20 fifths of a cent 10 times.

31. If a fruit jar hold $\frac{3}{4}$ of a gallon, how many jars will hold 6 gallons? 12 gallons? 18 gallons?

32. How many times is $\frac{3}{4}$ contained in 8? $\frac{3}{4}$ in 10?

33. How many times $\frac{3}{5}$ in 10? $\frac{3}{5}$ in 12? $\frac{3}{5}$ in 20?

34. How many times $\frac{2}{3}$ in 9? $\frac{5}{6}$ in 10? $\frac{7}{8}$ in 6?

35. How many times $\frac{3}{8}$ in 5? $\frac{7}{9}$ in 10? $\frac{3}{5}$ in 11?

36. Show that $8 \div \frac{3}{5} = 8 \times \frac{5}{3}$.

SUGGESTION.—$1 \div \frac{3}{5} = \frac{5}{3}$, and hence $8 \div \frac{3}{5} = 8 \times \frac{5}{3}$.

NOTE.—One divided by a fraction gives the *reciprocal* of the fraction, which is expressed by inverting the terms of the fraction. The reciprocal of $\frac{3}{5}$ is $\frac{5}{3}$; of $\frac{5}{8}$, $\frac{8}{5}$, etc.

37. Show that $12 \div \frac{5}{6} = 12 \times \frac{6}{5}$.

38. Show that $ \div \frac{3}{8} = 10 \times \frac{8}{3}$.

WRITTEN PROBLEMS.

39. What is the quotient of $25 \div \frac{7}{8}$?

PROCESS: $25 \div \frac{7}{8} = 25 \times \frac{8}{7} = \frac{200}{7} = 28\frac{4}{7}$, *Ans.*

Since $1 \div \frac{7}{8} = \frac{8}{7}$, $25 \div \frac{7}{8} = 25 \times \frac{8}{7} = \frac{200}{7} = 28\frac{4}{7}$. Hence an integer is divided by a fraction by multiplying it by the *reciprocal* of the fraction—that is, by multiplying the integer by the denominator of the fraction and dividing the product by the numerator.

Divide:

40. 21 by $\frac{7}{12}$.	**44.** 96 by $\frac{17}{30}$.	**48.** $75 \div 6\frac{1}{4}$.
41. 42 by $\frac{14}{15}$.	**45.** 125 by $\frac{21}{50}$.	**49.** $120 \div 3\frac{1}{3}$.
42. 24 by $\frac{24}{25}$.	**46.** 75 by $\frac{7}{15}$.	**50.** $225 \div 5\frac{1}{2}$.
43. 100 by $\frac{30}{37}$.	**47.** 108 by $\frac{9}{25}$.	**51.** $150 \div 7\frac{1}{2}$.

ART. 99. To divide an integer by a fraction:

Rules.—*1. Multiply the integer by the denominator of the fraction, and divide the product by the numerator. Or,*

2. Divide the integer by the numerator, and multiply the quotient by the denominator.

CASE III.

FRACTIONS DIVIDED BY FRACTIONS.

52. How many times is $\frac{2}{5}$ of an inch contained in $\frac{4}{5}$ of an inch? $\frac{2}{5}$ of an inch in $\frac{6}{5}$ of an inch?

53. How many times $\frac{3}{8}$ in $\frac{6}{8}$? $\frac{3}{8}$ in $\frac{9}{8}$? $\frac{5}{8}$ in $\frac{10}{8}$?

54. How many times $\frac{4}{9}$ in $\frac{2}{9}$? $\frac{4}{9}$ in $\frac{12}{9}$? $\frac{5}{7}$ in $\frac{10}{7}$?

55. How many times $\frac{5}{7}$ in $\frac{15}{7}$? $\frac{6}{7}$ in $\frac{15}{7}$? $\frac{5}{12}$ in $\frac{16}{12}$?

56. How many times is $\frac{1}{3}$ contained in $\frac{3}{4}$? $\frac{2}{3}$ in $\frac{3}{4}$?

SOLUTION.—1 is contained in 3 fourths $\frac{3}{4}$ of a time; $\frac{1}{3}$ is contained in 3 fourths 3 times $\frac{3}{4}$ of a time, which is $\frac{9}{4}$ times; $\frac{2}{3}$ is contained in 3 fourths $\frac{1}{2}$ of $\frac{9}{4}$ times, which is $\frac{9}{8}$ times.

57. How many times $\frac{2}{3}$ in $\frac{5}{6}$? $\frac{3}{5}$ in $\frac{3}{4}$? $\frac{1}{3}$ in $\frac{7}{8}$?

58. How many times $\frac{2}{7}$ in $\frac{9}{14}$? $\frac{3}{8}$ in $\frac{5}{6}$? $\frac{5}{6}$ in $\frac{3}{8}$?

59. How many times $\frac{3}{10}$ in $\frac{4}{5}$? $\frac{3}{4}$ in $\frac{7}{8}$? $\frac{2}{3}$ in $\frac{3}{7}$?

60. Show that the quotient of two fractions equals the dividend multiplied by the reciprocal of the divisor.

WRITTEN PROBLEMS.

61. Divide $\frac{7}{8}$ by $\frac{3}{5}$.

PROCESS: $\frac{7}{8} \div \frac{3}{5} = \frac{7}{8} \times \frac{5}{3} = \frac{35}{24} = 1\frac{11}{24}$, *Ans.*

Since $\frac{7}{8} \div 1 = \frac{7}{8}$, $\frac{7}{8} \div \frac{1}{5} = \frac{7 \times 5}{8}$, and $\frac{7}{8} \div \frac{3}{5} = \frac{7 \times 5}{8 \times 3}$. Hence, $\frac{7}{8} \div \frac{3}{5} = \frac{7}{8} \times \frac{5}{3}$; that is, $\frac{7}{8} \div \frac{3}{5}$ equals $\frac{7}{8}$ multiplied by $\frac{3}{5}$ with *the terms inverted*.

Or, $1 \div \frac{3}{5} = \frac{5}{3}$, and $\frac{7}{8} \div \frac{3}{5} = \frac{7}{8}$ of $\frac{5}{3} = \frac{7}{8} \times \frac{5}{3}$; that is, $\frac{7}{8} \div \frac{3}{5}$ equals $\frac{7}{8}$ multiplied by the *reciprocal* of $\frac{3}{5}$.

NOTE.—The correctness of this process may also be shown by reducing the fractions to equivalent fractions with a common denominator and dividing the numerators, thus:

$\frac{7}{8} = \frac{7 \times 5}{40}$, and $\frac{3}{5} = \frac{8 \times 3}{40}$; $\frac{7}{8} \div \frac{3}{5} = \frac{7 \times 5}{40} \div \frac{8 \times 3}{40} = \frac{7 \times 5}{8 \times 3} = \frac{7}{8} \times \frac{5}{3}$.

What is the quotient of :

62. $\frac{7}{10} \div \frac{14}{15}$? **66.** $3\frac{1}{2} \div 2\frac{1}{3}$? **70.** $\frac{7}{12} \div \frac{4}{5}$ of $\frac{15}{16}$?

63. $\frac{12}{13} \div \frac{8}{11}$? **67.** $5\frac{1}{2} \div 3\frac{1}{4}$? **71.** $\frac{5}{6}$ of $\frac{9}{10} \div \frac{3}{8}$ of 4 ?

64. $\frac{9}{20} \div \frac{18}{25}$? **68.** $6\frac{2}{3} \div 12\frac{1}{2}$? **72.** $\frac{7}{11}$ of $3\frac{2}{3} \div \frac{2}{9}$ of $2\frac{1}{4}$?

65. $\frac{18}{25} \div \frac{9}{10}$? **69.** $16\frac{2}{3} \div 3\frac{1}{3}$? **73.** $\frac{12}{13} \div \frac{1}{9}$ of $\frac{5}{6}$ of $3\frac{3}{5}$?

74. Divide each dividend in the above problems from 62 to 73 by $\frac{3}{5}$; by $\frac{5}{6}$.

75. Divide each divisor in the above problems from 62 to 73 by $\frac{3}{5}$; by $\frac{5}{6}$.

76. Divide $\frac{2}{5} + \frac{5}{6}$ by $\frac{4}{5} - \frac{2}{3}$.

77. Divide $2\frac{1}{2} - 1\frac{1}{5}$ by $\frac{3}{5}$ of $2\frac{1}{2} \times \frac{3}{4}$.

78. Divide $6\frac{1}{2} \times 3\frac{1}{3}$ by $4\frac{1}{2} \div 5\frac{1}{3}$.

PRINCIPLE AND RULE.

ART. 100. **Principle.**—*The quotient of two fractions equals the dividend multiplied by the reciprocal of the divisor.*
$\frac{5}{6} \div \frac{3}{4} = \frac{5}{6} \times \frac{4}{3}$.

ART. 101. To divide a fraction by a fraction :

Rule.—*Invert the terms of the divisor, and multiply the numerators together and also the denominators.*

NOTES.—1. Since the quotient of two fractions having a common denominator equals the quotient of their numerators ($\frac{6}{8} \div \frac{3}{8} = 6 \div 3$), a fraction may be divided by a fraction *by first reducing them to equivalent fractions with a common denominator, and then dividing the numerator of the dividend by the numerator of the divisor.* See "Elementary Arithmetic," Art. 76.

2. Since the multiplying of both dividend and divisor by the same number does not change the quotient, a fraction may be divided by a fraction *by multiplying both dividend and divisor by the least common multiple of the denominators of the fractions and then dividing the resulting dividend by the resulting divisor.* Thus, $\frac{3}{4} \div \frac{2}{3} = \frac{3}{4} \times 12 \div \frac{2}{3} \times 12 = 9 \div 8 = 1\frac{1}{8}$; and $6\frac{2}{3} \div 5\frac{1}{2} = 6\frac{2}{3} \times 6 \div 5\frac{1}{2} \times 6 = 40 \div 33 = 1\frac{7}{33}$. Compound fractions should be first reduced to simple fractions.

3. It is not necessary that the pupil be made equally familiar with the different methods of dividing one fraction by another. He should thoroughly master one method.

N. C. A.—7.

COMPLEX FRACTIONS.

ART. 102. A complex fraction is an expressed division, the numerator being the dividend and the denominator the divisor. It is reduced to its simplest form *by performing the division as expressed.* Thus:

$$\frac{\frac{4}{5}}{\frac{6}{7}} = \frac{4}{5} \div \frac{6}{7} = \frac{4}{5} \times \frac{7}{6} = \frac{14}{15}.$$

Reduce to the simplest form:

1. $\dfrac{\frac{3}{8}}{\frac{9}{10}}$.

5. $\dfrac{16\frac{2}{3}}{25}$.

9. $\dfrac{\frac{5}{6} \text{ of } \frac{6}{7}}{\frac{2}{3} \text{ of } \frac{3}{8}}$.

13. $\dfrac{\frac{3}{8} + \frac{3}{10}}{\frac{3}{8} - \frac{3}{10}}$.

2. $\dfrac{\frac{6}{7}}{24}$.

6. $\dfrac{25}{16\frac{2}{3}}$.

10. $\dfrac{\frac{2}{7} \text{ of } 2\frac{1}{3}}{5\frac{1}{2}}$.

14. $\dfrac{\frac{5}{7} - \frac{1}{3}}{\frac{3}{4} + \frac{8}{9}}$.

3. $\dfrac{15}{\frac{5}{9}}$.

7. $\dfrac{12\frac{1}{2}}{\frac{5}{8}}$.

11. $\dfrac{\frac{3}{8} \text{ of } \frac{4}{9}}{\frac{5}{12}}$.

15. $\dfrac{\frac{7}{8}}{\frac{3}{4}} \times \dfrac{\frac{5}{9}}{\frac{1}{6}}$.

4. $\dfrac{2\frac{1}{3}}{3\frac{1}{2}}$.

8. $\dfrac{\frac{5}{8}}{12\frac{1}{2}}$.

12. $\dfrac{\frac{6}{11}}{\frac{4}{7} \text{ of } \frac{14}{33}}$.

16. $\dfrac{\frac{2}{9}}{\frac{3}{4}} \div \dfrac{\frac{3}{4}}{\frac{5}{9}}$.

NOTE.—A complex fraction may be changed to a fraction with integral terms *by multiplying both of its terms by the least common multiple of the denominators of its fractions.* (Art. 101, note 2.) Compound fractions must first be reduced to simple fractions. Each of the above problems may be solved by this method.

---

17. How many village lots, each containing $\frac{5}{8}$ of an acre, can be sold from a tract containing 15 acres?

18. The product of two numbers is $6\frac{2}{3}$, and one of the numbers is 21: what is the other number?

19. By what number must $\frac{2}{5}$ be multiplied to give $26\frac{2}{3}$ as a product?

20. If a family use $\frac{4}{9}$ of a barrel of flour in a month, how long will $2\frac{1}{3}$ barrels last? $9\frac{1}{3}$ barrels?

21. If a bushel of corn cost $\$\frac{5}{8}$, how many bushels can be bought for $\$6\frac{1}{2}$? For $\$4\frac{7}{8}$? For $\$9\frac{3}{4}$?

22. If 13 yards of silk cost $\$17\frac{1}{3}$, how many yards can be bought for $\$48\frac{4}{5}$? For $\$50$? For $\$62\frac{1}{2}$?

23. If a man walk $3\frac{3}{10}$ miles an hour, in how many hours will he walk $20\frac{1}{4}$ miles? $30\frac{2}{5}$ miles?

24. At $\$33\frac{1}{3}$ an acre, how many acres of land can be bought for $\$841\frac{2}{3}$? For $\$4208\frac{1}{3}$?

NUMBERS PARTS OF OTHER NUMBERS.

ORAL PROBLEMS.

1. If $\frac{1}{3}$ of a barrel of flour cost $\$3$, what will a barrel cost?

2. If $\frac{1}{5}$ of a ream of note paper cost 75 cents, what will a ream cost?

3. Charles gave Henry 7 marbles, which were $\frac{1}{8}$ of all he had: how many marbles had Charles?

4. 15 is $\frac{1}{6}$ of what number?

5. 16 is $\frac{1}{10}$ of what number?

6. $12\frac{1}{2}$ is $\frac{1}{8}$ of what number?

7. $16\frac{2}{3}$ is $\frac{1}{12}$ of what number?

8. $22\frac{2}{5}$ is $\frac{1}{9}$ of what number?

9. 24 is $\frac{2}{5}$ of what number?

SOLUTION.—If 24 is $\frac{2}{5}$ of a number, $\frac{1}{5}$ of it is $\frac{1}{2}$ of 24, which is 12, and $\frac{5}{5}$ of it is 5 times 12, which is 60. 24 is $\frac{2}{5}$ of 60.

10. 27 is $\frac{3}{8}$ of what number?

11. 45 is $\frac{5}{12}$ of what number?

12. 64 is $\frac{8}{15}$ of what number?

13. $27\frac{1}{2}$ is $\frac{3}{5}$ of what number?

14. $46\frac{2}{3}$ is $\frac{9}{10}$ of what number?

15. $37\frac{1}{2}$ is $\frac{8}{9}$ of what number?

16. $87\frac{1}{3}$ is $\frac{7}{12}$ of what number?

17. 45 is $\frac{5}{7}$ of how many times 9?

18. 63 is $\frac{7}{8}$ of how many times 12?

19. 80 is $\frac{8}{15}$ of how many times 20?

20. 108 is $\frac{12}{25}$ of how many times 15?

21. What part of 4 is 1? What part of 4 is 3?

22. What part of 6 is 5? 9 is 8? 12 is 6?

What part of:

23. 11 is 7? 16 is 12? 20 is 15? 18 is 12?

24. 21 is 7? 32 is 8? 27 is 9? 30 is 15?

25. 39 is 13? 72 is 18? 25 is 15? 90 is 60?

26. $\frac{3}{4}$ is $\frac{1}{4}$? $\frac{4}{5}$ is $\frac{1}{5}$? $\frac{5}{7}$ is $\frac{2}{7}$? $\frac{7}{9}$ is $\frac{5}{9}$?

27. $\frac{1}{2}$ is $\frac{1}{3}$? $\frac{3}{4}$ is $\frac{2}{3}$? $\frac{5}{6}$ is $\frac{3}{5}$? $\frac{9}{14}$ is $\frac{4}{7}$? $\frac{11}{12}$ is $\frac{5}{6}$?

28. 3 is $\frac{2}{3}$? 4 is $\frac{3}{7}$? 10 is $\frac{5}{6}$? 8 is $\frac{4}{7}$? 10 is $\frac{5}{7}$?

29. $16\frac{1}{2}$ is $5\frac{1}{2}$? $33\frac{1}{3}$ is $6\frac{2}{3}$? $37\frac{1}{2}$ is $12\frac{1}{2}$? $33\frac{1}{3}$ is $16\frac{2}{3}$?

30. $6\frac{1}{2}$ is $3\frac{2}{3}$? $5\frac{1}{2}$ is $2\frac{3}{4}$? $2\frac{1}{4}$ is $3\frac{1}{3}$? $6\frac{1}{4}$ is $16\frac{2}{3}$?

ART. 103. To find what part one number is of another:

Rule.—*Divide the number denoting the part by the number denoting the whole.*

NOTE.—Only like numbers can be compared.

REVIEW PROBLEMS.

ORAL PROBLEMS.

1. A boy having $$\frac{7}{8}$ gave $$\frac{2}{5}$ for a knife: how much money had he left?

2. If $\frac{5}{7}$ be added to a certain fraction, the sum will be $\frac{9}{10}$: what is the fraction?

3. A laborer spends $\frac{3}{5}$ of his wages for board and $\frac{1}{3}$ for clothing: what part has he left?

4. A man did $\frac{1}{3}$ of a piece of work the first day, $\frac{1}{4}$ of it the second day, $\frac{1}{6}$ of it the third day, and the remainder the fourth day: what part of the work did he do the fourth day?

5. A man bought a farm, paying $\frac{2}{5}$ of the price down, $\frac{1}{3}$ of it the first year, $\frac{1}{6}$ the second year, and the remainder the third year: what part did he pay the third year?

6. A man is 42 years of age, and $\frac{2}{7}$ of his age equals the age of his son: how old is the son?

7. A man bought a cow for 33\frac{1}{3}$, and sold her for $\frac{5}{6}$ of what she cost: how much did he lose?

8. If a yard of velvet cost 8\frac{1}{3}$, what will $\frac{2}{5}$ of a yard cost? $\frac{2}{3}$ of a yard? $\frac{3}{4}$ of a yard?

9. Jane's age is $16\frac{2}{3}$ years, and Mary's age is $\frac{3}{4}$ of Jane's: how old is Mary?

10. A man owning $\frac{5}{6}$ of a mill sold $\frac{2}{3}$ of his share: what part of the mill did he sell? What part had he left?

11. Charles bought $\frac{3}{4}$ of a pound of candy and gave his sister $\frac{1}{8}$ of a pound, and his playmate $\frac{2}{3}$ of what remained: what part of a pound had he left?

12. A wife is 35 years of age, and her age is $\frac{5}{7}$ of the age of her husband: how old is her husband?

13. The difference between $\frac{5}{6}$ and $\frac{3}{5}$ of a certain number is 14: what is the number?

14. A farmer sold 50 sheep, which were $\frac{2}{5}$ of his flock: how many sheep had he before the sale?

15. When Charles is $\frac{2}{5}$ older than he now is, he will be 21 years of age: how old is he?

16. A farmer sold $\frac{3}{5}$ of his farm for $1645: at this rate, what was the value of the farm?

17. A man sold $\frac{3}{7}$ of his farm and had 64 acres left: how many acres had he at first?

18. A man sold a horse for $90, which was $\frac{1}{5}$ more than it cost him: what was the cost of the horse?

19. A lady paid $30 for a cloak, which was $\frac{3}{7}$ more than she paid for a dress: what was the cost of the dress?

20. $\frac{3}{7}$ of 42 is $\frac{2}{11}$ of what number?

21. A man is 45 years old, and $\frac{2}{5}$ of his age is $\frac{3}{7}$ of the age of his wife: how old is his wife?

22. Samuel is $\frac{3}{5}$ as old as Charles, and Harry, who is 9 years old, is $\frac{3}{4}$ as old as Charles: how old are Charles and Samuel?

23. A man gave \$150 for a watch and chain, and the chain cost $\frac{3}{7}$ as much as the watch: what did each cost?

24. If to A's age there be added $\frac{2}{3}$ and $\frac{2}{5}$ of his age, the sum will be 62 years: what is A's age?

25. A farmer's sheep are in 4 fields; the first contains $\frac{2}{9}$ of all, the second $\frac{1}{6}$, the third $\frac{1}{4}$, and the fourth 52 sheep: how many sheep in the 4 fields?

26. A harness cost \$35, and $\frac{2}{7}$ of the cost of the harness was equal to $\frac{5}{8}$ of the cost of a saddle and bridle: what was the cost of the saddle and bridle?

27. If to $\frac{5}{6}$ of a man's age 15 years be added, the sum will be $\frac{5}{4}$ of his age: how old is he?

28. The distance from Cleveland to Columbus is 138 miles, $\frac{15}{23}$ of which is $\frac{3}{4}$ of the distance from Columbus to Cincinnati: what is the distance from Columbus to Cincinnati?

29. $\frac{6}{7}$ is $\frac{3}{8}$ of what number? $3\frac{1}{3}$ is $\frac{4}{5}$ of what number?

30. If $\frac{2}{3}$ of the value of a house equal $\frac{4}{5}$ of the value of a lot, and the value of both is \$4400, what is the value of each?

31. If $\frac{2}{9}$ of A's money equal $\frac{6}{7}$ of B's, and both together have \$340, how much has each?

32. If $\frac{3}{4}$ of A's age is $\frac{3}{5}$ of B's, and B's age is 20 years, what is the age of each?

33. If $\frac{2}{7}$ of a yard of velvet cost $\$2\frac{2}{3}$, what will $\frac{4}{9}$ of a yard cost? $\frac{2}{3}$ of a yard? $1\frac{1}{3}$ yards?

34. How many pounds of honey, at $\$\frac{3}{8}$ a pound, can be bought for \$3? For $\$4\frac{1}{2}$? For \$6?

35. How many bushels of apples, at $\$\frac{3}{5}$ a bushel, can be bought for \$12? For \$15? For $\$16\frac{2}{3}$?

36. If a barrel hold $2\frac{3}{4}$ bushels, how many barrels will be required to pack 22 bushels of apples? 33 bushels? 55 bushels?

37. If $5\frac{1}{2}$ lb. of sugar cost \$1, how much will $16\frac{1}{2}$ lb. cost? 33 lb.? $38\frac{1}{2}$ lb.? $49\frac{1}{2}$ lb.?

38. If $\frac{3}{4}$ of a yard of silk cost \$$1\frac{1}{5}$, how many yards can be bought for \$8? For \$10? For \$$9\frac{3}{5}$?

39. If $3\frac{2}{3}$ yards of cloth cost \$$5\frac{1}{2}$, what will 6 yards cost? $6\frac{1}{2}$ yards? 10 yards? 20 yards?

40. If a train of cars run $\frac{3}{5}$ of a mile in $1\frac{2}{7}$ minutes, how many miles will it run in $6\frac{3}{7}$ minutes? $10\frac{5}{7}$ minutes? 15 minutes? 30 minutes?

41. If 4 pounds of coffee cost \$$\frac{8}{9}$, what will 6 pounds cost? 10 pounds? 7 pounds? 12 pounds?

42. If $12\frac{1}{2}$ tons of hay will feed 5 horses a year, how many tons will feed 8 horses a year? 12 horses?

43. If a rod 5 feet long casts a shadow $8\frac{1}{3}$ feet long, what is the length of a pole whose shadow, at the same time of day, is $17\frac{1}{2}$ feet?

44. If 3 men can do a piece of work in $10\frac{3}{4}$ days, how long will it take 8 men to do it? 12 men?

45. If a barrel of flour will supply 12 persons $4\frac{3}{5}$ weeks, how long will it supply 7 persons? 10 persons?

46. A can do a job of work in 12 days, and B in 10 days: how long will it take both to do it?

47. A and B can do a certain work in 8 days, and A can do it in 12 days: in what time can B do it?

48. A and B can mow a field in 6 days, and A can mow it in 10 days: what part of the field can each mow in 1 day? How long will it take B to mow the field?

49. How is the value of a proper fraction affected by adding the same number to both of its terms? By subtracting the same number? (Illustrate, taking the fraction $\frac{2}{5}$.)

50. How is the value of an improper fraction, greater than 1, affected by adding the same number to both of its terms? By subtracting the same number? (Illustrate, taking $\frac{5}{4}$.)

51. Add $\frac{5}{6}$, $\frac{7}{8}$, $\frac{3}{10}$ of $\frac{5}{12}$, and $3\frac{1}{6}$.

52. From $\frac{2}{3}$ of $1\frac{1}{8}$ take $\frac{5}{7}$ of $\frac{14}{15}$.

53. From the sum of $27\frac{3}{8}$ and $20\frac{2}{3}$ take their difference.

54. Multiply $1\frac{3}{15}$ by 35; 35 by $1\frac{3}{15}$; $1\frac{3}{15}$ by $\frac{10}{11}$; $3\frac{1}{2}$ by $2\frac{1}{3}$.

55. Divide $\frac{16}{21}$ by 32; 32 by $\frac{16}{21}$; $\frac{16}{21}$ by $\frac{7}{8}$; $4\frac{1}{2}$ by $3\frac{1}{5}$.

56. $\frac{11}{12} + \frac{7}{15} =$ what? $\frac{11}{12} - \frac{7}{15}$? $\frac{11}{12} \times \frac{7}{15}$? $\frac{11}{12} \div \frac{7}{15}$?

57. Multiply $2045\frac{3}{7}$ by 35; 806 by $84\frac{4}{5}$; $30\frac{1}{4}$ by $16\frac{2}{3}$.

58. Divide $347\frac{5}{6}$ by 15; 692 by $21\frac{5}{8}$; $19\frac{4}{9}$ by $16\frac{2}{3}$.

59. A farm is divided into five fields, containing respectively $21\frac{3}{4}$ A., $34\frac{2}{3}$ A., $45\frac{7}{8}$ A., $56\frac{5}{6}$ A., and $29\frac{1}{2}$ A.: how many acres in the farm?

60. There are $30\frac{1}{4}$ sq. yd. in a square rod: how many square rods in $786\frac{1}{2}$ sq. yd.? In $998\frac{1}{4}$ sq. yd.?

61. A man travels $5\frac{3}{4}$ miles an hour: how long will it take him to make a journey of $75\frac{2}{3}$ miles?

62. At $\$8\frac{2}{3}$ a ton, how many tons of hay can be bought for $\$52$? For $\$90$? For $\$108\frac{1}{3}$?

63. If $\frac{4}{15}$ of an acre of land cost $\$68$, what will 8 acres cost? $12\frac{2}{7}$ acres? $20\frac{2}{3}$ acres?

64. If $\frac{5}{8}$ of a yard of velvet cost $\$3\frac{4}{7}$, how many yards can be bought for $\$196\frac{4}{7}$? For $\$393\frac{1}{7}$?

65. If a number be diminished by $\frac{5}{7}$ of $\frac{12}{25}$ of itself, the remainder will be 69: what is the number?

66. A pedestrian walked $\frac{5}{12}$ of his journey the first day, $\frac{3}{8}$ of it the second day, and then had 24 miles to travel: how long was the journey?

67. A man pays $\$350$ a year for house rent, which is $\frac{14}{55}$ of his income: what is his income?

68. A man bequeathed to his wife $\$4860$, which was $\frac{12}{35}$ of his estate: what was the value of his estate?

69. A graded school enrolls 208 boys, and $\frac{7}{15}$ of the pupils are girls: how many pupils in the school?

70. A man owning $\frac{5}{9}$ of a ship, sells $\frac{3}{7}$ of his share for $3480: at this rate, what is the value of the ship?

71. A owning $\frac{2}{3}$ of a mill, sold $\frac{2}{5}$ of his share to B, and $\frac{1}{2}$ of what he then owned to C for $460: what part of the mill did C buy? What was the value of the mill at the rate of C's purchase?

72. A owns $\frac{7}{12}$ of a section of land; B, $\frac{7}{16}$ of a section; and C, $\frac{3}{7}$ as much as both A and B: what part of a section does C own?

73. A bought $\frac{2}{3}$ of a factory, and sold $\frac{3}{7}$ of his share to B, and $\frac{2}{5}$ of his share to C: what part of the factory did A then own?

74. A and B together own 396 acres of land, and $\frac{3}{5}$ of A's farm equals $\frac{3}{4}$ of B's: how many acres does each own?

75. A stock of goods is owned by three partners, A owning $\frac{3}{8}$, B $\frac{5}{11}$, and C the remainder; the goods were sold at a profit of $6160: what was each partner's share?

76. $\frac{5}{8}$ of a stock of goods was destroyed by fire, and $\frac{3}{5}$ of the remainder was damaged by water, and the uninjured goods were sold at cost for $5280: what part of the goods was sold? What was the cost of the entire stock?

77. A man paid $\frac{2}{5}$ of his money for a farm, $\frac{1}{3}$ of what remained for repairs, $\frac{1}{3}$ of what then remained for stock, $\frac{1}{2}$ of what then remained for utensils, and then had left $650: what part had he left? How much money had he at first?

78. A merchant-tailor has $67\frac{2}{5}$ yards of cloth, from which he wishes to cut an equal number of coats, pants, and vests: how many of each can he cut if they contain $3\frac{3}{4}$, $2\frac{7}{8}$, and $1\frac{4}{5}$ yards respectively?

79. An estate was divided between two brothers and a sister; the elder brother received $\frac{3}{8}$ of the estate, the younger $\frac{3}{10}$, and the sister the remainder, which was $450 less than the elder brother received: what part of the estate did the sister receive? What was the value of the estate? What was each brother's share?

DECIMAL FRACTIONS.

NUMERATION AND NOTATION.

1. If a unit be divided into ten equal parts, what is one part called?

2. If a tenth of a unit be divided into ten equal parts, what is one part? What is $\frac{1}{10}$ of $\frac{1}{10}$?

3. If a hundredth of a unit be divided into ten equal parts, what is one part? What is $\frac{1}{10}$ of $\frac{1}{100}$?

4. What part of a tenth is a hundredth? What part of a hundredth is a thousandth?

5. How do the fractions $\frac{3}{10}$, $\frac{3}{100}$, and $\frac{3}{1000}$ compare with each other in value? $\frac{7}{10}$, $\frac{7}{100}$, and $\frac{7}{1000}$?

ART. 104. Since the fractional units, tenths, hundredths, thousandths, etc., decrease in value like the successive orders of integers, they can be expressed on *a scale of ten.* This is done by extending the orders to the right of units, and calling the first fractional order *tenths*, the second *hundredths*, the third *thousandths*, etc., and placing a period at the left of the order of tenths. Thus, $\frac{5}{10}$ is written .5; $\frac{5}{100}$ is written .05; $\frac{5}{1000}$ is written .005, etc.

Copy and read:

6.	7.	8.	9.	10.	11.
.4	.03	.002	.06	.07	.005
.7	.05	.004	.006	.004	.4
.6	.08	.006	.08	.8	.07
.9	.09	.007	.5	.09	.009

12. How many tenths and how many hundredths in .25? In .45? .63? .78? .84? .69? .39?

13. How many tenths, hundredths, and thousandths in .325? .246? .307? .405? .056? .407? .075?

14. How many tenths, hundredths, and thousandths in .045? In .407? .008? .065? .607? .325?

Art. 105. When the right-hand figure of a decimal denotes hundredths, the whole decimal denotes hundredths, and when the right-hand figure denotes thousandths, the whole decimal denotes thousandths. Thus, .25 is read 25 *hundredths ;* .325 is read 325 *thousandths.*

15. How many hundredths in $\frac{15}{100}$? $\frac{8}{100}$? .34? .42?

16. How many thousandths in $\frac{35}{1000}$? .325? .065? .205? .008? .046? .608? .078?

Copy and read:

17.	**18.**	**19.**	**20.**	**21.**
.15	.016	.245	.8	.007
.42	.024	.354	.63	.038
.36	.045	.403	.086	.462
.50	.083	.587	.369	.507
.06	.007	.067	.504	.45
.09	.072	.308	.675	.807

Art. 106. When fractions denoting tenths, hundredths, thousandths, etc., are expressed, like integers, on the decimal scale, they are said to be expressed or written *decimally.*

Write decimally :

22.	**23.**	**24.**	**25.**	**26.**
$\frac{3}{10}$	$\frac{4}{1000}$	$\frac{45}{1000}$	$\frac{75}{100}$	$\frac{18}{1000}$
$\frac{7}{10}$	$\frac{6}{1000}$	$\frac{63}{1000}$	$\frac{43}{1000}$	$\frac{208}{1000}$
$\frac{6}{100}$	$\frac{14}{1000}$	$\frac{215}{1000}$	$\frac{6}{100}$	$\frac{355}{1000}$
$\frac{8}{100}$	$\frac{56}{100}$	$\frac{407}{1000}$	$\frac{7}{1000}$	$\frac{43}{1000}$
$\frac{12}{100}$	$\frac{47}{100}$	$\frac{504}{1000}$	$\frac{106}{1000}$	$\frac{5}{1000}$

27. What is the name of the third decimal order? The fourth? The fifth? The sixth?

28. What does each significant figure of .0034 denote? Of .00275? Of .03405? Of .000325? Of .030056?

Copy and read:

29.	**30.**	**31.**	**32.**
.246	.0635	.00647	.0307
.0246	.00635	.000647	.03007
.708	.3464	.04056	.030007
.0708	.03464	.004056	.034005
.3425	.32875	.32453	.450605

ART. 107. When a decimal fraction is expressed decimally, the right-hand figure is written in the order indicated by the name of the decimal. Thus, $\frac{325}{100000}$ is written .00325

Write decimally:

33.	**34.**	**35.**	**36.**
$\frac{3}{100}$	$\frac{6}{10000}$	$\frac{7}{100000}$	$\frac{29}{1000000}$
$\frac{75}{100}$	$\frac{33}{10000}$	$\frac{37}{100000}$	$\frac{609}{1000000}$
$\frac{8}{1000}$	$\frac{405}{10000}$	$\frac{208}{100000}$	$\frac{4045}{1000000}$
$\frac{28}{1000}$	$\frac{3042}{10000}$	$\frac{3056}{100000}$	$\frac{33033}{1000000}$
$\frac{356}{1000}$	$\frac{5007}{10000}$	$\frac{38045}{100000}$	$\frac{20405}{1000000}$

Write decimally

37.	**38.**
7 tenths.	42 ten-thousandths.
24 hundredths.	506 ten-thousandths.
29 thousandths.	4008 ten-thousandths.
405 thousandths.	65 hundred-thousandths.
65 millionths.	6007 hundred-thousandths.
5064 millionths.	54008 hundred-thousandths.
40056 millionths.	3004 hundred-thousandths.

39. Eighty-five thousandths.

40. Four hundred seven thousandths.

41. Ninety-five ten-thousandths.

42. Six hundred forty-four ten-thousandths.

43. Seven thousand eighty-two ten-thousandths.

44. Fifty-seven hundred-thousandths.

45. Seven hundred eight hundred-thousandths.

46. Nine thousand forty-eight hundred-thousandths.

47. Six hundred four millionths.

48. Seven thousand six hundred forty-three millionths.

49. Forty thousand sixty-three millionths.

Art. 108. An integer and a decimal may be written together as one number, as 6.5; 25.07; 48.137. In reading such mixed decimal numbers, the integer and the decimal are connected by *and*. Thus, 4.5 is read 4 *and* 5 tenths.

50. Read 45.6; 30.25; 204.045; 84.0307

51. Read 2005.045; 408.00075: 3040.0046; 50060.00705

52. Read 400.045; 500.0063; 7000.0084; 60000.00006

Suggestion.—In such cases read the integer as *units;* as, four hundred units and forty-five thousandths. The word units should be inserted whenever its omission changes the mixed decimal to a pure decimal, or causes ambiguity. See Art. 116.

53. Read 5600.0084; 40508.0307; 75000.000605

54. Read 300000.000003; 35000000.000035

55. Write decimally $56\frac{3}{100}$; $604\frac{35}{1000}$; $400\frac{305}{100000}$.

56. Write decimally $207\frac{35}{100000}$; $2560\frac{4056}{1000000}$.

57. Write decimally three hundred units and three hundred forty-eight millionths.

58. Write decimally two thousand nine hundred units and twenty-nine millionths.

59. Write decimally two thousand nine hundred twenty-nine millionths

DEFINITIONS, PRINCIPLES, AND RULES.

ART. 109.   A **Decimal Fraction** is one or more of the
decimal parts of a unit.

It results from the division of a unit into tenths, a tenth into
hundredths, a hundredth into thousandths, etc., called the *decimal*
division.   The division of a unit into *any* number of equal parts is
a *common* division, and the resulting fraction is a *common fraction*
(Art. 74).   Decimal fractions are a *class* of common fractions.

The denominator of a decimal fraction is 10 or some
product of 10's as factors; as, 10, 100, 1000, etc.

ART. 110.   Decimal fractions may be expressed in
three ways:

1. By words; as, three tenths, twelve hundredths.
2. By writing the denominator under the numerator,
in the form of a common fraction; as, $\frac{3}{10}$, $\frac{12}{100}$.
3. By omitting the denominator and writing the frac-
tion in the decimal form; as, .3, .12; the denominator
being understood.

NOTE.—Three tenths, $\frac{3}{10}$, and .3 express the same decimal fraction, which is the *thing* expressed, and not its expression.   A decimal fraction can be expressed orally, and is so expressed when
read or dictated.   When a decimal fraction is expressed in words,
written or oral, the denominator is *necessarily given*.   It is an error
to teach that a decimal fraction depends on its expression with
a decimal point and without its denominator.   This is called the
decimal form, since only decimal fractions can be thus written.   A
decimal fraction may or may not be expressed in figures, and it
may or may not be written in the decimal form.

ART. 111.   The **Decimal Point** is a period placed at the
left of the order of tenths, to designate the decimal orders.

ART. 112.   A **Complex Decimal** is a decimal ending
at the right with a common fraction; as, $.6\frac{2}{3}$, $.033\frac{1}{3}$.

ART. 113.   A **Mixed Decimal** is an integer and a
decimal written together as one number; as, 7.5, 8.25.

ART. 114. The orders on the left of the decimal point are *integral,* and those on the right are *decimal.* The decimal orders are also called *Decimal Places.*

The following table gives the names of several integral and several decimal orders, and shows the relation between them:

Hundred-millions.	Ten-millions.	Millions.	Hundred-thousands.	Ten-thousands.	Thousands.	Hundreds.	Tens.	Units.	Decimal Point.	Tenths.	Hundredths.	Thousandths.	Ten-thousandths.	Hundred-thousandths.	Millionths.	Ten-millionths.	Hundred-millionths.
0	0	0	0	0	0	0	0	0	.	0	0	0	0	0	0	0	0

Integral Orders.　　　　　Decimal Orders.

ART. 115. **Principles.**—1. *The value of the successive decimal orders decreases from left to right and increases from right to left in the same manner as integral orders.* Hence,

2. *The removal of a decimal figure one place to the right divides its value by 10, and its removal one place to the left multiplies its value by 10.*

3. *The name of a decimal is the same as the name of its right-hand order.*

ART. 116. 1. To read a decimal:

Rule.—*Read it as if it were an integer, and add the name of the right-hand order.*

NOTES.—1. A decimal is read precisely as it would be were the denominator expressed.

2. In reading a mixed decimal, the word "units" should be supplied if its omission would render the meaning ambiguous. 300.006 should be read *three hundred units and six thousandths.*

3. While "and" must be used to connect the integral and decimal parts of a mixed decimal, it may also be used to connect the parts of an integer (Art. 22, note 2) and also of a pure decimal. Thus, .306 may be read *three hundred six thousandths* or *three hundred and six thousandths.* The latter is common usage, but the former is preferred by many teachers.

2. To write a decimal:

Rule.—*Write the numerator, and so place the decimal point that the right-hand figure shall stand in the order denoted by the name of the decimal.*

NOTES.—1. When the number does not fill all the decimal places, supply the deficiency by prefixing decimal ciphers.

2. Pupils should be taught to write decimals by first making the decimal point, and then filling the successive orders from left to right, with ciphers or significant figures, as may be required. Suppose, for example, that the decimal to be written is 2312 millionths. Since millionths is the *sixth* decimal order, and the numerator of the decimal contains only four figures, it is seen that there will be two orders to fill with ciphers, thus: .002312. The decimal may thus be written from left to right.

WRITTEN EXERCISES.

Write decimally :

60. Two hundred five ten-thousandths.

61. Forty thousand thirty-four millionths.

62. Two thousand four hundred-thousandths.

63. Six hundred fifteen ten-millionths.

64. Six hundred units and fifteen ten-thousandths.

65. Fifteen units and fifteen thousandths.

66. Three hundred thousand three hundred thirteen hundred-millionths.

67. Five million eighty-five ten-millionths.

68. Twelve hundred-thousandths.

69. Four hundred units and four hundred sixty-five millionths.

70. Twenty-five units and twenty-five thousandths.

71. Five thousand units and five thousandths.

72. Three hundred seventy-five units and three hundred seventy-five billionths.

73. Thirty thousand units and forty-six hundred-thousandths.

74. One million forty-five billionths.

75. Eighty thousand forty units and three hundred six ten-thousandths.

76. Fifteen thousand units and fifteen ten-thousandths.

77. Seventy-five units and five thousand forty-three millionths.

78. One million units and one millionth.

79. Fifteen million and fifteen millionths.

REDUCTION OF DECIMALS.

CASE I.

DECIMALS REDUCED TO LOWER OR HIGHER ORDERS.

1. How many tenths in 6 units? 7 units? 9 units? 15 units? 22 units? 25 units?

2. How many hundredths in 5 tenths? In .6? .8? .7? .3? .4? .9?

3. How many thousandths in .06? In .24? .47? .55? .37? .63? .75? .85?

4. How many tenths in .60? .90? .600? .700?

5. How many hundredths in .240? In .420? .5600?

WRITTEN PROBLEMS.

6. Reduce .875 to millionths.

PROCESS: .875 = .875000

7. Reduce .0674 to millionths; to ten-millionths.

8. Reduce .075 to hundred-thousandths; to millionths.

9. Reduce 62.7 to ten-thousandths; to hundred-thousandths.

10. Reduce 5.33 to ten-thousandths; to ten-millionths.

11. Reduce 3. to hundredths; to ten-thousandths.

12. Reduce 45. to ten-thousandths; to millionths.

13. Reduce .04500 to thousandths.

PROCESS: .04500 = .045

14. Reduce 5.24000 to hundredths; to thousandths.

N. C. A.—8.

ART. 117. **Principles.**—1. *Annexing ciphers to a decimal fraction multiplies both of its terms by the same number, and hence reduces it to a lower order without changing its value.* (Art. 83.)

2. *Cutting off ciphers from the right of a decimal fraction divides both of its terms by the same number, and hence reduces it to a higher order without changing its value.* (Art. 80.)

NOTE.—The annexing of decimal ciphers to an integer does not change its value. Thus, 12. = 12.0, or 12.00; that is, 12 units = 120 tenths = 1200 hundredths, etc.

CASE II.

DECIMALS REDUCED TO COMMON FRACTIONS.

15. How many fifths in $\frac{4}{10}$? $\frac{6}{10}$? .2? .8?

16. How many fourths in $\frac{25}{100}$? $\frac{50}{100}$? $\frac{75}{100}$? .25?

17. How many twentieths in $\frac{15}{100}$? $\frac{25}{100}$? .20? .25?

WRITTEN PROBLEMS.

18. Reduce .625 to a common fraction in its lowest terms.

PROCESS : $.625 = \frac{625}{1000} = \frac{25}{40} = \frac{5}{8}$, *Ans.*

Reduce to common fractions in lowest terms:

19. .225	**25.** .004	**31.** 62.025
20. .75	**26.** .5625	**32.** 37.625
21. .075	**27.** .0125	**33.** $56.37\frac{1}{2}$
22. .0625	**28.** .3525	**34.** $247.33\frac{1}{3}$
23. .1625	**29.** 3.525	**35.** $16.66\frac{3}{4}$
24. .2250	**30.** 37.75	**36.** $214.00\frac{1}{4}$

ART. 118. To reduce a decimal to a common fraction :

Rule.—*Omit the decimal point and supply the denominator, and then reduce the fraction to its lowest terms.*

CASE III.

COMMON FRACTIONS REDUCED TO DECIMALS.

37. How many tenths in $\frac{1}{2}$? In $\frac{1}{5}$? $\frac{2}{5}$? $\frac{3}{5}$?

38. How many hundredths in $\frac{1}{4}$? $\frac{3}{4}$? $\frac{3}{5}$? $\frac{4}{5}$?

39. How many hundredths in $\frac{1}{20}$? $\frac{3}{20}$? $\frac{7}{20}$? $\frac{11}{20}$?

40. How many hundredths in $\frac{1}{25}$? $\frac{4}{25}$? $\frac{8}{25}$? $\frac{12}{25}$?

WRITTEN PROBLEMS.

41. Change $\frac{3}{125}$ to a decimal.

PROCESS.

125)3.000(.024, *Ans.*

  2 50

   500

   500

Since annexing decimal ciphers to a number does not change its value (Art. 117, note), $\frac{3}{125} = 3.000 \div 125 = .024$. Or, Multiplying both terms of $\frac{3}{125}$ by 1000 gives $\frac{3000}{125000}$, and dividing both terms of $\frac{3000}{125000}$ by 125 (the denominator of $\frac{3}{125}$) gives $\frac{24}{1000} = .024$

Reduce to decimal fractions:

42. $\frac{5}{8}$	**48.** $\frac{32}{25}$	**54.** $\frac{13}{40}$	**60.** $\frac{5}{600}$
43. $\frac{9}{16}$	**49.** $\frac{87}{24}$	**55.** $\frac{7}{400}$	**61.** $\frac{23}{300}$
44. $\frac{3}{75}$	**50.** $\frac{12}{125}$	**56.** $\frac{23}{250}$	**62.** $\frac{14}{111}$
45. $\frac{25}{32}$	**51.** $\frac{3}{40}$	**57.** $\frac{4}{1250}$	**63.** $12\frac{3}{20}$
46. $\frac{64}{125}$	**52.** $\frac{7}{80}$	**58.** $\frac{1}{750}$	**64.** $26\frac{4}{125}$
47. $\frac{80}{125}$	**53.** $\frac{19}{200}$	**59.** $\frac{21}{480}$	**65.** $37\frac{13}{80}$

ART. 119. To reduce a common fraction to a decimal:

Rule.—*Annex decimal ciphers to the numerator and divide by the denominator, and point off as many decimal places in the quotient as there are annexed ciphers.*

NOTES.—1. When a sufficient number of decimal places is obtained, the remainder may be discarded, or the quotient may be expressed as a complex decimal.

2. When the denominator of a common fraction in its lowest terms contains other prime factors than 2 and 5, the process will not terminate.

3. When the quotient repeats the same figure, or the same set of figures, as in problems 60, 61, and 62, it is called a *Repeating Decimal*, or a *Circulating Decimal*, and the figure or figures repeated are called a *Repetend*. See Appendix.

ADDITION OF DECIMALS.

1. Add 16.25, 48.037, 90.0033, and .864

PROCESS.

16.25
48.037
90.0033
.864
———
155.1543, *Ans.*

Since only like orders can be added (Art. 28), write the figures of the same order in the same column. Since ten units of any order equal one unit of the next higher order, begin at the right and add as in simple numbers. Place the decimal point at the left of the tenths' order.

2. Add .375, 80.06, 45.0084, .00755, and 84.635

3. Add 84.08, 16.075, 2.9, 1.96, 1.003, and 5.0008

4. Add $15.34, $65.048, $9.083, $12., 16.66\frac{2}{3}$, $18.06, 95.37\frac{1}{2}$, and $35.75

5. Add 26.37$\frac{1}{2}$, 19.08$\frac{1}{4}$, 23.042$\frac{1}{5}$, 38.5, 6.00$\frac{3}{4}$, and 7$\frac{1}{12}$.

6. Add 256 thousandths, 3005 millionths, 207 ten-thousandths, 34 ten-millionths, 604 hundred-millionths, and 94 hundred-thousandths.

7. Add fifteen thousandths, eighty-one ten-thousandths, fifty-six millionths, seventeen ten-millionths, and two hundred five hundred-thousandths.

8. How many rods of fence will inclose a field, the four sides of which are respectively 46.6 rd., 50.65 rd., 24.33$\frac{1}{3}$ rd., and 27 rd.?

9. Five bars of silver weigh respectively .75 lb., 1.15 lb., .86$\frac{1}{3}$ lb., 1.34 lb., and .9 lb.: what is their total weight?

10. The usual average amount of rain in San Francisco in the winter months is 11.25 inches; in the spring, 8.81 inches; in the summer, .03 inches; and in the autumn, 2.75 inches: what is the amount for the year?

Art. 120. To add decimals:

Rule.—1. *Write the numbers so that figures of the same order shall stand in the same column.*

2. *Add as in the addition of integers, and place the decimal point at the left of the tenths' order in the amount.*

Note.—If a complex decimal does not contain as many decimal places as either of the other numbers, change the terminal common fraction to a decimal, and continue the division until the requisite number of decimal places is secured.

SUBTRACTION OF DECIMALS.

1. From 47.625 take 28.7

1st process.	2d process.
47.625	47.625
28.700	28.7
18.925	18.925

Since only like numbers can be subtracted, write the numbers so that figures of the same order shall stand in the same column; and since ten units of any decimal order equal one unit of the next higher order, subtract as in simple numbers. Place the decimal point at the left of the tenths' order.

2. From 46.7 take 29.825

1st process.	2d process.
46.700	46.7
29.825	29.825
16.875	16.875

A comparison of the two processes shows that it is unnecessary to fill the vacant orders with ciphers.

3. From 7.245 take 4.09; 4.05 take 2.0075

4. From .062 take .0056; .6¼ take .0087½

5. From 2.04 take .0078; 12. take .0005

6. From six tenths take six thousandths.

7. From forty-four thousandths take forty-four millionths.

8. From 301 ten-thousandths take 4005 millionths.

9. From 50065 ten-millionths take 1307 billionths.

10. From seven thousand forty-five millionths take three thousand seven hundred six ten-millionths.

11. From eight hundred fifty-six ten-thousandths take five thousand six hundred sixteen millionths.

12. A man walked 33.7 miles the first day and 28.75 miles the second: how much farther did he walk the first day than the second?

13. The usual average amount of rain at Cincinnati in the summer months is 13.7 inches, and in the winter months it is 11.15 inches: what is the difference?

14. The mean height of the barometer at Boston is 29.934 inches, and at Pekin it is 30.154 inches: what is the difference?

ART. 121. To subtract decimals:

Rule.—1. *Write the numbers so that figures of the same order shall stand in the same column.*

2. *Subtract as in the subtraction of integers, and place the decimal point at the left of the tenths' order in the difference.*

MULTIPLICATION OF DECIMALS.

1. How much is 7 times $\frac{1}{10}$? 7 times $\frac{4}{10}$? 8 times $\frac{7}{10}$? 9 times $\frac{8}{10}$?

2. How much is 8 times $\frac{1}{100}$? 8 times $\frac{7}{100}$? 6 times $\frac{9}{100}$?

3. What is the product of $\frac{1}{10} \times \frac{1}{10}$? $\frac{5}{10} \times \frac{6}{10}$? $\frac{8}{10} \times \frac{9}{10}$? $\frac{7}{10} \times \frac{8}{10}$?

4. What is the product of $\frac{1}{10} \times \frac{1}{100}$? $\frac{4}{10} \times \frac{7}{100}$?

5. What is the product of $\frac{1}{100}$ by $\frac{1}{100}$? $\frac{7}{100}$ by $\frac{5}{100}$?

6. What is the denominator of the product when tenths are multiplied by units? Tenths by tenths? Tenths by hundredths? Hundredths by hundredths?

7. What is the denominator of the product of any two fractions whose denominators are powers of 10?

WRITTEN PROBLEMS.

8. Multiply .625 by .23.

PROCESS.

.625

.23

———

1875

1250

———

.14375

.625 $= \frac{625}{1000}$, and .23 $= \frac{23}{100}$, and hence .625 $\times$ .23 $= \frac{625}{1000} \times \frac{23}{100} = \frac{14375}{100000} = .14375$. Thousandths multiplied by hundredths produce *hundred-thousandths,* and hence the product contains *five* decimal places, or as many as both of the factors.

Multiply:

9. 6.5 by .75	**14.** 4.36 by .27	**19.** .085 by 30.
10. .043 by 6.5	**15.** 64. by .032	**20.** 2.56 by 250.
11. .0432 by 5.4	**16.** 30.3 by .018	**21.** 3.24 by .33⅓
12. .048 by 24.	**17.** .056 by 24.	**22.** 5.75 by 8⅗
13. 5.6 by .056	**18.** 50. by .08	**23.** 16¾ by .045

24. Multiply sixteen thousand by sixteen thousandths.

25. Multiply 205 millionths by 46 thousandths.

26. Multiply the multiplicand in each of the above problems, from 9 to 23 inclusive, by .015; by 2.04.

27. Multiply 6.25 by 10; by 100.

PROCESS.

6.25 $\times$ 10 $= 62.5$

6.25 $\times$ 100 $= 625$.

Since the removal of a decimal figure one place to the left multiplies its value by 10 (Art. 115, Pr. 2), the removal of the decimal point one place to the right multiplies 6.25 by 10, and the removal of the point two places to the right multiplies 6.25 by 100.

28. Multiply 3.406 by 100; by 1000; by 10000.

29. Multiply .00048 by 1000; by 100000.

30. Multiply .0000256 by 10000; by 1000000.

31. Multiply .000405 by 2500; by 16000.

32. Multiply .0001006 by 1800; by 9000.

ART. 122.   **Principle.**—*The number of decimal places in the product equals the number of decimal places in both factors.*

ART. 123.   1. To multiply one decimal by another:

Rule.—*Multiply as in the multiplication of integers, and point off as many decimal places in the product as there are decimal places in both multiplicand and multiplier.*

NOTE.—If there be not enough decimal figures in the product, supply the deficiency by prefixing decimal ciphers.

2. To multiply a decimal by 10, 100, 1000, etc.:

Rule.—*Remove the decimal point as many places to the right as there are ciphers in the multiplier.*

NOTE.—If there be not enough decimal places in the product, supply the deficiency by annexing ciphers.

DIVISION OF DECIMALS.

1. How many times are 5 tenths contained in 10 tenths? 7 tenths in 35 tenths? 8 tenths in 48 tenths?

2. How many times are 7 hundredths contained in 21 hundredths? 7 hundredths in 35 hundredths?

3. What is $\frac{9}{10} \div \frac{3}{10}$? $\frac{27}{100} \div \frac{9}{100}$? $\frac{75}{1000} \div \frac{25}{1000}$?

4. What is $.8 \div .4$? $.21 \div .07$? $.084 \div .012$?

5. What is $\frac{3}{10} \div \frac{6}{1000}$? $\frac{12}{100} \div \frac{6}{1000}$? $\frac{15}{100} \div \frac{15}{1000}$?

SUGGESTION.—Reduce the fractions to thousandths.

6. What is $.3 \div .15$? $.25 \div .125$? $.12 \div .012$?

7. Of what order is the quotient when tenths are divided by tenths? Hundredths by hundredths? Thousandths by thousandths?

8. Of what order is the quotient when any order is divided by a like order? When any number is divided by a like number?

9. Divide 8.05 by .35

PROCESS.

.35) 8.05 (23., *Ans.*   35 hundredths are contained in 805
  7 0   hundredths, a like number, 23 times, and
  ――   hence 8.05 ÷ .35 = 23. *The quotient is*
  1 05   *units.*
  1 05

10. Divide 80.5 by .35

PROCESS.

.35)80.50(230., *Ans.*   By annexing a decimal cipher to
  70   80.5, which does not change its value
  ――   (Art. 117), the dividend and divisor
  10 5   are made like numbers, and hence
  10 5   *their quotient is units.*
  ――
  00

11. Divide .805 by .35

PROCESS.

.35).805(2.3, *Ans.*   Since .35 and .80, the first partial
  70   dividend, are like numbers, the first
  ――   quotient figure (2) denotes *units;* and
  105   if the first figure denotes units, the
  105   second must denote tenths.

The pointing in all cases in the division of decimals, may also be explained on the principle, that the dividend is the product of the divisor and quotient, and hence it *must contain as many decimal places as both divisor and quotient.*

In the 9th example, the divisor and dividend contain an equal number of decimal places, and hence there are no decimal places in the quotient.

In the 10th example, the divisor contains one more decimal place than the dividend, and hence a decimal cipher must be added to the dividend before the division is possible.

In the 11th example, the divisor contains *two* decimal places, and the dividend *three*, and hence the quotient contains *one* decimal place.

Divide:

12.	32.4 by 1.8	**25.**	6.241 by .0079
13.	2.56 by .64	**26.**	67.5 by .075
14.	.288 by .036	**27.**	.675 by 75.
15.	82.5 by 2.75	**28.**	6.75 by 750.
16.	62.5 by .025	**29.**	256. by .075
17.	9. by .45	**30.**	.256 by 250.
18.	4.53 by .0302	**31.**	.0025 by 50.
19.	.3 by .0125	**32.**	25. by .00125
20.	.625 by 12.5	**33.**	.001 by 100.
21.	.0256 by .32	**34.**	100 by .001
22.	17.595 by 8.5	**35.**	.045 by 900.
23.	3.3615 by 12.45	**36.**	$13.50 by $.37$\frac{1}{2}$
24.	.031812 by 4.82	**37.**	$12. by $.06$\frac{1}{4}$

38. Divide the dividend in each of the above problems, from 12 to 24 inclusive, by .25; by 200.

39. Divide the dividend in each of the above problems, from 25 to 37 inclusive, by 1.25; by 2000.

40. Divide twenty-four thousandths by sixteen millionths.

41. Divide seventy-eight by thirty-four thousandths.

42. Divide fifteen millionths by six hundredths.

43. Divide 45.7 by 10; by 100.

PROCESS.

$45.7 \div 10 = 4.57$
$45.7 \div 100 = .457$

Since the removal of a decimal figure one place to the right divides its value by 10 (Art. 115, Pr. 2), the removal of the decimal point one place to the *left* divides a decimal by 10, and the removal of the point two places to the left divides it by 100.

44. Divide 483.75 by 100; by 1000; by 10000.

45. Divide 54.50 by 100; by 10000; by 1000.

46. Divide .005 by 10; by 100; by 1000.

47. Divide 62.5 by 500; by 5000; by 25000.

48. Divide 172.8 by 600; by 3600; by 9000.

ART. 124. **Principles.**—1. *Since the dividend is the* PRODUCT *of the divisor and quotient, it contains as many decimal places as both divisor and quotient.* Hence,

2. *The quotient must contain as many decimal places as the number of decimal places in the dividend exceeds those in the divisor.*

ART. 125. 1. To divide one decimal by another:

Rule.—*Divide as in the division of integers, and point off as many decimal places in the quotient as the number of decimal places in the dividend exceeds the number in the divisor.*

NOTES.—1. When the divisor and dividend contain the same number of decimal places, the quotient is *units.*

2. The dividend must contain at least as many decimal places as the divisor before division is possible, and hence when the divisor contains more decimal places than the dividend, supply the deficiency in the dividend by *annexing* decimal ciphers.

3. When the quotient has not enough decimal figures, supply the deficiency by *prefixing* decimal ciphers.

4. When there is a remainder, the division may be continued by annexing ciphers, each cipher thus annexed adding one decimal place to the dividend. Sufficient accuracy is usually secured by carrying the division to three or four decimal places.

2. To divide a decimal by 10, 100, 1000, etc.:

Rule.—*Remove the decimal point as many places to the left as there are ciphers in the divisor.*

REVIEW PROBLEMS.

1. Reduce $\frac{3}{125}$ to a decimal.
2. Reduce $\frac{7}{2500}$ to a decimal.
3. Change .325 to a common fraction.
4. Change .0045 to a common fraction.

5. From the sum of 67.5 and .54 take their difference.

6. From the sum of 64.5 and .015 take their product.

7. Multiply 6.25 + .075 by 6.25 — .075

8. Divide .0512 by .032 × .005

9. From 25.6 ÷ .064 take 32.4 × .015

10. Divide $5.33 × 2.5 by .075.

11. What is $(.08\frac{1}{4} \times 1.2\frac{1}{2}) \div (.006\frac{1}{4} \times .016)$?

12. Multiply 15 millionths by 7 millions.

13. Divide 16 ten-millionths by 25 thousandths.

14. Divide 205 millions by 41 ten-thousandths.

15. The product of three decimals is .0189, and one of them is .54 and another 2.5 : what is the third?

NOTE.—United States money will furnish numerous practical problems involving the use of decimals.

UNITED STATES MONEY.

ART. 126. The denominations of United States money, used in business and accounts, are *dollars, cents,* and *mills*—mills being used only in making calculations.

A dollar equals 100 cents, and a cent equals 10 mills.

ART. 127. The first two figures at the right of dollars denote cents, and the third figure denotes mills. The two figures denoting cents express *hundredths* of a dollar, and the figure denoting mills expresses *tenths* of a cent, or *thousandths* of a dollar.

The three figures denoting cents and mills may be read together as so many *thousandths* of a dollar.

ART. 128. The figures denoting dollars are preceded by the *dollar sign,* $, and they are separated from those denoting cents by a decimal point, called a *separatrix.* Thus, $24.354 is read *twenty-four dollars thirty-five cents four mills.*

NOTES.—1. United States Money consists of *Coin* and *Paper Money.* Coin is called Specie Currency, or *Specie*, and paper money is called *Paper Currency.*

2. The principal gold coins are the double eagle ($20), eagle ($10), half-eagle, quarter-eagle, and dollar.

The silver coins are the dollar, half-dollar, quarter-dollar, and dime. The smaller coins are the five-cent piece, three-cent piece, two-cent piece, and cent. The first two coins are made of copper and nickel, and the last two of bronze, which is an alloy of copper, tin, and zinc.

3. Gold and silver coins are alloyed to make them harder and more durable. The gold coins contain 9 parts of gold and 1 part of copper; and the silver coins contain 9 parts of silver and 1 part of copper. Nickel and copper coins are made in the proportion of 1 part nickel to 3 parts copper. The bronze coins are 19 parts copper and 1 part tin and zinc.

4. Paper money consists of notes issued by the United States, called Treasury Notes, and bank notes issued by banks.

NOTATION AND REDUCTION.

1. Express in words, $75.50; $105.08; $5; $.87½; $.375

2. Express in words, $37.507; $250.075; $80.005; $.075

3. Read decimally, $70.25; $140.05; $387.60; $105.805

4. Read decimally, $.255; $16.455; $300.05; $475.005

WRITTEN PROBLEMS.

5. Write, in figures, ten dollars fifty cents.

6. Write forty dollars sixty cents five mills.

7. Write 100 dollars 37 cents 4 mills.

8. Write 25 dollars 6 cents 5 mills; 50 cents 8 mills.

9. Write 75 cents 6 mills; 6 cents 5 mills; 10 mills.

10. How many cents in $25? $100? $350?

11. How many mills in $47? $150? $.75? $.625?

12. How many cents in $5.37? $16.85? $40.08?

13. How many mills in $.37½? $4.62½? $10? $1.01?

14. Reduce 1500 cents to dollars.

15. Reduce 15000 mills to dollars.

16. Reduce 450 mills to cents; $25.08 to mills.

17. Reduce $100.01 to cents; $10.10 to mills.

ADDITION AND SUBTRACTION.

ORAL PROBLEMS.

1. A man paid $7.50 for a pair of boots, and $5.50 for a hat: how much did he pay for both?

2. A lady paid $15 for a shawl, $5.75 for a hat, $2.25 for a pair of gloves, and $4 for a pair of gaiters: what was the amount of her purchases?

3. A drover bought cows at $36.50 a head, and sold them at $40 a head: how much did he gain?

4. A man bought a coat for $24.25, and a vest for $4.50, and handed the merchant three $10 bills: how much money did he receive back?

5. A mechanic earns $20 a week, and his family expenses amount to $16.75 a week: how much has he left?

6. A book-seller bought a set of maps for $17, and a set of charts for $6.50, and sold both sets for $28.50: how much did he gain?

WRITTEN PROBLEMS.

7. What is the sum of $.65, $15.44, $60.62½, $100, $94.05, $5.065, $50.37½, $625, and $.87½?

8. From $100.15 take $62.37½?

9. To the sum of $308.60 and $190.125 add their difference.

10. From the sum of $2750 and $1680.62½ take their difference.

11. A merchant's sales for a week were as follows: Monday, $125.60; Tuesday, $98.50; Wednesday, $190.30; Thursday, $215; Friday, $175.80; Saturday, $247.90: what was the amount of his sales for the week?

12. A farmer's sales in one year were as follows: wheat, $460.50; corn, $387.85; oats, $96.25; hay, $137.65; and stock, $340.75. What was the amount of his sales?

13. A man exchanged three city lots, valued respectively at $900, $1200, and $750, for a farm valued at $3075; paying the difference in money: how much money did he pay?

14. A man receiving a salary of $1600 a year, pays $325 for house rent, $450.80 for provisions, $200.60 for clothing, and $245 for all other expenses: how much has he left?

15. A man deposits in a bank, at different times, $75, $230.80, $180.40, and $95; and he draws out, at different times, $40, $87.50, $331.45, $20.15, and $18.60: what is his bank balance?

ART. 129. To add or subtract sums of money:

Rule.—*Write units of the same denomination in the same column, add or subtract as in simple numbers, and separate dollars and cents by a decimal point, and prefix the dollar sign.*

THE ADDING OF LEDGER COLUMNS.

ART. 130. A **Ledger** is a book in which business men keep a summary of accounts.

The items on a ledger page often make long columns of figures, which are added (footed) with absolute accuracy.

Many accountants write the partial footings, obtained by adding the successive columns or double columns, on a separate piece of paper. This permits the re-adding of any column, or set of columns, as the case may be, without the trouble of re-adding the preceding columns, and it also avoids the defacing of the ledger page by corrections.

Let the pupil foot the following ledger columns by adding two columns at a time (Art. 23), being as careful to obtain accurate results as he would be in actual business:

16.	17.	18.	19.
$1.25	$19.50	$75.50	$1912.88
8.14	20.00	184.30	806.40
2.75	12.45	111.10	1000.00
.65	14.52	43.95	1250.86
.75	25.48	263.55	943.82
8.37	40.50	100.00	607.55
12.50	8.60	90.00	400.33
4.65	9.35	7.15	148.67
.83	.65	13.48	249.50
7.16	.73	2.75	2040.00
10.28	.84	52.30	4508.70
1.20	12.10	900.25	3406.30
.95	.86	625.80	1280.75
.48	.93	314.87	1300.00
13.47	2.95	64.50	877.77
23.00	14.63	49.87	620.14
3.08	9.82	302.58	8.60
6.15	20.60	10.10	7.45
24.92	19.30	100.98	13.33
.83	22.33	78.60	286.45
.92	9.81	44.50	1300.80
.45	8.76	79.88	1440.00
14.86	12.57	320.65	986.70
5.80	18.19	19.10	87.80
7.26	7.63	8.50	137.40
12.00	14.60	436.75	1500.00
5.00	4.85	135.20	885.73
4.37	9.63	44.88	236.40
6.45	12.83	65.90	13483.86
17.83	18.10	6.01	11456.20
2.65	7.63	7.83	88.00
1.50	2.20	4.22	24.30
6.15	7.25	8.42	106.75
12.36	3.67	1.68	46.24
$279.01	$	$	$

20. Copy and add the upper half of 16 and the upper half of 17 together as one example.

21. Copy and add the lower half of 16 and the lower half of 17 together as one example.

22. Copy and add the upper half of 18 and the upper half of 19 together as one example.

23. Copy and add the lower half of 18 and the lower half of 19 together as one example.

MULTIPLICATION AND DIVISION.

ORAL PROBLEMS.

1. A mechanic earns $2.50 a day: how much will he earn in 6 days? 10 days? 20 days?

2. What will 8 barrels of flour cost, at $7.25 a barrel? At $6.50? At $6.25? At $7.50?

3. What will 10 yards of carpeting cost, at $1.75 a yard? At $1.25? At $1.50? At 75 cts.?

4. A drover paid $38.70 for 9 sheep: what did they cost apiece?

5. A man paid $42 for 8 tons of coal: what did it cost per ton?

6. If a man earn $39 in 6 days, how much will he earn in 5 days? In 10 days? 20 days? 8 days?

7. At 25 cents a dozen, how many dozens of eggs can be bought for $4.50? For $5? $6? $8?

WRITTEN PROBLEMS.

8. A farmer sold 45 hogs, at $22.45 apiece: how much did he receive for them?

9. A miller sold 237 pounds of flour, at $7.62½ a barrel: how much did he receive?

10. A man sold a farm of 260 acres, at $33⅓ per acre: what was the amount received?

11. A farm containing 125 acres was sold for $5093.75: what was the price per acre?

12. How many chairs, at $1.25 apiece, can be bought for $80? For $75? For $100?

13. At $12.37½ a ton, how many tons of hay can be bought for $4653? For $1163.25?

14. A farmer sold 3 hogs, weighing respectively 278, 309, and 327 pounds, at $.07½ a pound: how much did he receive?

15. A farmer sold in one year 536 pounds of butter, at 30 cts. a pound; 1200 pounds of cheese, at 16⅔ cts.; and 19 tons of hay, at $8.75 a ton: how much did he receive?

16. A grocer bought 540 pounds of coffee for $81, and 420 pounds of tea for $525; he sold the coffee at 18 cts. a pound, and the tea at $1.60 a pound: how much did he gain?

ART. 131. 1. To multiply or divide sums of money by an abstract number:

Rule.—*Multiply or divide as in simple numbers, separate dollars and cents in the result by a decimal point, and prefix the dollar sign.*

2. To divide one sum of money by another:

Rule.—*Reduce both numbers to the same denomination, and divide as in simple numbers.*

ALIQUOT PARTS.

ART. 132. When the price of an article is an aliquot part of a dollar, the cost of any number of such articles may be found more readily than by multiplying.

The aliquot parts of a dollar commonly used in business, are:

50 cts. $= \frac{1}{2}$ of \$1.00	$12\frac{1}{2}$ cts. $= \frac{1}{8}$ of \$1.00
25 " $= \frac{1}{4}$ of 1.00	$6\frac{1}{4}$ " $= \frac{1}{16}$ of 1.00
20 " $= \frac{1}{5}$ of 1.00	$33\frac{1}{3}$ " $= \frac{1}{3}$ of 1.00
10 " $= \frac{1}{10}$ of 1.00	$16\frac{2}{3}$ " $= \frac{1}{6}$ of 1.00

The following aliquot parts of aliquot parts of a dollar are also used:

25 cts. $= \frac{1}{2}$ of 50 cts.	$16\frac{2}{3}$ cts. $= \frac{1}{2}$ of $33\frac{1}{3}$ cts.
$12\frac{1}{2}$ " $= \frac{1}{4}$ of 50 "	$12\frac{1}{2}$ " $= \frac{1}{2}$ of 25 "
$6\frac{1}{4}$ " $= \frac{1}{8}$ of 50 "	$6\frac{1}{4}$ " $= \frac{1}{4}$ of 25 "

ORAL PROBLEMS.

17. What will 56 pounds of grapes cost, at $12\frac{1}{2}$ cts. a pound?

SOLUTION.—At \$1 a pound, 56 pounds will cost \$56, and at $12\frac{1}{2}$ cts., which is $\frac{1}{8}$ of \$1, 56 pounds will cost $\frac{1}{8}$ of \$56, which is \$7.

18. What will 120 spellers cost, at 25 cts. apiece? At $33\frac{1}{3}$ cts.? At $16\frac{2}{3}$ cts.? At 20 cts.?

19. What is the cost of 96 dozens of eggs, at $16\frac{2}{3}$ cts. a dozen? At 20 cts.? At 25 cts.? At $33\frac{1}{3}$ cts.?

20. What will 240 pounds of sugar cost, at $12\frac{1}{2}$ cts. a pound? At $16\frac{2}{3}$ cts.? At 20 cts.?

21. At $16\frac{2}{3}$ cts. a dozen, how many dozens of eggs can be bought for \$15?

SOLUTION.—At $16\frac{2}{3}$ cents a dozen, \$1 will buy 6 dozens of eggs, and \$15 will buy 15 times 6 dozens, or 90 dozens.

22. At $12\frac{1}{2}$ cts. a pound, how many pounds of lard can be bought for \$12? For \$25? For \$40?

23. How many pounds of butter, at $33\frac{1}{3}$ cts. a pound, can be bought for \$15? For \$33? For \$40?

24. At $6\frac{1}{4}$ cts. a quart, how many quarts of currants can be bought with 30 quarts of cherries, at 10 cts. a quart?

WRITTEN PROBLEMS.

25. What will 348 yards of carpeting cost, at $1.62½ cts. a yard?

PROCESS.

$1.62½ = $1 + 50 cts. + 12½ cts.

$$
\begin{array}{rl}
\$348 & = \text{cost at \$1 a yard.} \\
\tfrac{1}{2} \,\big|\, 174 & = \text{``  `` 50 cts. a yard.} \\
\tfrac{1}{4} \,\big|\, 43.50 & = \text{``  `` 12½ ``  ``} \\
\hline
\$565.50 & = \text{``  `` \$1.62½ ``}
\end{array}
$$

26. What will 1600 bushels of oats cost, at 37½ cts. a bushel? At 45 cts. a bushel? At 62½ cts.?

27. What will 2464 bushels of wheat cost, at $1.25 a bushel? At $1.37½? At $1.50? At $1.62½?

28. What will 1250 yards of carpeting cost, at $1.37½ a yard? At $1.50? At $1.25? At $1.75? At $1.87½.

29. What will 640 bottles of ink cost, at 87½ cents a bottle? At 62½ cts.? At 50 cts.? At 75 cts.?

30. At 25 cts. a dozen, how many dozens of eggs can be bought for $12? For $25? For $42? For $105?

31. At 33⅓ cts. a yard, how many yards of cloth can be bought for $50? For $75? For $90? For $120?

32. What will 5 lb. 10 oz. of butter cost, at 35 cts. a pound?

PROCESS.

$$
\begin{array}{rl}
\$\ .35 & = \text{cost of 1 lb.} \\
\$1.75 & = \text{``  `` 5 lb.} \\
.175 & = \text{``  `` 8 oz. (½ lb.)} \\
.044 & = \text{``  `` 2 `` (⅛ lb.)} \\
\hline
\$1.969 & = \text{``  `` 5 lb. 10 oz.}
\end{array}
$$

33. What will 9 lb. 13 oz. of cheese cost, at 15 cts. a pound? At 16 cts.? At 18 cts.? At 20 cts.?

34. What will 16 gal. 3 qt. of sirup cost, at $.90 a gallon? At $1.10? At $1.25? At $1.62½?

35. What will 7 bu. 3 pk. 4 qt. of cherries cost, at $4.25 a bushel? At $3.50? At $4? At $4.50?

Art. 133. 1. To find the cost of a number of articles when the price is an aliquot part of a dollar:

Rule.—*Find the cost at $1, and take such part of the result as the price is of $1.*

2. To find the number of articles which can be purchased for a given sum of money when the price is an aliquot part of a dollar:

Rule.—*Find the number of articles that can be purchased for $1, and multiply the result by the given sum of money, considered as an abstract number.*

BILLS.

Art. 134. Each of the following bills should be neatly made out on paper, in proper form, and receipted:

1.   CINCINNATI, O., Jan. 1, 1883.
  THOMAS KNIGHT,
                     Bought of BAKER, SMITH & CO.
     1882.

						$	
Nov.	18,	48 lb.	Castile Soap,	@ 16⅔c. . . .		$8	00
"	"	25 "	Starch,	@ 6¼ . . .		1	56
"	30,	65 "	Sugar,	@ 15		9	75
"	"	33 gal.	Vinegar,	@ 20		6	60
Dec.	12,	16 lb.	Rio Coffee,	@ 23		3	68
"	"	5 "	Star Candles,	@ 20		1	00
"	"	56 "	Butter,	@ 33⅓ . . .		18	67
"	15,	10 "	Cheese,	@ 15		1	50

$

Received Payment,

                     BAKER, SMITH & CO.
                          Per COONS.

CLEVELAND, O., Nov. 24, 1882.

...AM JONES,

　　　　　To CHARLES C. WILHELM, *Dr.*

...s' Work,	@ $2.75	. . . .	$
...Nails,	@ 6¼	. . . .	
" ... .. Pine Lumber,	@ 2.50 per C.	. . . .	
" 4 M. Shingles,	@ 4.33⅓	. . . .	

　　　　　　　　　　　　　　　　　　$

Cr.

Oct. 16, by cash,	. . . .	$25
" 23, " "	. . . .	44
Medical Services to date,	. . . . . .	15

　　　　　　　　　　　　　　　　　　$

Received payment, by due-bill,　　$

　　　　　　　CHARLES C. WILHELM.

What is the amount of the due-bill?

3 Mrs. C. B. Jones bought of Cole, Steele & Co., of Indianapolis, as follows: Nov. 12th, 1882, 23 yds. muslin, @ 16⅔ cts..; 45 yds. sheeting, @ 12½ cts.; Dec. 7th, 12 yds. silk, @ $1.62½; 8 handkerchiefs, @ 45 cts.; 2 pairs kid gloves, @ $1.37½; 6 neckties, @ 75 cts. Make out and receipt the above bill.

4. Daniel Hough bought of George F. Wheeler, Columbus, Ohio, Jan. 15th, 1883, 45 lb. of sugar at 11 cts., 48 lb. of flour at 4½ cts., and 36 lb. of Rio coffee at 27 cts.; Feb. 15th, 17 lb. of butter at 28 cts., 15 lb. of lard at 7½ cts., 36 lb. of ham at 14 cts., 8 lb. of cheese at 12½ cts., and 25 lb. of tea at 95 cts. Make out and receipt this bill as clerk of Mr. Wheeler.

5. Luther Day bought of William Taylor, Lafayette, Ind., Sept. 10th, 1882, 7 tons of hard coal at $6.45 per ton, and 6 tons of soft coal at $3.75; Oct. 5th, 5 cords of wood at $5.25; Oct. 7th, 13 tons hard coal at $6.95 per ton, 20 tons of soft coal at $4.10 per ton, and 16 bushels of charcoal at 24 cts. Mr. Day paid Oct. 9th, $50, Dec. 1st, $75, Dec. 10th, $50, Dec. 15th, $25, and the balance by due-bill Dec. 31st. Make out and receipt this bill, using Bill 2 as a model.

NOTE.—The pupils should be required to make out original bills until they are able to complete any business transaction involving a receipted bill.

DEFINITIONS.

ART. 135. An **Account** is a record of business transactions between two parties, with statements of debts and credits.

The party owing the debts specified, is called the *Debtor*, and the party to whom they are due, is called the *Creditor*.

ART. 136. A **Bill** is a written statement of an account. It is drawn by the creditor against the debtor, and gives the time and place of the transaction, and the names of the parties.

When the debtor has made payments on the account, or has charges against the creditor, such payments or charges are called *Credits*. They are entered as in Bill 2, p. 110.

ART. 137. A bill is receipted by writing the words *"Received Payment"* at the bottom, and affixing the creditor's name. This may be done by the creditor, or by a clerk, agent, or any other authorized person.

If the debtor is not able to pay a bill when presented, it may be accepted by writing the word *"Accepted"* across its face, with date and signature. When a bill is paid by a promissory note or due-bill, the fact may be added to the words *"Received Payment,"* as in Bill 2.

ART. 138. A **Bill of Goods** is a written statement of goods sold, with the amount and price of each article, and the entire cost. It is also called an *Invoice*.

DENOMINATE NUMBERS.

MEASURES OF WEIGHT.

ART. 139. Avoirdupois Weight is used in weighing all articles except gold, silver, and the precious stones.

The denominations are *ounces* (oz.), *pounds* (lb.), *hundred-weights* (cwt.), and *tons* (T.).

TABLE.

16 *oz.* = 1 *lb.*
100 *lb.* = 1 *cwt.*
20 *cwt.* = 1 *T.*

ALSO:

196 *lb. flour* = 1 *barrel.*
200 *lb. beef* = 1 "

200 *lb. pork* = 1 *barrel.*
100 *lb. fish* = 1 *quintal.*
100 *lb. of grain* = 1 *cental.*
114 *lb. lead or iron* = 1 *stone.*
56 *lb. corn or rye* = 1 *bushel.*
60 *lb. wheat* = 1 "
60 *lb. potatoes* = 1 "
32 *lb. oats* = 1 "

NOTES.—1. The standard avoirdupois pound contains 7000 troy grains.

2. At the United States custom houses, and in weighing coal and iron at the mines, the ton used contains 2240 pounds. It is called the *long* or *gross* ton.

3. The dram ($\frac{1}{16}$ of an ounce) is seldom used.

4. The legal weight of a bushel of grain or potatoes varies slightly in several States from the weight given above.

5. The legal weight of a bushel of coal varies in different States, the weight being from 70 to 80 pounds. Coal is usually sold by the ton.

ORAL EXERCISES.

1. How many ounces in 2 pounds? 4 lb.? $25\frac{1}{2}$ lb.?

2. How many pounds in 32 ounces? 48 oz.? 96 oz.?

3. How many pounds in 2 cwt.? $3\frac{1}{2}$ cwt.? $4\frac{3}{4}$ cwt.?

4. How many cwt. in $2\frac{1}{2}$ tons? $3\frac{1}{4}$ tons? $5\frac{1}{4}$ tons?

5. How many pounds in 5 bushels of wheat? $10\frac{1}{2}$ bu.?

6. How many bushels of wheat in 240 lbs.? 360 lbs.?

7. How many pounds of corn in 5 centals? 6½ centals? 7 centals? 8¼ centals?

8. How many bushels of oats in 96 pounds? 160 lb.?

TROY WEIGHT.

Art. 140. **Troy Weight** is used in weighing gold, silver, and the precious stones.

The denominations are *grains* (gr.), *pennyweights* (pwt.), *ounces* (oz.), and *pounds* (lb.).

TABLE.

$$24 \; gr. = 1 \; pwt.$$
$$20 \; pwt. = 1 \; oz.$$
$$12 \; oz. = 1 \; lb.$$

Notes.—1. In weighing diamonds, the unit commonly used is the carat, which is 3⅕ troy grains (nearly).

2. In determining the *fineness* of gold, it is considered as composed of twenty-four parts, called *carats*, and the number of carats specified is the number of twenty-fourths of pure gold which it contains. A sixteen-carat chain contains $\frac{16}{24}$ of pure gold and $\frac{8}{24}$ of alloy.

9. How many ounces of gold in 3 lb.? 4½ lb.? ⅓ lb.?

10. How many pounds of silver in 48 oz.? 72 oz.?

11. How many pounds troy in 32 oz.? 80 oz.?

12. How many pennyweights in 5 oz.? 3½ oz.? 4⅗ oz.?

13. How many ounces in 40 pwt.? 60 pwt.? 90 pwt.?

14. How many grains in 3 pwt.? 2½ pwt.? 3⅓ pwt.?

APOTHECARIES' WEIGHT.

Art. 141. **Apothecaries' Weight** is used by physicians in prescribing, and by apothecaries in mixing and compounding, medicines.

The denominations are *grains* (gr.), *scruples* (℈), *drams* (℥), *ounces* (℥), and *pounds* (lb.).

TABLE.

		APOTHECARIES' FLUID MEASURE.
20 *gr.* = 1 ϶		60 *minims* (♏︎) = 1 *dram*, *f ℥.*
3 ϶ = 1 ℥		8 *f ℥* = 1 *ounce*, *f ℥.*
8 ℥ = 1 ℥		16 *f ℥* = 1 *pint*, *O.*
12 ℥ = 1 *lb.*		

NOTE.—Medicines are bought and sold in quantities by avoirdupois weight.

15. How many drams in 3 ℥ of quinine? $2\frac{1}{2}$ ℥? $4\frac{1}{3}$ ℥?
16. How many scruples in 4 drams? $7\frac{1}{3}$ ℥? $8\frac{2}{3}$ ℥?
17. How many grains in 2 scruples? 5 ϶? $6\frac{1}{2}$ ϶?
18. How many fluid ounces in 2 O.? 4 O.? 5 O.?
19. How many fluid drams in 3 *f ℥*? $4\frac{1}{2}$ *f ℥*?

MEASURES OF CAPACITY.

DRY MEASURE.

ART. 142. **Dry Measure** is used in measuring grain, fruit, most vegetables, coal, and many other dry articles.

The denominations are *pints* (pt.), *quarts* (qt.), *pecks* (pk.), and *bushels* (bu.).

TABLE.

$$2 \ pt. = 1 \ qt.$$
$$8 \ qt. = 1 \ pk.$$
$$4 \ pk. = 1 \ bu.$$

NOTES.—1. The standard bushel is $18\frac{1}{2}$ inches in diameter and 8 inches deep. It contains $2150\frac{2}{5}$ cubic inches, or nearly $1\frac{1}{4}$ cubic feet.

2. Grain, potatoes, coal, etc., are also sold by weight. See Art. 139.

LIQUID MEASURE.

ART. 143. **Liquid Measure** is used in measuring liquids.

The denominations are *gills* (gi.), *pints* (pt.), *quarts* (qt.), and *gallons* (gal.).

TABLE.

$$4 \ gi. = 1 \ pt.$$
$$2 \ pt. = 1 \ qt.$$
$$4 \ qt. = 1 \ gal.$$

NOTES.—1. The standard liquid gallon contains 231 cubic inches. In measuring cisterns, etc., $7\frac{1}{2}$ gallons are allowed to the cubic foot.

2. The size of casks for liquids is variable. Barrels contain from 30 to 40 gallons, or more. The size of vats, cisterns, etc., is usually estimated in barrels of $31\frac{1}{2}$ gallons.

ORAL EXERCISES.

1. How many pints in 2 quarts? 5 qt.? 12 qt.?

2. How many quarts in 3 pecks? 5 pk.? 10 pk.?

3. How many pecks in 16 quarts? 30 qt.? 44 qt.?

4. How many quarts in 8 pt.? 13 pt.? 21 pt.? 25 pt.?

5. How many pecks in 3 bu.? $6\frac{1}{2}$ bu.? $10\frac{3}{4}$ bu.?

6. How many bushels in 36 pk? 41 pk.? 46 pk.?

7. How many gills in 5 pints? 8 pt.? $10\frac{1}{2}$ pt.?

8. How many quarts in 4 gallons? $7\frac{1}{2}$ gal.? $12\frac{1}{4}$ gal.?

9. How many gallons in 24 quarts? 30 qt.? 43 qt.?

10. How many pints in 16 quarts? 20 qt.? $25\frac{1}{2}$ qt.?

11. How many pecks in 16 pints? 32 pt.? 48 pt.?

12. How many bushels in 32 quarts? 64 qt.? 80 qt.?

MEASURES OF EXTENSION.

LONG MEASURE.

ART. 144. Long Measure is used in measuring lines or distances. It is also called *Linear Measure.*

The denominations are *inches* (in.), *feet* (ft.), *yards* (yd.), *rods* (rd.), and *miles* (mi.).

TABLE.

12 *in.* = 1 *ft.*	4 *in.* = 1 *hand.*
3 *ft.* = 1 *yd.*	3 *ft.* = 1 *pace.*
$5\frac{1}{2}$ *yd.* or $16\frac{1}{2}$ *ft.* } = 1 *rd.*	6 *ft.* = 1 *fathom.*
	3 *mi.* = 1 *league.*
320 *rd.* = 1 *mi.*	60 *geog. mi.* = 1 *degree.*
	$69\frac{1}{6}$ *st. mi.* = 1 *degree.*

NOTES.—1, The standard unit of length is the yard. The standard yard of the United States is a metal bar kept at Washington.

2. The mile is commonly divided into halves, fourths, eighths, etc. The furlong ($\frac{1}{8}$ of a mile) is seldom used.

3. In measuring cloth, ribbons, etc., the width is not considered, and the yard is divided into halves, fourths, eighths, and sixteenths. In the United States custom house the yard is divided into tenths and hundredths.

ORAL EXERCISES.

1. How many inches in 2 feet? 5 ft.? 8 ft.?

2. How many feet in 36 inches? 60 in.? 84 in.?

3. How many feet in 3 yards? $5\frac{2}{3}$ yd.? $10\frac{1}{3}$ yd.?

4. How many yards in 2 rods? 4 rd.? 5 rd.?

5. How many rods in 11 yards? 22 yd.? $27\frac{1}{2}$ yd.?

6. How many feet in 2 rods? 4 rd.? 10 rd.?

7. How many rods in 2 miles? 5 mi.? 10 mi.?

8. How many feet in 9 yards? $12\frac{1}{3}$ yd.? $16\frac{2}{3}$ yd.?

9. How many rods in $\frac{1}{4}$ of a mile? $\frac{1}{8}$ mi.? $\frac{1}{16}$ mi.?

10. How many feet in 5 fathoms? 8 fathoms? $9\frac{1}{2}$ fathoms? 11 fathoms? $12\frac{1}{2}$ fathoms?

SQUARE MEASURE.

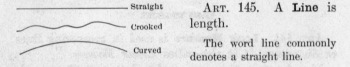
Straight
Crooked
Curved

ART. 145. A Line is length.

The word line commonly denotes a straight line.

ART. 146. An **Angle** is the divergence of two lines from a common point.

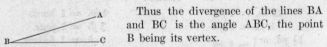

Thus the divergence of the lines BA and BC is the angle ABC, the point B being its vertex.

ART. 147. When a line so meets another line as to make the two adjacent angles equal, each angle is a *Right Angle*, and each line is *perpendicular* to the other.

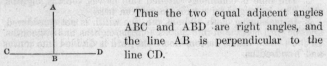

Thus the two equal adjacent angles ABC and ABD are right angles, and the line AB is perpendicular to the line CD.

ART. 148. An **Obtuse** angle is greater than a right angle, and an **Acute** angle is less than a right angle.

Thus the angle ABD is an obtuse angle, and the angle ABC is an acute angle. The line AB is an *oblique* line.

ART. 149. A **Surface** is that which has length and width, but not depth or thickness.

A flat surface, as the surface of still water, is called a *plane surface*, or, more briefly, a *plane*.

NOTE.—To determine whether the surface of any object, as a table, is a plane, take a ruler with a straight edge and apply it to the surface in many different directions. If the edge rests uniformly upon the surface, it is a plane.

ART. 150. A **Rectangle** is a plane surface bounded by four straight lines and having four right angles.

ART. 151. A **Square** is a rectangle with its four sides equal.

A **Square Inch** is a square each side of which is an inch in length.

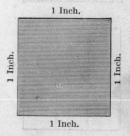

The figure at the right represents a square inch of real size.

A *square foot, square yard, square rod,* etc., are squares whose sides are respectively 1 foot, 1 yard, 1 rod, etc., in length.

ART. 152. The **Area** of a surface is the number of times it contains another surface taken as a unit of measure.

The unit of surface measure is a square; as, a *square inch,* a *square foot,* etc.

Art. 153. **Square Measure** is used in measuring the areas of surfaces. It is also called *Superficial Measure.*

The denominations are *square inches* (sq. in.), *square feet* (sq. ft.), *square yards* (sq. yd.), *square rods* (sq. rd.), *acres* (A.), and *square miles* (sq. mi.).

TABLE.

$$144 \; sq. \; in. = 1 \; sq. ft.$$
$$9 \; sq. \; ft. = 1 \; sq. \; yd.$$
$$30\tfrac{1}{4} \; sq. \; yd. = 1 \; sq. \; rd.$$
$$160 \; sq. \; rd. = 1 \; acre.$$
$$640 \; A. = 1 \; sq. \; mi.$$

Notes.—1. A square rod is also called a *perch* (P.); and 100 square feet is called a *square*, used in measuring flooring and roofing.

2. For surveyors' measure and the United States Government surveys of townships, see Mensuration, Arts. 196, 197.

ORAL EXERCISES.

1. How many square feet in a piece of zinc 3 feet long and 1 foot wide?

2. How many square feet in a piece of zinc 3 feet long and 3 feet wide?

3. How many square feet in a square yard?

4. How many square feet in 2 sq. yd.? 4 sq. yd.? 8 sq. yd.?

5. How many square yards in 9 sq. ft.? 18 sq. ft.? 27 sq. ft.?

6. How many square inches in a piece of paper 12 inches long and 1 inch wide?

7. How many square inches in a piece of paper 12 inches long and 12 inches wide?

8. How many square inches in a square foot?

9. How many square inches in 2 sq. ft. ? 5 sq. ft. ?

10. How many sq. ft. in 288 sq. in. ? 1440 sq. in. ?

11. How many square rods in a piece of land 16 rods long and 1 rod wide? 16 rd. long and 10 rd. wide? How many acres?

12. How many square rods in $\frac{1}{2}$ of an acre? $\frac{3}{4}$ of an acre? $\frac{3}{8}$ of an acre? $\frac{5}{8}$ of an acre?

13. How many acres in a sq. mile? $\frac{1}{2}$ sq. mile? $\frac{1}{4}$ sq. mile? $\frac{1}{8}$ sq. mile? $\frac{3}{8}$ sq. mile?

CUBIC MEASURE.

ART. 154. A **Solid** body has length, width, and depth or thickness. It is also called a *Volume* or *Body.*

A line has only length; a surface has length and width; and a solid has length, width, and depth.

ART. 155. A **Cube** is a body bounded by six equal squares. All its edges are equal.

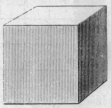
Cubic Inch.

ART. 156. A **Cubic Inch** is a cube whose edges are each one inch in length.

A *cubic foot, cubic yard,* etc., are cubes whose edges are respectively 1 foot, 1 yard, etc.

ART. 157. **Cubic Meaure** is used in measuring the contents of solids. It is also called *Solid Measure.*

The denominations are *cubic inches* (cu. in.), *cubic feet* (cu. ft.), *cubic yards* (cu. yd.), and *cords* (cd.).

TABLE.

$$1728 \ cu. \ in. = 1 \ cu. \ ft.$$
$$27 \ cu. \ ft. = 1 \ cu. \ yd.$$
$$128 \ cu. \ ft. = 1 \ cord.$$

NOTE.—For measurements of wood, stone, and masonry, see Mensuration, Art. 202.

1. How many cubic feet in a block of wood 3 ft. long, 1 ft. wide, and 1 ft. high?

NOTE.—All the solids referred to in this and the following examples are *rectangular*. See Art. 198.

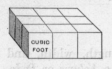

2. How many cubic feet in a block 3 ft. long, 3 ft. wide, and 1 ft. high?

3. How many cubic feet in a block 3 ft. long, 3 ft. wide, and 3 ft. high?

4. How many cubic feet in a cubic yard? In 2 cu. yd.? 5 cu. yd.? 8 cu. yd.? 10 cu. yd.?

5. How many cubic yards in 27 cu. ft.? 36 cu. ft.? 81 cu. ft.? 54 cu. ft.?

6. How many cubic feet in a block of granite 6 ft. long, 3 ft. wide, and 1 ft. high?

7. How many cubic feet in a block of granite 6 ft. long, 3 ft. wide, and 3 ft. high?

8. How many cubic inches in a solid 12 in. long, 1 in. wide, and 1 in. high?

9. How many cubic inches in a solid 12 in. long, 12 in. wide, and 1 in. high? 12 in. long, 12 in. wide, and 12 in. high?

10. How many cubic inches in a cubic foot? In 2 cu. ft.? 10 cu. ft.?

11. How many cubic feet in $\frac{1}{3}$ of a cubic yard? In $\frac{2}{3}$ cu. yd.? $2\frac{1}{3}$ cu. yd.? $3\frac{2}{3}$ cu. yd.?

12. How many cubic feet in $\frac{1}{8}$ of a cord of wood? In $\frac{1}{4}$ cord? $\frac{3}{4}$ cord? $\frac{5}{8}$ cord?

CIRCULAR MEASURE.

ART. 158. **Circular Measure** is used in measuring arcs of circles, and angles, and in estimating latitude and longitude. It is also called *Angular Measure.*

The denominations are *seconds* (″), *minutes* (′), *degrees* (°), *signs* (s.), and *circumferences* (cir.).

TABLE.

$$60″ = 1′$$
$$60′ = 1°$$
$$30° = 1 \ s.$$
$$\left.\begin{array}{c} 12 \ s. \ \text{or} \\ 360° \end{array}\right\} = 1 \ cir.$$

NOTES.—1. Circular Measure is used by surveyors in surveying land; by navigators in determining latitude and longitude at sea; and by astronomers in measuring the motion of the heavenly bodies, and in computing difference in time.

2. The portion of surface represented by the annexed figure is a *circle.* The curved line which bounds the circle is its *circumference.* Any portion of a circumference is an *arc.* Every circumference may be divided into 360 equal parts, called degrees.

3. One half of a circumference is a *semi-circumference;* one fourth, a *quadrant;* one sixth, a *sextant;* and one twelfth, a *sign.* A semi-circumference contains 180°; a quadrant, 90°; a sextant, 60°; and a sign, 30°.

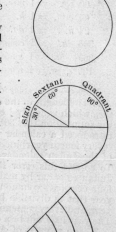

4. Since every circumference contains 360 degrees, the length of a degree depends upon the size of the circle. A degree of the earth's surface at the equator contains 69⅙ statute miles, or 60 geographical miles—a minute of space being a geographical or nautical mile.

5. The size of an *angle* is the same, whether the arc included between its sides be a portion of a large or small circle. Hence, the measure of an angle is *definite,* whatever be the length of a degree of the included arc.

Angle of 45°

ORAL EXERCISES.

1. How many minutes in 5 degrees?   10 degrees?

2. How many signs in 1 quadrant?   3 quadrants?

3. How many degrees in $\frac{1}{6}$ of a quadrant?

4. How many degrees in 2 signs? $2\frac{1}{3}$ signs?

5. How many signs in $\frac{1}{6}$ of a circumference? $\frac{1}{2}$ cir.?

6. How many degrees in $\frac{1}{4}$ cir.? $\frac{1}{8}$ cir.? $\frac{1}{12}$ cir.?

TIME MEASURE.

ART. 159. **Time Measure** is used in measuring time or duration.

The denominations are *seconds* (sec.), *minutes* (min.), *hours* (h.), *days* (da.), *years* (yr.), and *centuries* (cen.).

TABLE.

	ALSO:
60 *sec.* = 1 *min.*	7 *da.* = 1 *week* (*w.*)
60 *min.* = 1 *h.*	4 *w.* = 1 *lunar month* (*lr. mo.*)
24 *h.* = 1 *da.*	13 *lr. mo.* 1 *da.* 6 *hr.* = 1 *Julian yr.*
365 *da.* = 1 *common yr.*	12 *calendar mo.* = 1 *civil yr.*
365¼ *da.* = 1 *solar yr.*	366 *da.* = 1 *leap yr.*
100 *s. yr.* = 1 *century.*	

NOTES.—1. A solar day (24 h.) is the unit of time.

2. The length of the solar year 1880 was 365 da. 5 hr. 48 min. 47$\frac{1}{3}$ sec., which is nearly $\frac{1}{4}$ of a day longer than the common year. On the supposition that 365¼ days was the true solar year, Julius Cæsar introduced a calendar in which every year exactly divisible by 4 (every fourth year) included 366 days—called leap year. The error of the Julian calendar amounts to 3.1142 days in four centuries. To correct this error Pope Gregory XIII., in 1582, modified the Julian calendar by making three of the centennial years in every four centuries common years and one a leap year. Hence every year that is divisible by 4 and is *not* a centennial year, is a leap year, and every centennial year that is divisible by 400 is a leap year. The year 1900 will be a common year, and the year 2000 a leap year.

3. The months of April, June, September, and November contain 30 days each; the month of February, in common years, contains 28 days; and in leap years, 29 days; each of the other calendar months contains 31 days. In most business transactions 30 days are considered a month.

ORAL EXERCISES.

1. How many hours in 2 days? 3 days? 10 days?

2. How many days in 48 hours? 96 hr.? 240 hr.?

3. How many days in 5 weeks? 7 w.? $10\frac{2}{7}$ w.?

4. How many weeks in 21 days? 56 da.? 65 da.?

5. How many months in 3 years? $5\frac{1}{2}$ yr.? $10\frac{1}{4}$ yr.?

6. How many years in a quarter of a century? $\frac{1}{2}$ of a century? $\frac{3}{4}$ of a century?

7. How many days in February in 1882? 1884? 1900? 2000?

MISCELLANEOUS TABLES.

NUMBERS.

12 *things*	= 1 *dozen.*
12 *doz.*	= 1 *gross.*
12 *gross*	= 1 *great gross.*
20 *things*	= 1 *score.*

PAPER.

24 *sheets*	= 1 *quire.*
20 *quires*	= 1 *ream.*
2 *reams*	= 1 *bundle.*
5 *bundles*	= 1 *bale.*

BOOKS.

A sheet folded in 2 leaves is called a folio.

"	"	4	"	*a quarto, or 4to.*
"	"	8	"	*an octavo, or 8vo.*
"	"	12	"	*a duodecimo, or 12mo.*
"	"	16	"	*a 16mo.*
"	"	24	"	*a 24mo.*

NOTE.—In estimating the size of the leaves, as above, the double medium sheet (23 by 26 inches) is taken as a standard.

EQUIVALENTS.

1 *T.* = 20 *cwt.* = 2000 *lb.* = 32000 *oz.*

1 *bu.* = 4 *pk.* = 32 *qt.* = 64 *pt.*

1 *mi.* = 320 *rd.* = 1760 *yd.* = 5280 *ft.* = 63360 *in.*

1 *A.* = 160 *sq. rd.* = 4840 *sq. yd.* = 43560 *sq. ft.*

1 *cu. yd.* = 27 *cu. ft.* = 46656 *cu. in.*

1 *da.* = 24 *h.* = 1440 *min.* = 8640 *sec.*

REDUCTION OF DENOMINATE NUMBERS.

ORAL PROBLEMS.

1. How many mills in 9 cents? In $12\frac{1}{2}$ cts.?

2. How many cents in 7 dimes? 25 dimes?

3. How many dollars in 50 dimes? 120 dimes?

4. How many dollars in 800 cents? 2400 cts.?

5. How many ounces in 5 lb. avoir.? $10\frac{1}{2}$ lb.?

6. How many pounds in 64 oz. avoir.? 19.2 oz.?

7. How many grains in 5 pwt.? $10\frac{1}{2}$ pwt.? 2.5 pwt.?

8. How many pwt. in 7 oz.? 6.5 oz.? $12\frac{2}{5}$ oz.?

9. How many ounces of gold in 7 lb.? $12\frac{2}{3}$ lb.?

10. How many pounds of gold in 48 oz.? 14.4 oz.?

11. How many scruples in 12 ℨ? $8\frac{2}{3}$ ℨ? 14.5 ℨ?

12. How many drams in 15 ℥? $12\frac{3}{4}$ ℥? 11.5 ℥?

13. How many ounces in 9 lb.? 5.5 lb.? 10.5 lb.?

14. How many inches in $8\frac{1}{3}$ ft.? $12\frac{1}{2}$ ft.? $33\frac{1}{3}$ ft.?

15. How many yards in 12 rd.? 1.6 rd.? 3.2 rd.?

16. How many rods in 11 yd.? 33 yd.? 6.6 yd.?

17. How many feet in 36 inches? 4.8 in.? 46.8 in.?

18. How many sq. ft. in $3\frac{1}{3}$ sq. yd.? $10\frac{2}{3}$ sq. yd.?

19. How many sq. in. in 12.6 sq. ft.? 49.5 sq. ft.?

20. How many quarts in 7 pk.? $12\frac{1}{2}$ pk.? $30\frac{1}{4}$ pk.?

21. How many gallons in 35 qt.? 14.8 qt.? 2.56 qt.?

WRITTEN PROBLEMS.

22. Reduce 7 bu. 3 pk. 5 qt. to quarts.

PROCESS.

7 bu. 3 pk. 5 qt.
  4
―――――
31 pk.
  8
―――――
253 qt. *Ans.*

In 7 bu. there are 7 times 4 pk., which is 28 pk., and 28 pk. and 3 pk. are 31 pk.; in 31 pk. there are 31 times 8 qt., which is 248 qt., and 248 qt. and 5 qt. are 253 qt. Hence, 7 bu. 3 pk. 5 qt. = 253 qt.

23. Reduce 253 quarts to higher denominations.

PROCESS.

8)253 qt.

4) 31 pk. 5 qt.

7 bu. 3 pk.

7 bu. 3 pk. 5 qt. *Ans.*

In 253 qt. there are as many pk. as 8 qt. are contained times in 253 qt., which is 31 times, with 5 qt. remainder; in 31 pk. there are as many bu. as 4 pk. are contained times in 31 pk., which is 7 times, with 3 pk. remainder. Hence 253 qt. = 7 bu. 3 pk. 5 qt.

24. Reduce 12 bu. 5 qt. to pints; 778 pt. to bushels.

25. Reduce 5124 quarts to bushels.

26. Reduce 23 bu. 3 pk. 5 qt. to pints.

27. Reduce 2288 pints to bushels.

28. Reduce 13 mi. 200 rd. 3 yd. to yards.

29. Reduce 11 A. 142 sq. rd. to square rods.

30. Reduce 324 gi. to gallons; 380 pt. to gallons.

31. Reduce 10280 ft. to miles; 11880 ft. to miles.

32. Reduce 12840 yards to miles.

33. Reduce 13 mi. 220 rd. to inches.

34. Reduce 113420 inches to miles.

35. Reduce 12460″ to degrees; 450′ to degrees.

36. Reduce 30684 sec. to higher denominations.

37. How many sq. rods in 95 A.? 320¾ A.?

38. How many cwt. in 4080 oz. avoir.? 372051 oz.?

39. Reduce 3450 cu. feet to cubic yards.

40. Reduce 16 common years to hours.

41. Reduce 45040 hours to common years.

42. How many seconds in the year 1880? 1882?

43. Reduce 4 com. yr. 45 da. to minutes.

44. Reduce 3.7 bu. to pints; 1184 pt. to bushels.

45. Reduce 4.5 rods to feet; 15.85 ft. to rods.

46. Reduce 3.65 lb. troy to ounces; 21.6 oz. to pounds.

47. Reduce 15° 40′ 36″ to seconds; 588487″ to degrees.

48. Reduce 12.3 miles to feet; 21.648 ft. to miles.

49. Reduce 365¼ days to weeks.

50. How many acres in 12⅗ sq. miles?

51. How many sq. rods in ⅔ of an acre? 5⅕ A.?

ART. 160. 1. To reduce a denominate number from a higher to a lower denomination:

Rule.—1. *Multiply the number of the highest denomination by the number of units of the next lower which equals a unit of the higher, and to the product add the number of the lower denomination, if any.*

2. *Proceed in like manner with this and each successive result thus obtained, until the number is reduced to the required denomination.*

NOTE.—The successive denominations of the compound number should be written in their proper orders, and the vacant denominations, if any, filled with ciphers.

2. To reduce a denominate number from a lower to a higher denomination:

Rule.—1. *Divide the given denominate number by the number of units of its denomination which equals one unit of the next higher, and place the remainder, if any, at the right.*

2. *Proceed in like manner with this and each successive quotient thus obtained, until the number is reduced to the required denomination.*

3. *The last quotient, with the several remainders annexed in proper order, will be the answer required.*

NOTE.—The above rules also apply to the reduction of denominate fractions, both common and decimal, as shown below.

REDUCTION OF DENOMINATE FRACTIONS.

ORAL PROBLEMS.

1. What part of a peck is $\frac{1}{16}$ of a bushel? $\frac{3}{16}$ bu.?

SOLUTION.—$\frac{1}{16}$ bu. $= \frac{1}{16}$ of 4 pk. $= \frac{4}{16}$ pk. or $\frac{1}{4}$ pk., and $\frac{3}{16}$ bu. $= 3$ times $\frac{1}{4}$ pk. $= \frac{3}{4}$ pk. Hence, $\frac{3}{16}$ bu. $= \frac{3}{4}$ pk.

2. What part of a quart is $\frac{1}{12}$ of a peck? $\frac{5}{12}$ pk.?

3. What part of a day is $\frac{2}{15}$ of a week? $\frac{8}{15}$ w.?

4. What part of an hour is $\frac{1}{30}$ of a day? $\frac{7}{30}$ d.?

5. What part of an inch is $\frac{3}{40}$ of a foot? $\frac{5}{40}$ ft.?

6. What decimal part of an inch is .03 of a foot?

SOLUTION.—.03 ft. = .03 of 12 in., or 12 times .03 in. = .36 in.

7. What decimal of an hour is .05 of a day? .025 da.?

8. What decimal of a day is .12 of a week? .012 w.?

9. What decimal of a quart is .125 of a peck? .35 pk.?

10. What part of an inch is $\frac{2}{25}$ of a foot? .08 ft.?

11. What part of a pint is $\frac{3}{40}$ of a gallon? .06 gal.?

12. What part of a foot is $\frac{5}{8}$ of an inch?

SOLUTION.—$\frac{5}{8}$ in. = $\frac{5}{8}$ of $\frac{1}{12}$ ft. = $\frac{5}{96}$ ft.

13. What part of a week is $\frac{5}{12}$ of a day? $\frac{6}{13}$ da.?

14. What part of an hour is $\frac{7}{10}$ of a minute? $\frac{7}{20}$ min.?

15. What part of a gallon is $\frac{4}{5}$ of a pint? $\frac{5}{6}$ pt.?

16. What part of a pound avoir. is $\frac{4}{5}$ of an ounce?

17. What decimal of a foot is .48 of an inch?

SOLUTION.—.48 in. = .48 of $\frac{1}{12}$ ft. = $\frac{1}{12}$ of .48 ft. = .04 ft.

18. What decimal of a week is .49 of a day? 6.3 d.?

19. What decimal of a bushel is .12 pk.? 3.6 pk.?

20. What decimal of a pound troy is .144 oz.? 44.4 oz.?

WRITTEN PROBLEMS.

21. Reduce $\frac{7}{18000}$ of a day to the fraction of a minute.

PROCESS: $\frac{7}{18000}$ d. = $\frac{7 \times 24}{18000}$ h. = $\frac{7 \times 24 \times 60}{18000}$ min. = $\frac{14}{25}$ min.

NOTE.—Denominate fractions are reduced to a lower denomination by multiplying, and to a higher denomination by dividing, the same as denominate integers; but in reduction descending there are no units of a lower order to add, and in reduction ascending there are no remainders.

22. Reduce $\frac{13}{3200}$ of a pound avoir. to the fraction of an ounce.

23. Reduce $\frac{13}{24}$ of a yard to inches.

24. Reduce $\frac{11}{12}$ of a pound troy to pennyweights.

25. Reduce .0065 w. to the decimal of an hour.

26. Reduce 9.6 pwt. to the decimal of a pound troy.

27. Reduce 3.96 inches to the decimal of a rod.

28. Reduce 30.8 rods to the decimal of a mile.

29. Reduce .096 of a bushel to the decimal of a pint.

30. Reduce $\frac{20}{33}$ of a rod to the fraction of a league.

31. Reduce $\frac{8}{9}$ of a minute to the fraction of a day.

32. Reduce 11.2 sq. rods to the decimal of an acre.

33. Reduce $56\frac{5}{8}$ lb. troy to grains.

34. Reduce $\frac{11}{120}$ of a gallon to the fraction of a pint.

35. Reduce 2.43 miles to feet.

36. Reduce 1.408 ft. to the decimal of a mile.

37. Reduce 143.35 sq. in. to the decimal of a sq. rd.

DENOMINATE FRACTIONS REDUCED TO LOWER INTEGERS.

ORAL PROBLEMS.

1. How many months in $\frac{2}{3}$ of a year? $\frac{3}{4}$ yr.? $\frac{5}{6}$ yr.?

2. How many hours in $\frac{5}{6}$ of a day? $\frac{7}{8}$ day?

3. How many minutes in $\frac{7}{12}$ of an hour? $\frac{7}{15}$ hr.?

4. How many yards in $\frac{7}{11}$ of a rod? $\frac{2}{3}$ rd.? $\frac{7}{16}$ rd.?

5. How many quarts in .75 of a peck? 1.25 pk.?

6. How many months in .25 of a year? $.33\frac{1}{3}$ yr.?

7. How many days in .35 of a week? 4.5 w.? 7.3 w.?

8. How many pecks and quarts in .8 of a bushel?

SOLUTION.—.8 bu. = .8 of 4 pk. = 3.2 pk., and .2 pk. = .2 of 8 qt. = 1.6 qt. Hence .8 bu. = 3·pk. 1.6 qt.

9. How many pecks and quarts in .55 of a bushel?

10. How many feet and inches in .75 of a yard?

11. How many quarts and pints in $\frac{3}{5}$ of a gallon?

12. How many days and hours in $\frac{7}{8}$ of a week?

WRITTEN PROBLEMS.

13. Reduce $\frac{7}{16}$ of a day and .415 of an hour each to integers of lower denominations.

(1)   PROCESSES.   (2)

$$\frac{7}{16} \text{ da.} = \frac{7 \times 24}{16} \text{ h.} = 10\frac{1}{2} \text{ h.}$$

$$\frac{1}{2} \text{ h.} = \frac{60}{2} \text{ min.} = 30 \text{ min.}$$

$$\frac{7}{16} \text{ da.} = 10 \text{ h. } 30 \text{ min.}$$

$$\begin{array}{r} .415 \text{ h.} \\ 60 \\ \hline 24.900 \text{ min.} \\ 60 \\ \hline 54.000 \text{ sec.} \end{array}$$

.415 h. = 24 min. 54 sec.

Reduce to integers of lower denominations:

14. $\frac{7}{9}$ of a mile.

15. $\frac{5}{12}$ of a week.

16. $\frac{7}{15}$ of a lb. troy.

17. $\frac{13}{16}$ of a rod.

18. $\frac{11}{12}$ of an acre.

19. $\frac{7}{8}$ of a bushel.

20. .85 of a lb. avoir.

21. .325 of a ton.

22. .08$\frac{1}{3}$ of a yard.

23. .9375 of a gallon.

24. .5625 of a cwt.

25. .0135 of a day.

ART. 161. To reduce a denominate fraction to integers of lower denominations:

Rule.—1. *Multiply the fraction by the number of units of the next lower denomination which equals a unit of its denomination.*

2. *Proceed in like manner with the fractional part of the product and of each succeeding product, until the lowest denomination is reached.*

3. *The integral parts of the several products, written in proper order, will be the lower integers sought.*

NOTE.—When the last product contains a fraction, it should be united with the integer of the lowest denomination, forming a mixed number.

DENOMINATE INTEGERS REDUCED TO FRACTIONS OF HIGHER DENOMINATIONS.

1. What part of a dollar is 25 cents?   50 cts.?
2. What part of a foot is 8 inches?   10 in.?
3. What part of a day is 9 hours?   15 h.?
4. What part of a yard is 2 ft. 6 in.?

SOLUTION.—1 yd. = 36 in., and 2 ft. 6 in. = 30 in.; 1 in. = $\frac{1}{36}$ of a yd., and 30 in. = $\frac{30}{36}$ yd. = $\frac{5}{6}$ yd., or .8$\frac{1}{3}$ yd.

5. What part of a gallon is 3 qt. 1 pt.?
6. What part of a bushel is 2 pk. 5 qt.?
7. What part of a rod is 3 yd. 2 ft.?
8. What part of 3 pecks is 2 pk. 4 qt.?
9. What part of 5 yards is 2 yd. 2 ft.?

SUGGESTION.—Each of the above answers may be expressed either as a common fraction or as a decimal.

WRITTEN PROBLEMS.

10. Reduce 15 w. 5 da. to the fraction of a common year.

PROCESS.

$$15 \text{ w. } 5 \text{ da.} = 110 \text{ da.}$$

$$110 \div 365 = \frac{110}{365} = \frac{22}{73}. \quad \frac{22}{73} \text{ yr., } Ans.$$

11. Reduce 1 yd. 2 ft. 6 in. to the fraction of a rod.
12. Reduce 1 pk. 2 qt. 1$\frac{1}{5}$ pt. to the fraction of a bushel.
13. Reduce 9 h. 36 min. to the decimal of a year.
14. Reduce 2 pk. 3 qt. 1.2 pt. to the decimal of a bushel.
15. Reduce 8 oz. 8 pwt. to the decimal of a pound.
16. Reduce 18 rd. 1 yd. to the decimal of a mile.
17. What part of 1 bu. 3 pk. is 5 pk. 6 qt.?
18. What part of 3 w. 4 da. is 3 da. 8 h.?
19. What part of 12 A. 80 P. is 1 A. 90 P.?
20. What part of 3 barrels of flour is 110 lb. 4 oz.?
21. What part of 2 rods is 3 yd. 2 ft.?

ART. 162. To reduce a denominate number, simple or compound, to the fraction of a higher denomination:

Rule.—*Reduce the number which is a part and the number which is a whole to the same denomination, and write the former result as a numerator and the latter as a denominator of a fraction.*

NOTES.—1. The answer may be expressed decimally by changing the common fraction to a decimal.

2. When the whole is a unit and the part a compound number, the process may be somewhat shortened *by reducing the number of the lowest denomination to a fraction of the next higher, prefixing the higher number, if any, and then reducing this result to a fraction of the next higher denomination, and so on, until the required fraction is reached.* Thus, in the 14th problem above, the 1.2 pt. = .6 qt.; and 3.6 qt. = .45 pk.; and 2.45 pk. = .6125 bu.

DEFINITIONS.

ART. 163. A **Denominate Number** is a number composed of concrete units of one or several denominations.

It may be an integer, a mixed number, or a fraction.

ART. 164. Denominate numbers are either *Simple* or *Compound.*

A **Simple Denominate Number** is composed of units of the same denomination; as, 7 quarts.

A **Compound Denominate Number** is composed of units of several denominations; as, 5 bu. 3 pk. 7 qt. It is also called a *Compound Number.*

Every compound number is necessarily denominate. but all denominate numbers are not compound.

ART. 165. Denominate numbers express *Currency, Weights,* and *Measures.*

A standard unit of currency, or weight, or extension, or capacity, or time, is properly a *measure,* but the term is usually limited to the standard units of extension, capacity, and duration.

ART. 166. The following diagram represents the three general classes of denominate numbers, their subdivisions, and the tables included under each:

I. CURRENCY,   { 1. Coin,
                  2. Paper Money. }   1. United States Money.

II. WEIGHTS,   { 1. Avoirdupois Weight.
                  2. Troy Weight.
                  3. Apothecaries Weight.

III. MEASURES, { 1. Of extension, { 1. Lines } 1. Long Measure.
                                       and arcs. } 2. Circular Measure
                                      2. Surfaces: Square Measure.
                                      3. Volume: Cubic Measure.

                  2. Of capacity.   { 1. Dry Measure,
                                      2. Liquid Measure.

                  3. Of duration: Time Measure.

ART. 167. The **Reduction** of a denominate number is the process of changing it from one denomination to another without altering its value.

The process of changing a denominate number from a higher to a lower denomination is **Reduction Descending**; and the process of changing a denominate number from a lower to a higher denomination is **Reduction Ascending**.

PRACTICAL REVIEW PROBLEMS.

1. Reduce 5 bu., $\frac{3}{8}$ bu., and 5 bu. each to quarts.
2. Reduce 13 pk., $\frac{4}{5}$ pk., and .24 pk. each to bushels.
3. Reduce 3 gal., $\frac{5}{8}$ gal., and .25 gal. each to pints.
4. Reduce 15 pt., $\frac{8}{9}$ pt., and .24 pt. each to gallons.
5. Reduce .25 ft. to inches; 4.8 in. to feet.
6. Reduce $\frac{5}{12}$ yd. to inches; $\frac{36}{55}$ in. to yards.
7. What part of a dime is $\frac{5}{8}$ of a cent? 3.5 cts.?
8. What part of a gallon is $1\frac{1}{2}$ of a pint? .64 pt.?
9. How many half-pint bottles can be filled with $2\frac{1}{2}$ gallons of sweet-oil?

10. A boy bought $\frac{3}{4}$ of a bushel of chestnuts for \$2, and sold them at 10 cents a quart: how much did he gain?

11. If a workman can do a job of work in 120 hours, how many days will it take him if he work 8 hours a day? If he work 10 hours a day?

12. How much will $\frac{3}{5}$ of a cwt. of sugar cost, at $16\frac{2}{3}$ cents a pound? At $12\frac{1}{2}$ cts.?

13. If a man spend $\frac{1}{3}$ of each day in sleep, how many days will he sleep in the last three months of the year? How many hours?

WRITTEN PROBLEMS.

14. Reduce 5 rd. 11 ft. 5 in. to inches; 138 ft. to rods.

15. How many pennyweights of gold in 1 lb. $6\frac{2}{5}$ oz.?

16. Reduce 13° 45″ to seconds; 255′ to degrees.

17. Reduce 252 cu. ft. to cubic yards; $33\frac{1}{3}$ cu. yd. to cubic feet.

18. Reduce $\frac{17}{25}$ of a day to minutes.

19. Reduce $\frac{16}{21}$ of a week to hours.

20. Reduce $\frac{7}{15}$ of an hour to the fraction of a day.

21. Reduce .012 of a mile to yards.

22. Reduce $\frac{4}{5}$ of a yard to the decimal of a mile.

23. What part of a rod is 3 ft. 4 in.?

24. What part of $3\frac{1}{5}$ acres is 32 sq. rods?

25. What part of a week is 8 h. 24 min.?

26. It requires 240 steps, each $7\frac{1}{4}$ inches high, to reach the top of a tower: what is the height of the tower in feet?

27. How many rings, each weighing 4 pwt. 15 gr., can be made from a bar of gold weighing 1 lb. 10 oz.?

SUGGESTION.—Reduce both divisor and dividend to the same denomination.

28. How many kegs, each containing 5 gal. 1 qt., can be filled from a cask holding 63 gal.?

29. How many rotations will a wheel 12 ft. 6 in. in circumference make in rolling $\frac{5}{8}$ of a mile.

30. How many barrels, each holding 2 bu. 3 pk., will be required to pack 132 bushels of apples?

31. How many axes, each weighing 3 lb. 3 oz., can be made from a ton of iron?

32. A farmer sold 4 loads of wheat, weighing respectively 2465 lb., 2535 lb., 2594 lb., and 2286 lb., at 94 cts. a bushel: how much did he receive for the wheat?

33. If the weight of a cubic foot of water is 1000 ounces, what is the weight of a cubic yard of water? What decimal part of a ton?

34. How many doses, of 18 gr. each, in 5 ℥ 2 ℈ of tartar emetic?

35. How many pills, of 5 gr. each, can be made from 1 ℥ 2 ℨ 2 ℈ of calomel?

36. How many ounces of calomel will make 480 pills, each weighing 6 grains?

37. A lady bought a pearl necklace, weighing 8 oz. 15 pwt., at 75 cents a grain: what did it cost?

38. What will be the cost of a gold chain, weighing $3\frac{1}{2}$ oz., at 75 cents a pwt.?

39. How many ounces of gold in a gold chain 16 carats fine, weighing $3\frac{1}{8}$ ounces?

40. A grocer bought 5 barrels of cranberries, each containing 2 bu. 3 pk. 4 qt., at $8.75 a barrel, and sold 3 barrels of the berries at 12 cts. a quart, and 2 barrels at 10 cts. a quart: how much did he gain?

41. A grocer bought 4 cheeses, weighing respectively $15\frac{1}{4}$ lb., $16\frac{1}{2}$ lb., $17\frac{3}{8}$ lb., and $14\frac{5}{16}$ lb., at $8\frac{1}{2}$ cts. a pound; he sold the first cheese at 12 cts. a pound, the second at 11 cts., the third at 10 cts., and the fourth at 9 cts.: how much did he gain?

COMPOUND NUMBERS.

ADDITION AND SUBTRACTION OF COMPOUND NUMBERS.

WRITTEN PROBLEMS.

1. Add 13 w. 6 da. 13 h. 48 min.; 8 w. 13 h. 51 min. 37 sec.; 12 w. 5 da. 22 h. 16 min. 44 sec.; 1 w. 10 h. 15 min.; and 1 da. 10 h. 26 sec.

PROCESS.

w.	d.	h.	min.	sec.
13	6	13	48	
8	0	13	51	37
12	5	22	16	44
1	0	10	15	00
	1	10	00	26
36	1	22	11	47, *Ans.*

Since only like numbers can be added, write the numbers of the same denomination in the same column. Beginning at the right hand, add the numbers of the successive denominations and divide the sum in each case by the number of units of that denomination which equals a unit of the next higher denomination; write the remainder under the numbers added, and add the quotient with the numbers of the next higher denomination.

NOTE.—In the addition of both simple and compound numbers, *the sum of the numbers of each denomination is divided by the number of units of that denomination which equals one of the next higher denomination.* In simple addition this divisor is 10; in compound addition it is a varying number, since the several denominations are expressed on a *varying scale.*

2. Add 16 mi. 307 rd. 3 yd. 2 ft. $8\frac{1}{2}$ in.; 13 mi. 160 rd. 5 yd. 1 ft. $7\frac{3}{4}$ in.; 27 mi. 35 rd. 4 yd. $5\frac{1}{3}$ in.; and 264 rd. 3 yd. 2 ft.

3. Add 24 lb. 10 oz. 17 pwt. 22 gr.; 16 lb. 19 pwt.; 10 oz. 15 pwt. 21 gr.; 45 lb. 9 oz. 18 gr.; and 13 lb. 11 oz. 18 pwt. 23 gr.

4. Add 15 bu. 3 pk. 7 qt.; 27 bu. 5 qt.; 1 pt.; 8 bu. 2 pk. 1 pt.; 47 bu. 3 pk.; 12 bu. 2 pk. 1 qt. 1 pt.; and 19 bu. 1 pk. 3 qt.

5. Add 16° 32′ 43″; 28° 47′ 53″; 25° 53″; 4 s. 48′ 48″; 11 s. 16° 36′ 59″; and 5 s. 18° 7′ 8″.

6. From 104° 11′ 20″ take 83° 43′ 36″.

PROCESS.

104° 11′ 20″
83° 43′ 36″
―――――――――
20° 25′ 44″, *Ans.*

Write the subtrahend under the minuend, placing numbers of the same denomination in the same column. Beginning at the right hand, subtract each successive term of the subtrahend from the corresponding term of the minuend, and write the difference beneath. Since 36″ is greater than 20″, add 60″ to 20″, and from the sum, 80″, take 36″. To balance the 60″ added to the minuend add 1′ to the next term of the subtrahend (or take 1′ from the next term of the minuend). Proceed in like manner in subtracting the higher terms. *The process is similar to the subtraction of simple numbers.*

7. Boston is 71° 4′ 9″ W. longitude, and San Francisco is 122° 26′ 15″ W. longitude: what is their difference in longitude?

8. Baltimore is situated 76° 37′ W., and Chicago 87° 35′ W.: what is their difference in longitude?

9. A ship in latitude 37° 20′ north, sails 15° 45′ south, and then 12° 36′ north: what is her latitude?

10. A man was born Sept. 12, 1827, and his eldest son was born Apr. 6, 1855: what is the difference in their ages?

PROCESS.

yr. mo. da.
1855 4   6
1827 9 12
――――――――
27   6 24, *Ans.*

In finding the difference between two dates, allow 30 days to the month and 12 months to the year.

11. Washington died Dec. 14, 1799, and Lincoln died April 15, 1865: what is the difference in time between the two events?

12. Garfield was born Nov. 19, 1831, and died Sept. 19, 1881: what was his age?

13. A note was given July 23, 1873, and paid Nov. 16, 1878: how long did it run?

14. From 13 rd. 3 yd. 1 ft. 6.4 in. take 9 rd. 4 yd. 11.5 in.

15. From 30 mi. 14 rd. 3 yd. 1. ft. 4 in. take 25 m. 36 rd. 4 yd. 2 ft. 10 in.

16. From 33 rd. 2 ft. 11 in. take 16 rd. 3 yd. 8 in.

PROCESS.

rd.	yd.	ft.	in.
13	3	1	6.4
9	4	0	11.5
3	$4\frac{1}{2}$	0	6.9
	$\frac{1}{2}=1$		6
3	4	2	.9, *Ans.*

17. From 26 rd. 11 ft. take 18 rd. 13 ft. 9.8 in.

ART. 168. **Compound Addition** is the process of finding the sum of two or more compound numbers of the same kind.

ART. 169. **Compound Subtraction** is the process of finding the difference between two compound numbers of the same kind.

MULTIPLICATION AND DIVISION OF COMPOUND NUMBERS.

18. Multiply 65 rd. 3 yd. 1 ft. 5 in. by 11.

PROCESS.

65 rd. 3 yd. 1 ft. 5 in.

11

2 mi. 81 rd. 5 yd. 0 ft. 7 in., *Ans.*

Since the value of the units of the successive denominations increases from right to left, begin at the right hand and multiply each term of the multiplicand in order, reducing each product to the next higher denomination, writing the remainder under the term multiplied, and adding the quotient to the next product.

NOTE.—In the multiplication of both simple and compound numbers, *the successive products are each divided by the number of units of their denomination which equal one of the next higher denomination.*

19. Multiply 13 bu. 2 pk. 2 qt. 1 pt. by 15.

20. If a man can build 7 rd. 11 ft. 6 in. of fence in a day, how much can 15 men build?

21. How many bushels of wheat in 18 bins, each containing 124 bu. 3 pk. 5 qt.?

22. How much hay in 13 stacks, each containing 4 T. 13 cwt. 56 lb.?

23. What is the weight of 12 silver spoons, each weighing 2 oz. 13 pwt. 14 gr.?

24. Divide 19 mi. 180 rd. 2 yd. 9 in. by 7.

PROCESS.

7)19 mi. 180 rd. 2 yd. 0 ft. 9 in.

2 mi. 254 rd. 1 yd. 2 ft. 8¼ in.

Since the value of the units of the successive denominations decreases from left to right, begin at the left hand and divide each term of the dividend in order, writing the quotient under the term divided, and reducing the remainder, if any, to the next lower denomination, adding the result to the next term of the dividend, and then dividing as before. *The process is similar to the division of simple numbers.*

25. Divide 27 mi. 25 rd. 12 ft. 6 in. by 12.

26. A ship sailed 39° 12′ 40″ in 21 days: how far did it sail, on an average, each day?

27. If 15 equal bars of silver contain 24 lb. 8 oz. 16 pwt., what is the weight of each bar?

28. If 12 equal bins hold 430 bu. 2 pk. of wheat, how much wheat is there in each bin?

29. From 13 w. 5 d. 18 h. 40 min. take 7 w. 23 h. 45 min., and divide the difference by 15.

30. Add 4 mi. 23 rd. 3 yd. 2 ft. and 7 mi. 16 rd. 1 ft., and divide the sum by 22.

31. From the sum of 56 lb. 13 oz. and 47 lb. 15 oz. take their difference, and divide the result by 9.

32. The length of a solar year is 365 d. 5 h. 48 min. 48 sec.: how much time is $\frac{7}{12}$ of a solar year?

Art. 170. **Compound Multiplication** is the process of taking a compound number a given number of times. The multiplier is always an abstract number.

Art. 171. **Compound Division** is the process of dividing a compound number into equal parts.

LONGITUDE AND TIME.

Art. 172. **Longitude** is distance east or west from a given meridian. It is measured in degrees, minutes, and seconds. Thus, 15° 24′ 40″ east longitude denotes a position 15° 24′ 40″ east of the meridian from which longitude is reckoned.

Art. 173. A **Meridian** is an imaginary line passing around the earth through both poles.

All meridian lines run north and south, and when the rays of the sun are vertical at any point of a given meridian, it is mid-day, or noon, at all places on this meridian which are then lighted by the sun. One half of every meridian circle is in light, and the other half in darkness.

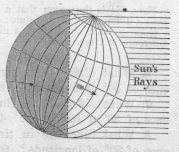

The rotation of the earth on its axis gives the unit of time, called a **day**. The day is divided into twenty-four equal parts, called **hours**. Since the earth rotates on its axis from west to east, the sun appears to revolve around the earth from east to west, and its rays move westward at the same rate over the earth's surface.

Hence, when it is noon, or twelve o'clock, at any place, it is past noon at all places east of its meridian, and before noon at all places west of its meridian. When for example it is noon at Cincinnati it is after noon at New York and before noon at St. Louis.

ORAL EXERCISES.

1. The earth rotates on its axis once every 24 hours: what part of a rotation does it make in 1 hour?

2. Since the earth rotates once every 24 hours, how many degrees of its surface pass under the sun's rays in 24 hours? In 1 hour? 2 hours?

3. How many degrees of longitude make a difference of 1 hour in time? 2 hours? 5 hours?

4. If a difference of 15° of longitude give a difference of 1 hour in time, what difference in longitude will give a difference of 1 minute in time?

SOLUTION.—If a difference of 15° of longitude give a difference of 1 hour, or 60 minutes, in time, a difference of 1° of longitude will give a difference of $\frac{1}{15}$ of 60 minutes of time, which is 4 minutes; and if 4 minutes of time require 1° of longitude, 1 minute of time will require $\frac{1}{4}$ of 1° of longitude, which is 15′.

5. If 15′ of difference in longitude give a difference of 1 minute in time, what difference in longitude will give a difference of 1 second in time.

NOTE.—It is thus seen that a difference of 15° in longitude gives a difference of 1 h. in time; a difference of 15′ in longitude, a difference of 1 m. in time; a difference of 15″ in longitude, a difference of 1 sec. in time.

6. What difference in time corresponds to a difference of 30° of longitude? 60°? 75°? 90°?

7. What difference in time corresponds to a difference of 30′ of longitude? 45′? 60′? 75′?

8. What difference in time corresponds to a difference of 30″ of longitude? 60″? 45″? 75″?

9. What difference in time corresponds to a difference of 45° of longitude? 45′? 90′? 45″? 90″?

10. What difference in longitude corresponds to a difference of 2 hours in time? 3 h.? 2 min.? 3 min.?

WRITTEN PROBLEMS.

11. The difference in longitude between two places is 31° 45′ 30″: what is the difference of time?

PROCESS.

15)31°   45′   30″
———————————————
2 h. 7 min. 2 sec.

Since 15° long. give 1 hour in time, 15′ long. 1 minute, and 15″ long. 1 second, divide 31° 45′ 30″ by 15, as in compound division, and the quotient will be the difference in time.

What is the difference in time between two places whose difference in longitude is:

12. 10° 35′?

13. 9° 20′?

14. 16° 14′?

15. 77° 1′?

16. 18° 25′ 30″?

17. 56° 36′ 12″?

18. 17° 35′ 15″?

19. 19° 45″?

20. The difference in time between two cities is 1 h. 35 min. 12 sec.: what is their difference in longitude?

PROCESS.

1 h. 35 min. 12 sec.
            15
———————————————
23°   48′   0″, *Ans.*

Since 1 h. in time corresponds to 15° in long., 1 min. to 15′, 1 sec. to 15″, multiply 1 h. 35 min. 12 sec. by 15, as in compound multiplication, and the product will be the difference in longitude.

What is the difference in longitude between two places whose difference in time is:

21. 1 h. 20 min.?

22. 2 h. 10 min.?

23. 3 h. 18 min. 12 sec.?

24. 5 h. 40 sec.?

25. 45 min. 50 sec.?

26. 6 h. 12 min. 24 sec.?

27. 3 h. 42 min.?

28. 46 min. 50 sec.?

29. The difference in longitude between two cities is 5° 31′: what is the difference in time?

DIFFERENCE IN CLOCK TIME.

Art. 174. Since the earth rotates from west to east, and the rays of the sun pass over the earth's surface from east to west, all places east of a given meridian have the faster clock time, and all places west of it the slower clock time.

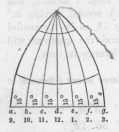

Take, for illustration, seven places 15° apart, as shown in the diagram. When it is 12 M., or noon, at the middle place (*d*) it is 1 P. M., 2 P. M., and 3 P. M. respectively at the three places (*e, f, g*) east of it, and 11 A. M., 10 A. M., and 9 A. M. respectively at the three places (*c, b, a*) west of it.

30. The difference in clock time between Cincinnati and Philadelphia is 37 min.: when it is noon at Cincinnati, what is the time at Philadelphia? When it is 3 P. M. at Philadelphia, what is the time at Cincinnati?

31. The difference in clock time between Cincinnati and Boston is 53 min. 25 sec.: when it is 4 P. M. at Boston, what is the time at Cincinnati? When it is 10 A. M. at Cincinnati, what is the time at Boston?

32. The difference in clock time between Philadelphia and San Francisco is 3 h. 9 min. 1 sec.: when it is 9 A. M. at Philadelphia, what is the time at San Francisco? When it is 1 P. M. at San Francisco, what is the time at Philadelphia?

33. When it is 6 o'clock at Boston what is the hour of day 30° east of Boston? 45° west of Boston?

34. When it is 9 o'clock at Chicago, what is the time 15° 15′ east of Chicago? 15° 45′ west of Chicago?

35. When it is 12 o'clock at St. Louis, what is the clock time 7° west of St. Louis? 16° 45′ east of St. Louis?

36. Berlin is 13° 23′ 53″ E. and Boston 71° 4′ 9″ W.: when it is noon at Boston, what is the time at Berlin?

37. Rome is 12° 27′ 14″ E. and Washington 77° 2′ 48″ W.: when it is 9 A. M. at Washington, what is the clock time at Rome?

---

38. The difference in time in the observations of an eclipse, on two vessels at sea, is 2 h. 15 min. 10 sec.: what is their difference in longitude?

39. The difference in time between New York and St. Louis is 1 h. 2⅓ min.: what is the difference in their longitude?

40. A gentleman left Omaha and traveled until his watch was 1 h. 3 min. too slow: how many degrees had he traveled, and in what direction?

41. Two captains observed an eclipse of the moon, one seeing it at 9 P. M., and the other at 11½ P. M.: what was the difference in their longitude?

42. An eclipse was observed at New York, 74° W., at 9.30 P. M., and the time of its observation on a vessel in the Atlantic Ocean, was 11.45 P. M.: what was the longitude of the vessel?

43. The difference in time between the chronometers of two observatories is 45 min. 30 sec., and the longitude of the observatory having the faster time is 85° 40′ W.: what is the longitude of the other observatory?

44. The difference between Greenwich time and Washington time is 5 h. 8 min. 16 sec., and the difference between Washington time and Chicago time is 42 min. 9 sec.: what is the longitude of Chicago, the longitude of Greenwich being 0?

45. The longitude of Baltimore is 76° 37′ W.; of Cincinnati, 84° 26′ W.; of Chicago, 87° 35′ W.; and of San Francisco, 122° 26′ 15″ W.: when it is noon at Cincinnati, what is the time of day at Baltimore? At Chicago? At San Francisco?

FORMULAS AND RULES.

Art. 175.   The correspondences between differences of longitude and differences of time are as follows:

> 15° *diff. in long. gives a diff. of* 1 *h. in time.*
> 15′ *diff. in long. gives a diff. of* 1 *m. in time.*
> 15″ *diff. in long. gives a diff. of* 1 *sec. in time.*

Art. 176.   1. To find the difference in time corresponding to any difference in longitude:

Rule.—*Divide the difference in longitude, expressed in degrees, minutes, and seconds, by 15, and the respective quotients will be hours, minutes, and seconds of time.*

2. To find the difference in longitude corresponding to any difference in time:

Rule.—*Multiply the difference in time, expressed in hours, minutes, and seconds, by 15, and the respective products will be degrees, minutes, and seconds of longitude.*

3. To find the time at one place when the time at another place and their difference of time are given:

Rule.—*When the second place is* EAST *of the first,* ADD *their difference of time; when it is* WEST *of the first,* SUBTRACT *their difference of time.*

Notes.—1. Since every circle is divided into 360 degrees, the length of a degree depends upon the size of the circle of which it is a part; and hence the length of a degree of longitude depends upon the latitude of the parallel on which it is measured. It is greatest at the equator, where it is 69⅙ miles, nearly; and least at the poles, where it is nothing. A degree of longitude at Washington contains about 54 miles, and a degree at Boston about 51 miles.

2. If the distance in miles between any two places on, or near, the same parallel be given, the difference in clock time may be found by first reducing the miles to degrees; but problems involving the conversion of distance in miles to time, and *vice versa*, have little practical value.

METRIC MEASURES.

ART. 177. The **Metric System** is a system of weights and measures expressed on the decimal scale.

The system, first adopted by France, is now in use in nearly all the countries of Europe. The use of the system in the United States was legalized by Congress in 1866, and it is employed, to some extent, in several departments of the government service. It has long been used by the Coast Survey. Its convenience and accuracy have secured its very general adoption in the sciences and in the arts.

ART. 178. The **Meter** is the primary unit of the system, all the other units of measure being derived from it. It is the length of a bar of metal kept at Paris as a standard.

The meter was intended to be the *ten-millionth* part of the distance from the equator to the north pole, but subsequent measurements of this quadrant show that its length is a little more than ten million meters.

A standard meter, copied from the one at Paris, is kept by each nation that has adopted the Metric System. The standard meter of the United States is kept at Washington. Its length is 39.37 inches.

ART. 179. The principal metric units are:

The Meter, for lengths.
The Square Meter, for surfaces.
The Cubic Meter, for large volumes.
The Liter (*lē'-ter*), for smaller volumes.
The Gram, for weights.

NOTE.—The teacher should be supplied with a meter, and the other more important metric measures.

ART. 180. The meter, liter, and gram are each multiplied by 10, 100, 1000, and 10000, giving *multiple units*, and they are also each divided by 10, 100, 1000, giving the decimal *subdivisions* of tenths, hundredths, thousandths, etc.

The multiples are named by prefixing to the name of the primary unit, or base, the Greek numerals, *deka* (10), *hekto* (100), *kilo* (1000), and *myria* (10000); and the subdivisions are named by prefixing the Latin numerals, *deci* (10th), *centi* (100th), and *milli* (1000th).

I. MEASURES OF LENGTH.

ART. 181. The principal unit is the **meter** (ᵐ). Its successive multiples and subdivisions correspond to the successive orders of units in the *decimal system*, the meter corresponding to units, the dekameter to tens, the hektometer to hundreds, etc.; and the decimeter to tenths, the centimeter to hundredths, and the millimeter to thousandths, as follows:

Myriameter (Mm)	Kilometer (Km)	Hektometer (Hm)	Dekameter (Dm)	Meter (m), *the unit*	Decimeter (dc)	Centimeter (cm)	Millimeter (mm)
5	4	3	2	1.	1	2	3

Multiples.   Subdivisions.

The correspondence between the metric denominations and those of United States money is noticeable, the meter corresponding to *dollars*, the decimeter to *dimes*, the centimeter to *cents*, and the millimeter to *mills*, as shown by the following scale:

Thou.-dols.	Hund.-dols.	Ten-dollars	Dollars		Dimes	Cents	Mills
4	3	2	1	.	1	2	3

The metric measures of length in common use are the *meter*, which, like the yard, is used in measuring short distances, and the *kilometer*, which, like the mile, is used in measuring long distances.

NOTE.—All the compound metric names are accented on the first syllable, as, mil′-li-meter, kil′-o-meter, etc.

ORAL EXERCISES.

1. How many meters in a dekameter? How many dekameters in a hektometer? How many hektometers in a kilometer?

2. What part of a meter is a decimeter? What part of a decimeter is a centimeter? What part of a centimeter is a millimeter?

3. How many units of any metric denomination of length equal one unit of the next higher?

4. How many meters in a hektometer? In a kilometer? In a dekameter?

5. What part of a meter is a centimeter? A millimeter? A decimeter?

6. Name the metric units of length from meter to myriameter, inclusive. From meter to millimeter.

7. Read 64.5^{m}; 13.5^{cm}; 62.4^{Km}; 10.14^{Dm}; 36.8^{Hm}

8. Read 4867.35^{m} in the different metric denominations that compose it.

WRITTEN EXERCISES.

9. Write 6^{Dm}, 4^{m}, 5^{cm}, 8^{mm} in one number as meters.

Ans. 64.058^{m}

10. Write 7^{Km}, 6^{Dm}, 3^{m}, 4^{dm}, 7^{cm} in one number as meters.

11. Write 5^{Hm}, 7^{m}, 6^{cm}, 4^{mm} in one number as meters.

12. Reduce 2.54^{Km} to meters; to centimeters.

PROCESS.

$2.54^{Km} = 2540^{m}$
$2540^{m} = 254000^{cm}$

Multiply 2.54^{Km} by 1000 by removing the decimal point three places to the right (Art. 123), and multiply 2540^{m} by 100 by removing the decimal point two more places to the right.

13. Reduce 4.82^{Hm} to meters.
14. Reduce 58.65^{Km} to dekameters.
15. Reduce 2.65^{dm} to millimeters.
16. Reduce 5.29^{Hm} to meters.
17. Reduce 14.6^{Dm} to decimeters.

18. Reduce 341.5^{mm} to centimeters; to meters.

PROCESS.

$341.5^{mm} = 34.15^{cm}$
$34.15^{cm} = .3415^{m}$

Divide 341.5^{mm} by 10 by removing the decimal point one place to the left (Art. 125), and this quotient by 100 by removing the decimal point two more places to the left.

19. Reduce 307.5^{cm} to meters.
20. Reduce 487.6^{dm} to dekameters.
21. Reduce 3076.24^{cm} to hektometers.

II. MEASURES OF SURFACE.

ART. 182. The principal unit is the **Square Meter.** The other units are the squares of the multiples and the squares of the subdivisions of the meter.

ART. 183. Since the square of 10 is 100, and the square of .1 is .01, the successive metric units of square measure occupy two orders of figures, thus:

Sq. Km	Sq. Hm	Sq. Dm	Sq. m	Sq. dm	Sq. cm	Sq. mm

$$0000000.000000$$

Square Centimeter.

The *square meter* is used in measuring ordinary surfaces, and the *square kilometer* in measuring large surfaces, as the areas of countries.

LAND MEASURE.

Art. 184. In measuring land the square meter is called the *centar* (ᶜᵃ), the square dekameter an *ar* (ᵃ), and the square hektometer a *hektar* (ʰᵃ), the principal unit being the **ar**.

Since 100 centars equal 1 ar, and 100 ars equal one hektar, the successive units occupy two orders of figures, thus:

$$\begin{array}{ccc} \text{Hektar} & \text{Ar} & \text{Centar} \\ 0\ 0\ 0 & . & 0\ 0 \end{array}$$

It is seen that the centars are written as hundredths of an ar, as cents are written as hundredths of a dollar.

ORAL EXERCISES.

1. How many sq. meters in a sq. dekameter?

2. How many sq. dekameters in a sq. hektometer?

3. What part of a sq. meter is a sq. decimeter?

4. What part of a sq. meter is a sq. millimeter?

5. Name the metric units of surface from sq. meter to sq. kilometer, inclusive. From sq. meter to sq. milimeter.

6. How many ars in a hektar? What part of an ar is a centar?

7. Read 87.5 $^{sq.\ m}$; 3.86 $^{sq.\ Km}$; 315.7 $^{sq.\ cm}$; 45.4 $^{sq.\ mm}$

8. Read 23.7ᵃ; 67.05ʰᵃ; 200ᶜᵃ; 307.6ᶜᵃ; 4.07ᵃ

WRITTEN EXERCISES.

9. Write 6 $^{sq.\ Dm}$, 5 $^{sq.\ m}$, 8 $^{sq.\ dm}$, in one number as sq. meters. *Ans.* 605.08 $^{sq.\ m}$

10. Write 6 $^{sq.\ m}$, 7 $^{sq.\ dm}$, 4 $^{sq.\ cm}$, in one number as sq. meters.

11. Write 9 ^{ha}, 4 ^{a}, 6 ^{ca}, in one number as ars.

12. Reduce 45.06 $^{sq.\ Dm}$ to sq. meters; to sq. decimeters.

PROCESS: 45.06 $^{sq.\ Dm}$ = 4506. $^{sq.\ m}$ = 450600. $^{sq.\ dm}$

13. Reduce 2.25 $^{sq.\ Km}$ to sq. hektometers; to sq. deka-meters; to sq. meters.

14. Reduce 2.005 $^{sq.\ m}$ to sq. centimeters.

15. Reduce 2400 $^{sq.\ cm}$ to sq. decimeters; to sq. meters.

PROCESS: $2400^{sq.\ cm} = 24^{sq.\ dm} = .24^{sq.\ m}$

16. Reduce 405 ^{a} to hektars; to centars.

III. Measures of Volume.

ART. 185. The primary unit of the measures of volume is the **Cubic Meter.**

The higher units are not used, and the chief use of the cubic decimeter and cubic centimeter is to furnish a basis for the measure of capacity and weight.

Since $.1 \times .1 \times .1 = .001$, $.01 \times .01 \times .01 = .000001$, each lower unit, or denomination, occupies three decimal orders, thus:

Cubic Centimeter.

Cu. m	Cu. dm	Cu. cm	Cu. mm

$$0 . 0 0 0 \ 0 0 0 \ 0 0 0$$

In measuring wood the cubic meter is called a **ster** (*stair*), and one tenth of a ster a **decister**, and ten sters a **dekaster**. The ster is not used in this country, and is not likely to take the place of the cord.

ORAL EXERCISES.

1. How many cu. centimeters in a cu. decimeter?

2. How many cu. decimeters in a cu. meter?

3. What part of a cu. meter is a cu. decimeter?

4. What part of a cu. decimeter is a cu. centimeter?

5. How many cu. centimeters in a cu. meter?

6. Name the metric units of volume from cu. meter to cu. millimeter, inclusive.

IV. MEASURES OF CAPACITY.

ART. 186. The principal unit is the **Liter**. It equals a cubic decimeter.

The successive multiples and subdivisions of the liter, like those of the meter, are written on the decimal scale thus:

Kiloliter (Kl)	Hektoliter (Hl)	Dekaliter (Dl)	Liter (l), the unit		Deciliter (dl)	Centiliter (cl)	Milliliter (ml)
0	0	0	0	.	0	0	0

The *liter* is used in measuring liquids, and the *hektoliter* in measuring grains, seeds, roots, etc. The kiloliter equals a cubic meter.

NOTE.—When the three dimensions of a regular solid are expressed in *decimeters*, their continued product will be the contents, or capacity, in *liters*.

ORAL EXERCISES.

1. Name the metric units of capacity from liter to kiloliter, inclusive. From liter to milliliter.

2. How many liters in a dekaliter? How many dekaliters in a hektoliter? How many hektoliters in a kiloliter?

3. What part of a liter is a deciliter? What part of a deciliter is a centiliter? What part of a centiliter is a milliliter?

4. How many units of any metric denomination of capacity equal one unit of the next higher?

5. How many liters in a kiloliter? In a hektoliter?

6. What part of a liter is a centiliter? A milliliter?

7. Read 64.35^{l}; 13.5^{cl}; 62.44^{Hl}; 10.74^{Kl}; 36.08^{Hl}; 37.45^{dl}; 1600^{ml}; 15.4^{Dl}.

8. Read 5876.347^{l} in the different metric denominations that compose it.

WRITTEN EXERCISES.

9. Write 7^{Dl}, 4^{l}, 5^{dl}, 6^{cl} in one number as liters.

10. Write 9^{Kl}, 6^{Dl}, 5^{l}, 3^{cl}, 9^{ml} in one number as liters.

11. Reduce 4.644^{Hl} to liters; to deciliters.

PROCESS: $4.644^{Hl} = 464.4^{l} = 4644.^{dl}$

12. Reduce 3.75^{Dl} to liters; to centiliters.

13. Reduce $.529^{Kl}$ to liters; to deciliters.

14. Reduce 3400^{cl} to liters.

PROCESS: $3400^{cl} = 34.^{l}$

15. Reduce 4.05^{l} to hektoliters; to kiloliters.

16. Reduce 45.6^{l} to hektoliters; to centiliters.

V. MEASURES OF WEIGHT.

ART. 187.   The principal unit is the **Gram,** the weight of a cubic centimeter of pure water at its greatest density.

The successive multiples and subdivisions are written on the decimal scale, thus:

Kilogram (Kg)	Hektogram (Hg)	Dekagram (Dg)	Gram (g), the unit		Decigram (dg)	Centigram (cg)	Milligram (mg)
0	0	0	0	.	0	0	0

A thousand kilograms is a *Metric Ton* (T.), which is the weight of a cubic meter of water.

A liter of water, at its greatest density, equals a kilogram, also called a *Kilo*.

The *gram*, *kilogram* (kilo), and the *metric ton* are the units of weight in use, the gram being used in weighing letters, gold, and jewels, and in mixing medicines, the kilogram in weighing such common articles as sugar, coffee, etc., and the metric ton in weighing such bulky articles as coal, hay, etc. The smaller weights are used by jewelers, druggists, chemists, etc., when great accuracy is required.

NOTE.—The nickel five-cent piece weighs 5 grams, and two silver half-dollars 25 grams. The weight of a letter for single postage (3 cts.) must not exceed the weight of 3 nickels (15 grams). The nickel is 2 centimeters in diameter.

ORAL EXERCISES.

1. Name the metric units of weight from gram to kilogram, inclusive. From gram to milligram.

2. How many grams in a dekagram? In a hektogram? In a kilogram?

3. What part of a gram is a decigram? A centigram? A milligram?

4. How many grams in 5 hektograms? 6 dekagrams? 7 kilograms?

5. How many decigrams in 5 grams? How many centigrams? How many milligrams?

6. Read 3.25^{Kg}; $.456^{\text{Hg}}$; 500^{cg}; 34.6^{g}; 740.78^{Dg}.

7. Read 708.03^{dg}; 989^{mg}; 7.83^{Hg}; 50.63^{g}.

8. Read 7806.587^{g} in the different metric denominations that compose it.

WRITTEN EXERCISES.

9. Write 5^{Kg}, 6^{Dg}, 8^{g}, 9^{cg} in one number as grams.

10. Write 9^{Hg}, 7^{Dg}, 5^{dg}, 6^{cg} in one number as grams.

11. Reduce 244.56^{Hg} to grams; to decigrams.

PROCESS: $234.56^{\text{Hg}} = 23456^{\text{g}} = 234560^{\text{dg}}$.

12. Reduce 745.8^{Kg} to dekagrams; to grams.

13. Reduce 690^{cg} to grams; to hektograms.

PROCESS: $690^{\text{cg}} = 6.9^{\text{g}} = .069^{\text{Hg}}$.

14. Reduce 746.35^{dg} to grams; to kilograms.

VI. METRIC EQUIVALENTS.

NOTE.—These tables should not be committed to memory.

LONG MEASURE.

1 *meter*   = $\begin{cases} 39.37 \ inches. \\ 1.0936 \ yards. \end{cases}$

1 *yard*   =   .9144 *meter.*

1 *kilometer* =   .6214 *mile.*

1 *mile*   =   1.6093 *Km.*

SQUARE MEASURE.

1 *sq. meter*   = 1.196 *sq. yards.*

1 *sq. yard*   =   .8361 *sq. m.*

1 *sq. decimeter* = .1076 *sq. ft.*

1 *sq. foot*   = 9.2903 *sq. dm.*

1 *hektar*   = 2.471 *acres.*

1 *acre*   =   .4047 *ha.*

CAPACITY MEASURE.

1 *liter*   = $\begin{cases} .908 \ dry \ qt. \\ .0284 \ bu. \end{cases}$

1 *dry qt.* =   1.101 *liters.*

1 *liter*   =   1.0567 *liq. qt.*

1 *liq. qt.* =   .9463 *liters.*

WEIGHT.

1 *gram*   = $\begin{cases} 15.432 \ gr. \ troy. \\ .0353 \ oz. \ avoir. \end{cases}$

1 *lb. av.*   =   .4536 *Kg.*

1 *kilogram* =   2.206 *lb. avoir.*

1 *met. ton* =   1.102 *com. ton.*

1 *com. ton* =   .907 *met. ton.*

CUBIC MEASURE.

1 *cubic meter* = 1.308 *cu. yards.*

1 *cubic yard* = .7646 *cu. meter.*

1 *ster*   = .2759 *cord.*

1 *cord*   = 3.624 *sters.*

1 *cu. cm. of water* = 1 *gram.*

1 *cu. dm. of water* = 1 *liter.*

1 *liter of water*   = 1 *kilogram.*

1 *cu. m. of water* = 1 *met. ton.*

WRITTEN EXERCISES.

1. How many yards in 220 meters?

PROCESS: 39.37 in. × 220 ÷ 12 ÷ 3 = 240.59+.   *Ans.* 240.59 yd.

2. How many miles in 44.5 kilometers?

3. How many inches in 24 centimeters?

4. How many bushels in 250 hektoliters of wheat?

5. How many gallons in 37½ liters of sirup?

6. How many pounds of butter in 150 kilos?

7. How many liters in 35 liquid quarts?

8. How many sters in 20 cords of wood?

9. How many ars in ¾ of an acre?

10. How many meters in 1760 feet?

PRACTICAL PROBLEMS.

1. Add 45.6 ^{m}, 3.48 ^{Dm}, 460 ^{dm}, 3.6 ^{m}, and 340 ^{cm}

2. Add 74.06 ^{l}, 88.8 ^{Dl}, .687 ^{Kl}, 47.6 ^{cl}, and 450 ^{ml}

3. From 8.46 ^{Kg} take 6.5 ^{g} + 340 ^{cg}

4. What is the weight of 54 ^{l} of water in kilograms?

5. How many liters of water in 94.5 ^{Kg}?

6. How many sq. decimeters in a piece of tin 6 ^{m} long and 2.5 ^{m} wide?

7. How many ars in a garden 54 ^{m} long and 30 ^{m} wide?

8. How many sq. meters in a floor 9.25 ^{m} long and 6.8 ^{m} wide? 12.45 ^{m} long and 8.6 ^{m} wide?

9. A farmer sold five loads of hay, weighing respectively 4286.5 ^{Kg}, 3987.45 ^{Kg}, 4536 ^{Kg}, 4098.6 ^{Kg}, and 4186.4 ^{Kg}, at $14.50 per metric ton: how much did he receive?

10. If a pipe discharge 6.54 ^{l} a minute, how many hektoliters will it discharge in an hour? In a day?

11. An empty bottle weighs 380 ^{g}, and when filled with water it weighs .985 ^{Kg}: what part of a liter does it hold?

12. How many pills, each weighing 1.2 ^{dg}, can be made from 2.4 ^{Hg} of calomel?

13. How many rings, each weighing 4.3 ^{g}, can be made from a bar of gold weighing 47.3 ^{g}?

14. Milk is 1.04 as heavy as water: how many kilograms of water in 16.5 ^{l} of milk?

15. A vessel holds 25.5 ^{Kg} of milk: what is the milk worth at 6 cts. a liter?

16. A merchant bought 160 ^{m} of broadcloth at $3.25 per meter, and sold ½ of it at $3.90 per meter, and the other half at $3.75 per meter: what did he gain?

17. A man sold 40.65 ^{ha} of land at $94 per hektar: what was the value of the land?

18. A farmer sold 150.85 ^{Hl} of potatoes at $2.40 per hectoliter: how much did he receive?

19. A grocer bought 5.4 ^{Hl} of cranberries at $6.50 per hektoliter, and sold them at 8 cts. a liter: what was his gain?

20. The large wheel of a bicycle is 5.8 ^m in circumference: how many times will it rotate in going 11.6 ^{Km}?

21. If a liter of air weighs 1.273 ^g, what is the weight in kilos of the air in a room which contains 78 ^{cu. m}?

22. If a pipe discharge 14.6 ^l in a minute, how many hektoliters will it discharge in 2 hours?

23. A gasometer holds 6400 ^{cu. m} of gas: if filled with gas, how many hours would it supply 50 jets, each burning 120 ^l an hour?

24. A milk dealer sold 8 cans of milk, each containing 42.5 ^l, at 5½ cts. a liter: how much did he receive?

25. A dairy of 10 cows yielded in one season 120 ^{Hl} of milk and 450 ^{Kg} of butter; the milk was sold at an average of 6½ cts. per liter; and the butter, at 56 cts. per kilo: what were the season's receipts in money?

26. A grocer bought 25 casks of N. O. sugar, weighing 260 ^{Kg} each, at 15½ cts per kilo, and sold the sugar at 18 cts. per kilo: how much did he gain?

27. How much will it cost to plaster the ceiling of a room that is 8.5 ^m square at 24 cts. a sq. meter?

28. A merchant imported 18288 ^m of silk at a cost of $2.40 per meter, and sold it at $2.75 per yard: how much did he gain?

29. A grocer bought 8808 ^l of molasses at 6½ cts. per liter, and sold it at 35 cts. a gallon: how much did he gain?

30. A merchant imported 4412 ^{Kg} of Malaga rasins at a cost of 30 cts. a kilo, and sold the lot at 25 cts. a pound: how much did he make?

MENSURATION.

MEASUREMENT OF PLANE SURFACES.

PRELIMINARY DEFINITIONS.

NOTE.—For the definitions of a *line, angle, surface, plane, rectangle, square,* and *area,* see Arts. 145–153. These definitions should here be reviewed.

ART. 188. A **Triangle** is a plane figure bounded by three straight lines and having three angles.

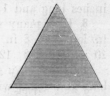

ART. 189. A **Right-angled Triangle** is a triangle having a right angle.

One of the sides including the right angle is called the *Base,* and the other the *Perpendicular* or *Altitude.* (Art. 370.)

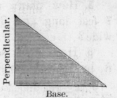

Base.

ART. 190. A **Circle** is a portion of a plane bounded by a curved line, all points of which are equally distant from a point within, called the *center.* (Art. 158, note 2.)

The curved line which bounds a circle is its *Circumference.*

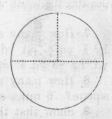

ART. 191. The **Diameter** of a circle is a straight line passing through the center and terminating on both sides in the circumference. One half of a diameter is a *Radius.*

All the diameters of a circle are equal.

(157)

ORAL PROBLEMS.

1. How many square inches in a piece of paper 5 inches long and 1 inch wide? 5 in. long and 3 in. wide?

NOTE.—All the surfaces referred to in this and the following sixteen problems are *rectangles*.

2. How many square inches in a piece of tin 12 inches long and 1 inch wide? 8 in. wide?

3. How many square inches in a pane of glass 10 in. long and 8 in. wide? 12 in. long and 10 in. wide? 10 in. square? 12 in. square?

4. How many square feet in a piece of zinc 4 feet long and 3 feet wide? 5 ft. long and 4 ft. wide?

5. How many square feet in a piece of oil-cloth 7 feet long and 3 feet wide? 8 ft. long and 6 ft. wide?

6. How many square feet in the floor of a room 20 ft. by 15 ft.? 30 ft. by 24 ft.? 50 ft. by 30 ft.?

NOTE.—The dimensions of a plane figure are usually expressed by writing the word "by," or the sign "×," between the figures denoting the length and width.

7. How many square yards in a pavement 40 yd. by 5 yd.? 50 yd. by 4 yd.? 80 yd. by 5 yd.? 50 yd. by 72 yd.? 50 yd. × 40 yd.?

8. How many square miles in a township 5 miles square? 6 miles square?

9. Show that the area of a piece of paper 6 inches long and 4 inches wide is 4 times 6 sq. inches.

10. Show that the area of any rectangle is found *by multiplying the number of square units corresponding to the number of linear units in its length by the number of linear units in its width.*

WRITTEN PROBLEMS.

11. How many square feet in a floor 37½ ft. by 23 ft.?

PROCESS: 37.5 sq. ft. × 23 = 862.5 sq. ft.

12. How many square yards in a walk 124.5 yd. by 3.25 yd.? 205.14 yd. by 5.5 yd.?

13. How many square feet in the walls of a room 24 ft. by 18¾ ft. and 10½ ft. high? In the ceiling? How many square yards in the walls and ceiling?

14. How many square rods in a farm 134 rods long and 52.5 rods wide? How many acres?

15. How many square feet in a city lot 62½ ft. front by 208 ft. deep? How many square yards?

16. A garden containing 3267 square yards is 49½ yards wide: how long is it?

17. A street containing 840 square rods is 252 rods long: how wide is it?

18. How many square inches in a right-angled triangle, whose base is 8 inches and whose altitude is 6 inches?

PROCESS.

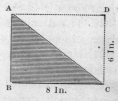

8 sq. in. × ½ of 6 = 24 sq. in. *Ans.*

Or, 8 sq. in × 6 ÷ 2 = 24 sq. in.

The area of a right-angled triangle is ½ of the area of a rectangle, having the same base and altitude. The triangle ABC is ½ of the rectangle ABCD. The area of any triangle equals *the base multiplied by one half the altitude.*

19. How many square yards in a triangular garden whose base is 54.5 yards, and altitude 33.2 yards?

20. How many acres in a triangular field whose base is 80 rods, and altitude 50 rods?

21. A triangle contains 270 sq. in., and the base is 36 in.: what is its altitude?

22. The diameter of a circle is 10 feet: what is its circumference?

PROCESS: 10 ft. × 3.1416 = 31.416 ft., *Ans.*

It is shown by geometry that the circumference of a circle is 3.1416 (nearly 3⅐) times the diameter.

23. The diameter of a circular pond is 60 yards: what is its circumference?

24. How many square inches in a circular piece of tin 12 inches in diameter?

PROCESS.

12 in. × 3.1416 = 37.6992 in., circum.

37.6992 sq. in. × ¼ of 12 = 113.0976 sq. in.

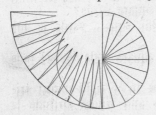

A circle may be considered as made up of triangles whose bases form the circumference, and whose altitude is the radius (½ diameter) of the circle. This is clearly illustrated by the cut at the left.

25. The diameter of a circular room is 40 feet: how many square feet in the floor?

26. The diameter of a circle is 16 inches: how many square inches in its area?

27. How many square feet in a circle whose diameter is 20 feet?

28. A horse is tied to a stake by a rope 40 feet long: on how much surface can the horse graze?

SUGGESTION.—The surface is a circle 80 feet in diameter.

ART. 192.   1. To find the area of a rectangle:

Rule.—*Multiply the number of square units corresponding to the linear units in its length by the number of linear units in its width.*

NOTE.—This is the true meaning of the common rule, "*Multiply the length by the width.*" The length is a *line*, and a line multiplied by any number does not give surface.

2. To find either side of a rectangle:

Rule.—*Divide the area by the number of square units corresponding to the linear units in the other side.*

3. To find the area of a triangle:

Rule.—*Multiply the number of square units corresponding to the linear units in the base by one half the altitude.*

4. To find the area of a circle:

Rule.—*Multiply the number of square units corresponding to the linear units in the circumference by one fourth of the diameter.*

NOTES.—1. The two dimensions of a surface (length and width) must be in the same denomination.

2. The multiplier in the 1st, 3d, and 4th rules above is an *abstract* number.

3. It is shown by geometry that the area of a circle is .7854 of the area of a square whose sides are equal to its diameter. Hence the area of a circle may be found *by multiplying the square of the diameter, considered as square units, by* .7854.

Cir.=.7854 of Square.

APPLICATIONS OF SURFACE MEASUREMENTS.

I. CARPETING ROOMS.

ART. 193. The number of yards of carpeting required to carpet a room is found *by multiplying the number of yards in each strip by the number of strips.*

NOTE.—The number of yards of carpeting required to carpet a room depends on the direction in which the strips or breadths run, whether lengthwise or across the room, and the amount of loss occasioned by the proper matching of the figures. If the width or length of the room, as the case may be, be not a multiple of the width of the carpeting, a part of an outside strip must be turned under or cut off, and the proper matching of figures may also require the turning under or cutting off of the carpet at one end. Carpets are sold by *Long Measure.*

WRITTEN PROBLEMS.

1. How many yards of carpeting 1 yard wide will be required for a floor 24 ft. long, 17 ft. 3 in. wide, if the strips run lengthwise, and there be a waste of 6 in. in matching figures? How much will be turned under or cut off at the side? At the end?

SUGGESTION.—It will require 6 strips of carpeting, each 8⅙ yards long.

2. How many yards of carpeting 1 yard wide will carpet the above room, if the strips run across the room, and there be a waste of 9 in. in matching figures?

3. How many yards of carpeting ¾ of a yard wide will be required for a room 18½ ft. long and 15 ft. 9 in. wide, if the strips run lengthwise, and there be a waste of ⅙ of a yard in matching figures? •

4. How many yards of Brussels carpeting ¾ of a yard wide will be required for a room 20 ft. square, there being a waste of 9 in. in matching figures? How much will the carpet cost at $1.60 a yard?

5. A room is 20 ft. long and 17 ft. wide : which way must the strips of carpeting run in order to carpet the room most economically, allowing no waste for matching the pattern?

6. How many yards of Brussels carpeting ¾ of a yard wide will cover a hall 45 ft. long and 32 ft. wide, the strips running lengthwise, and there being a waste of ¼ of a yard in matching the pattern? What part of a strip will have to be turned under or cut off at the sides? How much will the carpet cost at $1.62½ a yard?

7. How many yards of Brussels carpeting will carpet a flight of stairs consisting of 18 steps, including the landing, each step being 10 in. wide and 8 in high, if 1¼ yards be allowed for turnings? What will be the cost at $2.25 per yard?

ART. 194. Plastering, painting, and kalsomining are measured by the square yard. There is no uniform rule respecting the allowance to be made for doors and windows.

The surface of the walls of a room may be found *by multiplying the sum of the lengths of the four sides by the height.*

8. How much will it cost to plaster the walls and ceiling of a room 18 ft. 6 in. long, 16 ft. 9 in. wide, and 10 ft. high, at $33\frac{1}{3}$ cts. per sq. yard, if 18 sq. yards be deducted for doors and windows?

9. What will it cost to plaster a room, walls and ceiling, 25 ft. long, 18 ft. wide, and 12 ft. 6 in. high, at 35 cts. a sq. yard, allowing for two doors, each 9 ft. by $3\frac{1}{2}$ ft., and 3 windows, each 7 ft. by 3 ft.?

10. What will be the cost of plastering a dining-room, walls and ceiling, 36 ft. long, 25 ft. wide, and 14 ft. high, at 45 cts. per sq. yard, allowing for a double door, 10 ft. by 8 ft.; one single door, 8 ft. by $3\frac{1}{2}$ ft.; six windows, each 8 ft. by $3\frac{1}{2}$ ft.; and a dado, 2 ft. 10 in. high, extending around the room?

11. At 6 cts. a sq. yard, what will it cost to kalsomine the walls and ceiling of a dining-room 25 ft. long, 18 ft. wide, and 12 ft. 6 in. high, allowing for two doors, each 9 ft. by $3\frac{1}{2}$ ft.; 3 windows, each 7 ft. by 3 ft.; and a wainscot, 3 ft. high, extending around the room?

12. What will it cost to paint the walls of a parlor $18\frac{1}{2}$ ft. long, $16\frac{1}{2}$ ft. wide, and 12 ft. high, at 27 cts. per sq. yard, no allowance being made for doors and windows?

13. What will be the cost of papering the walls of a room 18 ft. 6 in. long, 16 ft. 9 in. wide, and 10 ft. high, with paper 18 in. wide and 8 yards in a roll, at

75 cts. a roll, if 22 sq. yards be deducted for doors, windows, and base-board?

NOTE.—Wall-paper is sold by the roll, a roll being usually 18 in. wide and 8 yd. in length. The measurement of the room only assists in making a general estimate of the number of rolls required, the actual number being determined by papering the room. The number of rolls used, in whole or in part, is the number paid for, only uncut rolls being returned.

14. What will it cost to paper the walls of a hall 35 ft. long, 27 ft. wide, and 14 ft. high, with paper at 65 cts. a roll and border at 5 cts. a yd., allowing 25 sq. yd. for doors, windows, base-board, and border, the amount of paper used corresponding to the measurement?

III. BOARD MEASURE.

ART. 195. Boards one inch or less in thickness are sold by the square foot, surface measure. Boards more than one inch in thickness, as joists, sills, and other square lumber, are measured *by multiplying the number of square feet in one surface by the thickness in inches.*

NOTES.—The number of square feet in the surface of a board is found *by multiplying the length in feet by the width in inches, and dividing the product by* 12. In practice, the width of a board is reckoned to the next smaller half inch; thus, a width of $9\frac{3}{8}$ in. is counted 9 in.; $9\frac{3}{4}$ in. is counted $9\frac{1}{2}$ in.

2. Round logs are measured by the amount of lumber that can be sawed from them. When they do not exceed 15 ft. in length, the length and the diameter of the small end are taken, and the number of feet of lumber is computed by means of a table, stamped upon calipers. In the case of logs over 16 ft. in length, the average diameter is taken.

3. Shingles are estimated at 9 shingles, laid 4 in. to the weather, to the square foot. Allowing for waste and defects, 1000 shingles are estimated to cover 100 sq. ft., called a *square*. In practice, 1000 shingles of the best quality will cover 125 sq. ft.

4. A bunch of lath contains 100 pieces, each 4 ft. long; and a bunch is estimated to cover 5 square yards of surface.

15. How many feet of lumber in a board 16 ft. long, 10 in. wide, and 1 in. thick? $\frac{3}{4}$ in. thick?

16. How many feet of lumber in a tapering board 14 ft. long, and 8 in. at one end and 5 in. at the other?

SUGGESTION.—The average width is one half of the sum of the two end widths. In practice, this would be found by measuring the board at its middle.

How many feet of lumber in:

17. 20 boards 14 ft. long, 6 in. wide, and 1 in thick?
18. 9 joists 12 ft. long, 8 in. wide, and 2 in. thick?
19. 5 joists 14 ft. long, and 4 in. by 3 in.?
20. 10 planks 16 ft. long, 10 in. wide, $2\frac{1}{2}$ in. thick?

21. Find the cost, at $18.00 per M., of:

34 boards 16 ft. long, 10 in. wide, and 1 in. thick.
16 boards 12 ft. long, 8 in. wide, and 1 in. thick.
16 scantling 14 ft. long, and 4 in. by 2 in.
9 joists 12 ft. long, and 6 in. by $2\frac{1}{2}$ in.
26 flooring 14 ft. long, and 5 in. by $\frac{7}{8}$ in.

22. What will be the cost of 4 sills, two of them being 24 ft. long, and 8 in. by 6 in., and two being 30 ft. long, and 8 in. by 6 in., at $16.00 per M.?

23. Find the cost of flooring, allowing nothing for waste, for a floor 21 ft. by 16 ft., at $22 per M.

24. How many feet of siding 5 in. wide will be required to cover the four sides of a house 40 ft. long, 28 ft. wide, 20 ft. high, if they be laid 4 in. to the weather, and 150 sq. ft. be deducted for doors, windows, and cornice?

25. How many thousand shingles will be required to cover a gable roof 50 ft. long and each of the two sides $22\frac{1}{2}$ ft. wide, allowing a thousand shingles to every 125 sq. ft.? At $3.25 per M., what will be the cost?

IV. LAND SURVEYS.

ART. 196. The public lands of the United States are divided by survey into *Townships* 6 miles square, and these are divided into 36 equal parts, called *Sections*, each being one mile square. The sections are subdivided into *half-sections, quarter-sections, half-quarter-sections,* and *quarter-quarter-sections.*

In the survey of the public lands by the United States Government, a line is run through a given territory north and south, and another line east and west. The north and south line is called the *Principal Meridian,* and the east and west line the *Base Line.*

Lines are then run parallel to the principal meridian six miles apart, and other lines parallel to the base line six miles apart, thus forming *Townships* six miles square.

The lines of townships running north and south are called *Ranges,* and these are numbered from the principal meridian east and west. The townships are numbered from the base line north and south; and hence the location of a township is accurately designated by its number and the number of the range. Thus T. 5 N., R. 3 E., designates the fifth township north of the base line, in the third range east of the principal meridian.

N.

6	5	4	3	2	1
7	8	9	10	11	12
18	17	16	15	14	13
19	20	21	22	23	24
30	29	28	27	26	25
31	32	33	34	35	36

W.   E.

S.

Township.

The sections of a township are numbered from the north-east corner across to the west, and back on the second line of sections to the east, and thus back and forth, as is shown in the diagram at the right.

Each section is divided into halves and quarters, and the quarters are subdivided into halves and quarters, and designated, as is shown in the diagram at the left. Thus, the N. W. ¼ of N. W. ¼, Sec. 8, designates the north-west quarter of the north-west quarter of section 8.

| N.W.¼ of N.W.¼ 40 A. | E.½ of N.W.¼ 80 A. | N.E.¼ 160 A. |
| S.½ 320 A. | | |

Section 1.

A section contains 640 acres; a half-section, 320 acres; a quarter-section, 160 acres, etc.

26. Write out the description in full, and give the number of acres in each of the following tracts of land:

(a) N. W. ¼, Sec. 12, T. 10, N. R. 6 W. *160*

(b) W. ½ of N. E. ¼, Sec. 23, T. 13, S. R. 4 E. *160*

(c) S. E. ¼ of N. E. ¼, Sec. 18, T. 7, N. R. 2 W. *40*

(d) S. ½ and W. ½ of N. W. ¼, Sec. 7, T. 11, N. R. 5 W.

(e) S. E. ¼ and S. E. ¼ of N. E. ¼ Sec. 6, T. 9, N. R. 6 E.

27. What will be the cost of a quarter-section and a half-quarter-section of land at $14.50 an acre? A half-section and a half-quarter-section?

Art. 197. In measuring land, surveyors use a chain 4 rods long, and made of 100 links of equal length.

A square chain is 16 square rods, and 10 square chains are an acre.

NOTE.—This chain is called Gunter's chain. Each link is $\frac{1}{100}$ of 66 ft., or $7\frac{92}{100}$ in.

28. How many acres in a tract of land 60 ch. long and 32 ch. 50 l. wide?

PROCESS: 60 sq. ch. × 32½ ÷ 10 = 195 acres.

29. How many acres in a field 15 ch. long and 8 ch. 40 l. wide? 32 ch. by 10 ch. 25 l.?

30. How many acres in a street 80 ch. 60 l. long and 90 l. wide?

31. How many acres in a field 64 rods long and 35¼ rods wide? What will be its cost at $36.50 an acre?

32. How many acres in a street ¾ of a mile long and 4 rods wide? 2½ miles long and 3⅓ rods wide?

33. A man bought a farm 80 ch. long and 40 ch. wide at $22.50 an acre: what part of a section did he buy, and how much did it cost?

MEASUREMENT OF SOLIDS.

DEFINITIONS.

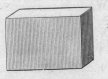

ART. 198. A **Rectangular Solid** is a body bounded by six rectangular surfaces.

The surfaces bounding a solid are called *Faces*, and the sides of these faces are called *Edges*. A rectangular solid has twelve edges. The face on which a solid is supposed to rest is called its *Base*.

ART. 199. A **Cylinder** is a solid whose two bases are equal and parallel circles, and whose lateral surface is uniformly curved.

ART. 200. The solid contents of a body is called its *Volume* or *Capacity*. It is expressed in some unit of measure; as a cubic inch, a cubic foot, etc.

ORAL PROBLEMS.

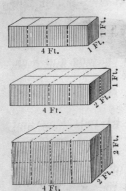

1. How many cubic feet in a rectangular solid 4 feet long, 1 foot wide, and 1 foot thick?

2. How many cubic feet in a rectangular solid 4 feet long, 2 feet wide, and 1 foot thick?

3. How many cubic feet in a rectangular solid 4 feet long, 2 feet wide, and 2 feet thick?

SOLUTION.—A rectangular solid 4 feet long, 1 foot wide, and 1 foot thick contains 4 cu. feet; a solid 4 feet long, 2 feet wide, and 1 foot thick contains 2 times 4 cu. feet, which is 8 cu. feet; and a solid 4 feet long, 2 feet wide, and 2 feet thick contains 2 times 8 cu. feet, which is 16 cu. feet.

4. How many cubic feet in a block of marble 6 ft. long, 3 ft. wide, and 2 feet thick? 10 ft. long, 5 ft. wide, and 4 ft. thick?

5. How many cubic feet in a piece of ice 5 ft. long, 2 ft. wide, and $\frac{1}{2}$ ft. thick?

6. How many cubic feet in a bin 6 ft. long, 3 ft. wide, and 3 ft. deep? 8 ft. long, 5 ft. wide, and 2 ft. deep? 6 ft. long, $3\frac{1}{3}$ ft. wide, and $1\frac{3}{4}$ ft. deep?

7. How many cubic yards in a room 5 yd. long, 4 yd. wide, and 3 yd. high?

8. If the number of cubic inches corresponding to the number of inches in the length or edge of a rectangular solid be multiplied by the number of inches in its width, what will the product represent? If this product be multiplied by the number of inches in the height of the solid, what will this product represent?

WRITTEN PROBLEMS.

9. How many cubic feet in a block of granite 16 ft. long, 8 ft. wide, and 5 ft. thick?

10. How many cubic feet in a pile of wood 45 ft. long, $3\frac{1}{2}$ ft. wide, and 7 ft. high?

PROCESS.

16 cu. ft.
8
___
128 cu. ft.
5
___
640 cu. ft.

11. How many cubic yards in a cellar 30 feet long, 21 feet wide, and 6 feet deep?

12. How many cubic feet in a cube, each of whose edges is 15 ft. in length? $12\frac{1}{2}$ ft. in length?

13. A building 65 ft. by 44 ft. has a foundation wall 12 ft. deep and 2 ft. thick: how many cubic feet in the foundations?

14. A pile of wood containing 840 cu. ft. is 30 ft. long and $3\frac{1}{2}$ ft. wide: how high is the pile?

15. If 27 bricks make a cu. ft., how many bricks will make a wall 45 ft. long, 27 ft. high, and $2\frac{1}{3}$ ft. thick?

16. The base of a cylinder is 12 in. in diameter, and its altitude is 25 in.: how many cubic inches in its solid contents?

PROCESS.

12 in. × 3.1416 = 37.6992 in., circum.

37.6992 sq. in. × 3 = 113.0976, sq. in., area of base.

113.0976 cu. in. × 25 = 2827.44 cu. in., solid contents.

17. How many cubic feet in a round block of timber 5 ft. long and 2 ft. in diameter?

NOTE.—The block of timber is a cylinder.

18. How many cubic feet in a round cistern 5 ft. in diameter and 8 ft. 6 in. deep?

19. How many cubic feet in a circular well 30 ft. deep and 3 ft. in diameter? 4 ft. in diameter?

ART. 201. 1. To find the solid contents of a rectangular solid:

Rule.—*Multiply the number of cubic units corresponding to the linear units in the length by the width, and this product by the thickness.*

NOTE.—The width and thickness are considered abstract numbers.

2. To find the length, width, or thickness of a rectangular solid:

Rule.—*Divide the solid contents by the number of cubic units corresponding to the product of the other two dimensions.*

NOTE.—The three dimensions of a solid (length, width, and height) must be in the same denomination.

3. To find the solid contents of a cylinder:

Rule.—*Multiply the number of cubic units corresponding to the square units in the area of the base by the altitude.*

APPLICATIONS OF SOLID MEASUREMENTS.

I. Wood and Stone.

ART. 202. A cord of wood is a pile 8 ft. long, 4 ft. wide, 4 ft. high, containing 128 cu. ft.

NOTE.—1 ft. in length of such a pile, or $\frac{1}{8}$ of a cord, is called a *cord foot* (little used).

WRITTEN PROBLEMS.

1. How many cords in a pile of wood 36 ft. long, 7 ft. high, and 4 ft. wide?

2. How many cords of wood in three piles, the first being 23 ft. long, 4 ft. wide, and 7 ft. high; the second, 28 ft. long, 4 ft. wide, and $6\frac{1}{2}$ ft. high; and the third 17 ft. long, 8 ft. wide, and $7\frac{1}{4}$ ft. high?

3. How many cords of four-foot wood in a pile 28 ft. long, 5 ft. high? 36 ft. long, 6 ft. high?

NOTE.—In practice, wood 4 ft. in length, or less, is measured *by multiplying the length by the height, and dividing the product by* 32. Short wood is sold at a less price per cord.

4. How many cords of wood in two piles, one 20 ft. long, $6\frac{1}{2}$ ft. high, and the other 26 ft. long, 8 ft. high?

5. How many cords of stove-wood in a pile 18 ft. long, 8 ft. high? 24 ft. long, 6 ft. high?

6. How much wood in a wagon-load piled in three lengths, each 3 ft. wide and 3 ft. high? What would be the cost at $4.80 per cord?

7. At 5.62\frac{1}{2}$ a cord, what would be the cost of a pile of three-foot wood 85$\frac{1}{2}$ ft. long, $6\frac{1}{3}$ ft. high?

8. How many perches of rough stone in a wall 36 rd. long, $2\frac{1}{2}$ ft. thick, and 5 ft. high?

NOTE.—Stone is usually measured by the *perch*, which is a mass of stone $16\frac{1}{2}$ ft. long, $1\frac{1}{2}$ ft. wide, and 1 ft. thick, containing $24\frac{3}{4}$ cu. ft. In some localities, the perch, used as a unit of measure, contains $16\frac{1}{2}$ cu. ft. Masonry is more generally measured by the cubic yard.

9. How many perches of stone in a pile 60 ft. long, 5 ft. wide, and 1 ft. 9 in. high?

10. How many perches of masonry in the wall of a cellar 45 ft. long, 34 ft. wide, 8 ft. high, and $2\frac{1}{6}$ ft. thick?

NOTE.—In measuring walls of cellars and buildings, masons take the distance round the *outside* of the walls (the girth) for the length, thus measuring each corner twice.

11. How many cubic yards of masonry in the foundation walls of a house, the two side walls being each 48 ft. long, $2\frac{1}{2}$ ft. wide, and 7 ft. high; and the two end walls, each 32 ft. long, $2\frac{1}{2}$ ft. wide, and 7 ft. high?

II. BINS, TANKS, AND CISTERNS.

ART. 203.   The capacity of bins for grain is usually measured in bushels; and the capacity of tanks, cisterns, etc., in gallons or barrels.

NOTE.—The United States standard bushel contains 2150.42 cu. in.; the liquid gallon, 231 cu. in.; and the dry gallon ($\frac{1}{8}$ bu.), 268.8 cu. in.; 6 dry gallons equal nearly 7 liquid gallons.

12. How many bushels of wheat will fill a bin 10 ft. long, 5 ft. wide, and 3 ft. deep?

PROCESS:
$$\begin{cases} 10 \text{ cu. ft.} \times 5 \times 3 = 150 \text{ cu. ft.} \\ 1728 \text{ cu. in.} \times 150 = 259200 \text{ cu. in.} \\ 259200 \text{ cu. in.} \div 2150.4 \text{ cu. in.} = 120.53 + \text{(bu.).} \end{cases}$$

NOTE.—Since a bushel contains $1\frac{1}{4}$ cu. ft. nearly, the capacity of a bin in bushels is found in practice *by taking $\frac{4}{5}$ of the number of cubic feet in it.*

13. How many bushels of wheat will fill a bin 4 ft. long, $2\frac{1}{2}$ ft. wide, and 2 ft. 9 in. deep?

14. How many bushels of oats will fill a wagon box 9 ft. long, 3 ft. 4 in. wide, and 15 in. deep?

NOTE.—Wheat and other grains are usually sold by weight, and hence the measurement of bins is of little practical value.

15. How many gallons of water will fill a tank 5 ft. square and 3 ft. deep?

PROCESS: $\begin{cases} 5 \text{ cu. ft.} \times 5 \times 3 = 75 \text{ cu. ft.} \\ 1728 \text{ cu. in.} \times 75 = 129600 \text{ cu. in.} \\ 129600 \text{ cu. in.} \div 231 \text{ cu. in.} = 561.038 \text{ (gals.).} \end{cases}$

NOTE.—In practice, $7\frac{1}{2}$ gallons are allowed for a cubic foot.

16. How many gallons of water will a tank hold that is 12 ft. long, 3 ft. 4 in. wide, and 1 ft. 8 in. deep? How many barrels of 31 gallons each?

17. How many gallons will a vat hold that is 5 ft. square and 20 in. deep? How many barrels?

18. How many gallons of water will a round cistern hold that is 5 ft. in diameter and 8 ft. deep?

SUGGESTION.—Find the area of a circle 5 ft. in diameter (the base of the cistern) and multiply this area by 8; the product will be the capacity of the cistern in cubic feet.

19. What is the capacity, in barrels, of a round cistern 4 ft. in diameter and 10 ft. deep?

20. How many gallons will a round tank hold that is 15 in. in diameter and 28 in. deep?

21. How many gallons of cider will fill a cask 16 in. in diameter and 27 in. long., no allowance being made for bulge?

ART. 204. 1. To find the capacity of a bin in bushels:

Rule.—*Divide the contents in cubic inches by* 2150.42. Or, *Take* $\frac{4}{5}$ *of the contents in cubic feet.*

2. To find the capacity of a vessel is liquid gallons:

Rule.—*Divide the contents in cubic inches by* 231. Or, *Multiply* $7\frac{1}{2}$ *gallons by the contents in cubic feet.*

NOTE.—The capacity in dry gallons is found by dividing the contents in cubic inches by 268.8.

III. Specific Gravity.

Art. 205.   The specific gravity of any substance is the number of times its weight contains the weight of an equal volume of water.

The specific gravity of a few common liquids and solids are as follows:

Pure cows milk,	1.03	*Iron (wrought),*	7.6 *to*	7.8
Human blood, .	1.0055	*Gold,* . . .	19. *to*	19.6
Alcohol, . . .	.791	*Silver,* . .	10.5	
Mercury, . .	13.596	*Copper,* . .	8.6 *to* 8.9	
Ice, ...	.92	*Quartz,* . .	2.65	

Since the weight of a cubic foot of water at its greatest density is 1000 oz., or 62½ lb., the weight of a cubic foot of any substance is found *by multiplying* 1000 oz. avoir. *by its specific gravity.*

22. What is the weight, in pounds, of a gallon of water, allowing 7½ gallons to the cubic foot?   A gallon of milk?

23. What is the weight of a cubic foot of ice?   A cubic foot of quartz rock?

24. What is the weight of a bar of wrought iron 1 in. square and 10 ft. long?

25. What is the weight of a brick of silver 2 in. by 4 in. and 8 in. long?

26. If 25^l of milk weigh 25.5^{Kg} is the milk pure? What would be the weight of the milk, if pure?

MISCELLANEOUS PROBLEMS.

1. What would be the cost of a township of land 6 miles square, at $10.50 an acre?

2. A park containing 40 acres is 50 rods wide: how long is it?

3. A circular park is 165 yards in diameter: how many acres does it contain?

4. How many bricks, 8 in. by 4 in., will pave a walk 60 ft. long and 12¾ ft. wide, with no allowance for edges or waste?

5. How many yards of carpeting ¾ of a yard wide will carpet a room 27 ft. long and 20⅓ ft. wide, if the strips run lengthwise, with a loss of 6 in. in matching?

6. How many yards of Brussels carpeting ¾ of a yard wide will carpet a room 18⅓ ft. long and 15 ft. wide, if the strips run lengthwise, with an allowance of 8 in. for matching figures?

7. What will it cost to plaster the walls and ceiling of a room 15 ft. long, 12 ft. wide, and 9 ft. high, at 50 cts. a square yard, with an allowance of 15 sq. yd. for doors and windows?

8. A bin is 8 ft. long, 3½ ft. wide, and 4 ft. deep: how many bushels of grain will it hold?

9. How many cubic feet in the capacity of a circular well 3⅓ ft. in diameter and 20 ft. deep?

10. A round cistern is 5 ft. in diameter and 6 ft. 4 in. deep: how many gallons of water will it hold?

11. How many barrels (31 gal.) will a round cistern hold that is 3 ft. in diameter and 10 ft. deep?

12. How many cubic blocks whose edges are 2 inches each, can be packed in a cubic box whose inside edges are 12 inches each?

13. What will it cost to excavate a cellar 10.5^m long, 7.6^m wide, and 1.8^m deep, at 25 cts. per cu. meter?

14. What will it cost to plaster the walls and ceiling of a room 8.5^m long, 6.4^m wide, and 3.8^m high, at 45 cts. per square meter, 10$^{sq.\ m}$ being allowed for doors and windows?

15. How many cubic meters of gas will fill a round gasometer 5.5^m in diameter and 3.25^m deep?

16. How many hektoliters of water will fill a cubic tank each of whose edges is 2.5^m? How many gallons?

PERCENTAGE.

NOTATION AND DEFINITIONS.

ART. 206. One per cent of a number is one hundredth of it, two per cent is two hundredths, and, generally, any per cent of a number is so many *hundredths* of it.

1. How many hundredths of a number is 4 per cent of it? 7 per cent of it? 15 per cent? 112 per cent?

2. How many hundredths of a number is $3\frac{1}{3}$ per cent of it? $12\frac{1}{2}$ per cent? $33\frac{1}{3}$ per cent? $133\frac{1}{3}$ per cent?

3. How many hundredths of a number is $\frac{1}{2}$ of one per cent of it? $\frac{3}{7}$ of one per cent? $\frac{2}{5}$ per cent?

4. What per cent of a number is $\frac{3}{100}$ of it? $\frac{7}{100}$ of it? $\frac{15}{100}$ of it? $\frac{45}{100}$ of it? $\frac{112}{100}$ of it?

5. What per cent of a number is .05 of it? .09 of it? $.03\frac{1}{2}$ of it? $.33\frac{1}{3}$ of it? $.00\frac{3}{7}$ of it? $.00\frac{1}{3}$ of it?

6. What decimal part of a number is 8 per cent of it? 15 per cent? $12\frac{1}{2}$ per cent? 125 per cent?

7. What decimal part of a number is $3\frac{1}{3}$ per cent of it? $33\frac{1}{3}$ per cent? $\frac{3}{4}$ per cent? $\frac{5}{8}$ per cent?

8. How much is 1 per cent of 400? 3 per cent?

9. How much is 2 per cent of $600? 4 per cent?

10. Express decimally 5 per cent; 8%; 15%.

NOTE.—The character % is often used for the words "per cent." Thus, 8% denotes 8 per cent.

11. Express decimally 1%; 3%; 6%; 7%; 8%; 9%.

12. Express decimally 15%; 20%; 25%; 33%; 45%.

13. Express decimally 112%; 125%; 150%; 220%.

14. Express decimally $6\frac{1}{2}\%$; $3\frac{1}{4}\%$; $12\frac{1}{2}\%$; $24\frac{2}{5}\%$.

SUGGESTION.—$6\frac{1}{2}\% = .06\frac{1}{2}$, or $.065$; $3\frac{1}{4}\% = .03\frac{1}{4}$, or $.0325$; etc.

15. Express decimally $7\frac{3}{5}\%$; $16\frac{2}{3}\%$; $10\frac{1}{2}\%$; $30\frac{1}{4}\%$.
16. Express decimally $\frac{1}{2}\%$; $\frac{3}{5}\%$; $\frac{1}{3}\%$; $\frac{3}{7}\%$; $\frac{7}{15}\%$.
17. Express decimally 5% ; $\frac{3}{10}\%$; $7\frac{3}{10}\%$; $\frac{1}{4}\%$; $20\frac{1}{4}\%$.
18. How much is 4% of \$450?

PROCESS : 4% of \$450. $=$ \$450 $\times$ .04 $=$ \$18.00.

19. How much is 5% of 80 hours? Of 160 hours?
20. How much is 6% of \$250? 15%? 20%?

DEFINITIONS.

ART. 207. When a given per cent of a number is taken, the result is called the *percentage;* the number of hundredths taken, the *rate per cent;* and the number itself, the *base.*

If, for example, 6% of 250 be taken, 15 (the result) is the percentage, $\frac{6}{100}$ the rate per cent (6 being the rate), and 250 the base.

ART. 208. These three terms may be defined as follows :

A **Percentage** of a number is the result obtained by taking any per cent of it.

The **Rate Per Cent** is the fraction denoting the number of hundredths taken.

The **Base** is the number of which a per cent is taken.

NOTES.—1. In this treatise the terms *rate per cent* and *rate* are not used as synonymous. The rate is the *numerator* of the fraction which is the rate per cent, the denominator being 100. The convenience, as well as accuracy, of this distinction will be made obvious by a comparison of the two rules in the following cases.

2. The rate per cent may be expressed in figures either in the form of a common fraction, as $\frac{6}{100}$, or in the form of a decimal, as .06. When written in the decimal form it is said to be *expressed decimally.*

Art. 209. The character % is read *per cent.*

Art. 210. Percentage is that branch of Arithmetic in which *one hundred* is the basis of computation.

The term per cent is a contraction of the Latin *per centum,* which means by the hundred.

THE THREE CASES OF PERCENTAGE.

Art. 211. The Base, Percentage, and Rate Per Cent have such relations to each other that, if any two of them are given, the other may be found. Hence, there are three distinct operations or processes in percentage, usually called *Cases.*

Art. 212.   These distinct processes may be thus stated:

1. The Base and Rate Per Cent given to find the Percentage.
2. The Base and Percentage given to find the Rate Per Cent.
3. The Percentage and Rate Per Cent given to find the Base.

Note.—A fourth case is usually given, including problems in which the sum or difference of the base and percentage and the rate per cent are given to find the base; but the percentage part of the process does not differ essentially from Case III. The sum or difference given is a percentage of the base, and the new rate per cent, found by adding the given rate per cent to or subtracting it from 100%, is the *Rate Per Cent.* The adding of the given rate per cent to or subtracting it from 100%, as the case may be, is not an operation of percentage, but is simply the adding or subtracting of numbers.

CASE I.

THE BASE AND THE RATE PER CENT GIVEN TO FIND THE PERCENTAGE.

1. How much is 5% of 800?

Solutions.—1. 5% of $800 = \frac{5}{100}$ of 800, which is 40. Or,
 2. 1% of $800 = \frac{1}{100}$ of 800, which is 8; and 5% of 800 = 5 times 8, which is 40.

2. What is 4% of 50? 6%? 8%? 10%?

3. What is 5% of 40? Of 60? 80? 120?

4. What is 3% of 200? 300? 500? 700?

5. What is 6% of 250 miles? 10%? 12%? 20%?

6. What is $\frac{1}{2}$% of 100 days? 200 days? 500 days?

7. What is $\frac{3}{4}$% of $800? $1200? $2000? $600?

WRITTEN PROBLEMS.

8. What is 8% of $674.50?

1ST PROCESS.	2D PROCESS.
$674.50	$6.745 = 1%
.08	8
$53.96 00	$53.960 = 8%

NOTE.—Let the pupil use the first process only until he is familiar with it. In the second process 1% of the base is found by removing the decimal point two places to the left (Art. 115).

What is:

9. 5% of 245?

10. 9% of 350?

11. 15% of 1200?

12. 25% of 37.5?

13. 33% of $150?

14. 8% of $37.50?

15. 3% of $180.25?

16. $1\frac{1}{3}$% of 1050 lb.?

17. $2\frac{1}{2}$% of 60.8 lb.?

18. $12\frac{1}{2}$% of 560 days?

19. $\frac{1}{2}$% of $540?

20. $\frac{1}{10}$% of $4000?

21. $\frac{3}{7}$% of 21700 ft.?

22. $\frac{3}{4}$% of $48.50?

23. $33\frac{1}{3}$% of 965 days?

24. $16\frac{2}{3}$% of $.54?

25. 15% of $\frac{5}{8}$? Of $\frac{9}{10}$?

26. $66\frac{2}{3}$% of $\frac{7}{15}$? Of $2\frac{2}{3}$?

27. 12% of .25? Of .45?

28. $6\frac{1}{4}$% of 50? Of .75?

29. What is the difference between 33% and $25\frac{1}{2}$% of 480 miles? Of 2670 miles?

30. If 70% of a certain ore is iron, how much iron is there in 3740 pounds of ore?

31. If 20% of air-dried wood is water, how much water is there in $143\frac{3}{4}$ tons of wood?

ART. 213.   **Formula.**—*Percentage = base × rate per cent.*

ART. 214.   To find a given per cent of any number:

Rules.—*1. Multiply the given number by the given rate per cent.* Or,

2. Remove the decimal point in the given number two places to the left, and multiply the result by the rate.

NOTE.—When the rate per cent is used in a written process as a multiplier or divisor it should be *expressed decimally.*

CASE II.

THE BASE AND THE PERCENTAGE GIVEN TO FIND THE RATE PER CENT.

1. What per cent of 16 is 4?

SOLUTION.—1 is $\frac{1}{16}$ of 16, and 4 is $\frac{4}{16}$, or $\frac{1}{4}$, of 16; $\frac{1}{4} = \frac{25}{100}$ or 25%.

2. What per cent of $50 are $5? $20?
3. What per cent of $300 are $12? $30?
4. What per cent of 150 lb. are 75 lb.?   50 lb.?
5. What per cent of 250 ft. are 50 ft.?   100 ft.?

WRITTEN PROBLEMS.

6. What per cent of 62.5 is 15?

1ST PROCESS.	2D PROCESS.
$15 \div 62.5 = .24$	1% of 62.5 = .625
$.24 = 24\%$, *Ans.*	$15 \div .625 = 24$, *Rate.*

NOTE.—The quotient obtained by the first process is the *rate per cent*, and the quotient obtained by the second process is the *rate*.

What per cent of:

7. 75 is 4.5?

8. 125 is 25?

9. 120 is 40?

10. $450 are $90?

11. $192 are $32?

12. $760 are $19?

13. $1000 are $5?

14. $6 are 45 cts.?

15. 75 lb. are 16.5 lb.?

16. 20 ft. are 1.2 ft.?

17. $37\frac{1}{2}$ yd. are 5 yd.?

18. .75 is .15?

19. .60 is .45?

20. $\frac{5}{6}$ is $\frac{1}{3}$?

21. $\frac{4}{5}$ is $\frac{2}{3}$?

22. $2\frac{1}{2}$ is $\frac{3}{4}$?

23. A farmer had 320 sheep and sold 48 of them: what per cent of the flock did he sell?

24. A gold ring is 18 carats fine: what per cent of it is gold? If it were 16 carats fine, what per cent of it would be gold?

25. What per cent of $45 is $16\frac{2}{3}\%$ of $150?

FORMULA AND RULES.

ART. 215. **Formula.**—*Rate% = percentage ÷ base.*

ART. 216. To find what per cent one number is of another:

Rules.—*1. Divide the number which is the percentage by the base, and the quotient expressed in hundredths will be the rate per cent. Or,*

2. Divide the number which is the percentage by one per cent of the base, and the quotient will be the rate.

CASE III.

PERCENTAGE AND RATE PER CENT GIVEN TO FIND THE BASE.

1. 45 is 15% of what number?

SOLUTION.—If 45 is 15 % of a number, 1% of it is $\frac{1}{15}$ of 45, which is 3, and 100 %, or the number, is 100 times 3, which is 300.

2. 320 is 16% of what number?

3. 7.2 pounds are 12% of how many pounds?

4. 75 miles are 25% of how many miles?

5. 208 rods are 104% of how many rods?

6. $540 are 108% of how many dollars?

7. 216 is 8% more than what number?

SUGGESTION.—If 216 is 8 % more than a number, 216 is 100 % + 8%, or 108% of the number.

8. 318 is 6% more than what number?

9. $480 is 20% more than what sum of money?

10. 560 lb. are 12% more than how many pounds?

11. 184 is 8% less than what number?

SUGGESTION.—184 is 100% — 8%, or 92% of the number.

12. 285 is 5% less than what number?

13. $356 are 11% less than how many dollars?

14. 425 feet are 15% less than how many feet?

WRITTEN PROBLEMS.

15. 256 is 35% of what number?

16. $107\frac{1}{2}$ is 15% of what number?

17. 99 is $33\frac{1}{3}$% of what number?

18. 30 lb. are 45% of how many pounds?

19. $12\frac{1}{2}$ is 8% of what number?

20. 125 is 30% of what number?

21. 7.15 is 20% of what number?

22. $5\frac{1}{3}$ is 50% of what number?

23. 240 men are $12\frac{1}{2}$% of how many men?

24. $78 are 10% of how many dollars?

25. $\frac{3}{5}$ is 20% of what number?

26. 540 sheep are 36% of how many sheep?

27. 5280 pounds are $66\frac{2}{3}$% of how many pounds?

28. $189.80 are 104% of what sum of money?

29. What number plus 16% of itself equals 87?

1ST PROCESS.	2D PROCESS.
$87 \div 1.16 = 75$, *Ans.*	$(87 \div 116) \times 100 = 75$, *Ans.*

30. What number plus 6% of itself equals 25.5?

31. What number plus 1½% of itself equals 243.6?

32. What number plus 8% of itself equals 13.5?

33. How many yards less 8% equal 42.78 yd.?

34. What sum of money less 7% of itself is $483.60?

35. What sum of money less 12½% of itself is $34.50?

36. What sum of money less 3⅓% of itself is $44.60?

37. What number less 6% of itself is 470?

38. What number plus 30% of itself equals 162.5?

39. What number less 16⅔% of itself equals 2035.8?

FORMULA AND RULES.

ART. 217. **Formula.**—*Base = percentage ÷ rate per cent.*

ART. 218. To find a number when a certain percentage of it is given:

Rules.—*1. Divide the number which is the percentage by the rate per cent expressed decimally.* Or,

2. Divide the number which is the percentage by the rate, and multiply the quotient by 100.

NOTE.—When the given number is a given per cent more or less than the required number, the true rate per cent is 1 *plus* or *minus the given rate per cent.* Art. 212, note.

THE RATE AN ALIQUOT PART OF 100.

ART. 219. When the rate is an aliquot part of 100, the percentage of a number may be found by taking the same aliquot part of it. Thus, 33⅓% of $48 = ⅓ of $48.

The process in finding a number when a percentage of it and the rate per cent are given, may likewise be shortened by using the aliquot fraction.

The aliquot parts of 100 % most frequently used are 12½ % (⅛), 16⅔ % (⅙), 20 % (⅕), 25 % (¼), 33⅓ % (⅓), and 50 % (½).

WRITTEN PROBLEMS.

1. What is $12\frac{1}{2}\%$ of 49.80? $16\frac{2}{3}\%$?   20%?
2. What is 25% of 6.4?   Of 26.32? $17\frac{1}{2}$? $21\frac{1}{3}$?
3. What is $33\frac{1}{3}\%$ of \$689.64?   Of \$1448.25?
4. What is 50% of 786.7 miles?   84.25 ft.?
5. 84.6 is $33\frac{1}{3}\%$ of what number?
6. $5\frac{1}{2}$ is $12\frac{1}{2}\%$ of what number?
7. 876.5 days are $16\frac{2}{3}\%$ of how many days?
8. \$85.90 are 50% more than what sum of money?
9. \$360.45 are 25% less that what sum of money?

NOTE.—Let the pupil solve the following problems in which the rate is an aliquot part of 100.

MISCELLANEOUS PRACTICAL PROBLEMS.

ORAL PROBLEMS.

1. What is $12\frac{1}{2}\%$ of 640? $16\frac{2}{3}\%$ of 360?
2. What is $33\frac{1}{3}\%$ of 672? $66\frac{2}{3}\%$ of 321?
3. 15 is what per cent of 60?   Of 90?
4. $16\frac{2}{3}$ pounds are what per cent of 50 lb.?   120 lb.?
5. 25% of 120 is what per cent of 90?   120?
6. $33\frac{1}{3}\%$ of 150 is what per cent of 250?
7. 80 is $12\frac{1}{2}\%$ of what number?
8. 20% of 105 is 25% of what number?
9. $33\frac{1}{3}\%$ of 225 is 15% of what number?
10. 45 is what per cent of 75% of 120?
11. 360 is 20% more than what number?
12. 60 is $33\frac{1}{3}\%$ more than what number?
13. $33\frac{1}{3}\%$ of 240 is $33\frac{1}{3}\%$ less than what number?
14. 25% of 280 is $16\frac{2}{3}\%$ more than what number?
15. What per cent of any number is $\frac{2}{3}$ of it? $\frac{3}{4}$ of it?
16. What per cent of any number is $\frac{4}{15}$ of it?
17. What per cent of any number is $\frac{5}{8}$ of it? $\frac{3}{25}$ of it?
18. What per cent of any number is $\frac{12}{3}$ of it?

19. A man is 60 years of age, and 20% of his age is 25% of the age of his wife: how old is his wife?

20. A company of 75 men lost 25 men in a certain battle: what per cent of the company remained?

21. Charles is 15 years old, and his age is 30% of his father's age: how old is his father?

22. A man's expenses are $28 a month, which is 70% of his wages: how much does he earn a month?

23. In a certain school 96 pupils study arithmetic, which is 24 per cent of the whole number of pupils in school: how many pupils in the school?

24. A horse cost $160, which was 20% less than the cost of a carriage: what was the cost of the carriage?

25. A school enrolls 230 boys, which is 15% more than the number of girls enrolled: how many pupils in the school?

WRITTEN PROBLEMS.

26. A man receives $1650 a year, and his expenses are $87\frac{1}{2}$% of his income: how much has he left?

27. A regiment of 750 men lost 160 in a certain battle: what per cent of the regiment remained?

28. The number of pupils in daily attendance in a certain school is 420, which is 80% of the number enrolled: how many pupils are enrolled?

2?. The number of youth of school age in a certain city is 5220, which is 36% of the number of inhabitants: what is the population of the city?

30. A man spent 60% of his money for a suit of clothes, 25% of it for books, and had $7.50 left: how much money had he at first?

31. A man invested $5400 in land, which was $37\frac{1}{2}$% of his property: what was the value of his property?

32. In a storm, a ship's crew threw overboard 250 barrels of flour, which was 40% of the number of barrels on board: how many barrels of flour were left?

N. C. A.—16.

33. A man owning 60% of a factory, sold 40% of his share for $9600: at this rate, what was the value of the factory?

34. The land surface of the earth is about 50000000 square miles, which is 33⅓% of the water surface: what is the extent of the water surface?

35. The population of a certain city in 1870 was 64000, which is 80% of the population in 1880: what was the population in 1880?

36. A farm was sold for $6390, which was 12½% more than it cost: what was the cost of the farm?

37. A grain dealer owning 58500 bushels of wheat, shipped 37½% of it by a steamer, 33⅓% of it by a schooner, and the rest of it by railroad: how many bushels did he ship by each?

38. The population of a certain city in 1870 was 63500, and the census of 1880 shows an increase of 17⅕%: what was the population in 1880?

39. A's farm contains 306 acres, which is 32% less than B's: how many acres in B's farm?

40. When gold was worth 25% more than currency, what was the gold value of $150 in currency?

41. When gold was worth 20% more than currency, what was the value in gold of a dollar bill?

42. The number of pupils in daily attendance at a school is 570, which is 5% less than the number enrolled: how many pupils are enrolled?

43. The number of pupils enrolled in a certain school is 920, which is 15% more than the average number of pupils in daily attendance: what is the average daily attendance?

44. The population of a certain city in 1880 was 171572, which is 18% more than its population in 1870: what was the population in 1870?

45. A farm contains 480 acres, of which 30% is meadow, 25¼% pasture, 16⅔% grain land, and the rest woodland: how many acres of each kind of land in the farm?

46. A merchant failed in business owing $10500, and having $6300 worth of property: what per cent of his indebtedness can he pay?

47. A clerk, receiving a yearly salary of $950, pays $275 a year for board, $180 for clothing, and $150 for other expenses: what per cent of his salary is left?

48. A lady pays $280 a year for board, $175 a year for clothing and other expenses, and lays up 35% of her income: what is her income?

49. A man's expenses are 80% of his income, and $33\frac{1}{3}\%$ of his income equals 10% of his property, which is valued at $27000: what is his income? What are his expenses?

50. A merchant sold a stock of goods for $10811, and gained $13\frac{4}{5}\%$: what was the cost of the goods?

51. A cargo of damaged corn was sold at auction for $9450, which was $33\frac{1}{3}\%$ less than cost: what was the cost of the corn?

52. An orchard contains 1200 trees, of which 45% are apple, 22% peach, $12\frac{1}{2}\%$ cherry, and the rest pear: how many trees of each kind in the orchard?

53. A owns $42\frac{1}{2}\%$ of a factory worth $35000, B owns 37% of it, and C owns the remainder: what is the value of each of their shares?

54. A man bequeathed $7560 to his wife, which was $62\frac{1}{2}\%$ of the sum bequeathed to his children, and the sum bequeathed to his wife and children was 80% of his estate: what was the value of the estate? What per cent of the estate did the wife receive?

55. The population of a city in 1880 was 41064, which was 16% more than in 1870, and the population in 1870 was $6\frac{1}{4}\%$ less than in 1875: what was the population in 1875?

56. The number of deaths in a certain city in 1879 was 1950, which was equal to $3\frac{1}{4}\%$ of the population: what was the population?

APPLICATIONS OF PERCENTAGE.

ART. 220. The principal applications of percentage are *Profit and Loss, Commission and Brokerage, Capital Stock, Insurance, Taxes, Customs, Bankruptcy, Interest, Discount, Stock Investments, Exchange,* and *Equation of Payments.* The last five involve the element of *time.*

All the problems are solved by the application of the principles of one or more of the three cases of percentage.

PROFIT AND LOSS.

ART. 221. The **Cost** of an article is the price paid for it, or the total expense incurred in producing it.

ART. 222. The **Selling Price** of an article is the amount asked or received for it by the seller.

The *selling price* of the seller is the *cost* to the buyer.

ART. 223. When an article is sold for more than its cost, it is said to be sold at a *profit* or *gain;* when it is sold for less than its cost, it is said to be sold at a *loss* or *discount.*

NOTE.—The terms *gain* and *loss* are not limited to business transactions. When any quantity undergoes an increase or decrease, from any cause, there is a gain or loss, and when such gain or loss can be expressed in hundredths, it may be computed by the principles of percentage.

ORAL PROBLEMS.

1. A merchant bought a piece of cloth for $80, and sold it at 25% profit: for how much did he sell it?

2. A dealer bought hats at $5 apiece, and sold them at 20% profit: what was the selling price?

3. Hats, costing $5 apiece, were sold at a loss of 20%: what was the selling price?

4. At what price must flour, costing $6 a barrel, be sold to gain $16\frac{2}{3}\%$? To gain 25%? $33\frac{1}{3}\%$?

5. A grocer bought sugar at 12 cts., 16 cts., and 18 cts. a pound: for how much must each kind be sold to gain 20%? To gain 25%? $33\frac{1}{3}\%$?

6. A merchant sells broadcloth, costing $4, for $5 a yard: what per cent does he gain?

7. When broadcloth, costing $5 a yard, is sold for $4 a yard, what is the loss per cent?

8. Teas costing $1.20, $1.40, and $1.50 a pound, are sold respectively at $1.50, $1.70, and $1.80 a pound: what is the gain per cent on each?

9. A merchant sold velvet at a profit of $2 a yard, and gained 20%: how much did it cost?

10. A dealer sold boots at $1.50 a pair less than cost, and thereby lost $33\frac{1}{3}\%$: what did they cost?

11. A grocer sold tea at 20 cents above cost, and gained $16\frac{2}{3}\%$: what was the cost of the tea? What was the selling price?

12. A man sold a horse for $90, and gained 20%: what was the cost of the horse?

13. A man sold a horse for $80, and lost 20%: what was the cost of the horse?

14. Sold butter at 40 cts. a pound, and gained 25%: how much did it cost?

15. A watch, costing $80, was sold at a loss of 10%: for how much was it sold?

16. How must shoes, costing $2, $2.50, and $3 a pair, be sold respectively to gain 25%? To gain 30%?

17. How must muslin that cost 10 cts., 15 cts., and 18 cts. a yard, be sold to gain 20%? To gain 25%?

18. Sold tea at 90 cts. a pound, and gained 20%: what would have been my gain per cent if sold at $1 a pound?

19. A merchant sells goods at retail at 30% above cost, and at wholesale at 10% less than the retail price: what is his gain per cent on goods sold at wholesale?

20. A merchant marked a piece of silk at 25% above cost, and then sold it at 20% less than the marked price: did he gain or lose, and how much?

21. An article that cost nothing was sold for $5: what was the gain per cent? What would have been the gain per cent if it had been sold for $10?

SUGGESTION.—The base is 0 and the gain $5.

22. Can an article be sold at a loss equal to or greater than 100%? Could it be sold at a gain greater than 100%? Explain each answer, supposing the cost to be $5.

WRITTEN PROBLEMS.

23. A house and lot which cost $6750 were sold at a gain of $12\frac{1}{2}$%: for how much were they sold?

24. Carriages costing $165 each are sold at 18% profit: what is the gain on each carriage?

25. A man paid $4500 for a farm, and sold it for $5400: what was the gain per cent?

26. A drover bought cattle at $65 a head, and sold them at $84.50 a head: what was the gain per cent?

27. A drover bought horses at $130 a head, expended $6 each in taking them to market, and then sold them at $153.50 a head: what was the gain per cent?

28. A cargo of wheat costing $16500, being damaged, was sold for $13750: what was the loss per cent?

29. A merchant sold a lot of goods at $12\frac{1}{2}$% profit, and gained $8160: what was the cost?

30. A grocer sold 82 barrels of apples at 22% profit, and gained $45.10: what was the cost per barrel?

31. A man sold a watch for $180, and lost $16\frac{2}{3}$%: what was the cost of the watch?

32. A house and lot were sold for $7762.50, at a gain of 15%: what was the cost?

33. A firm sold $45000 worth of goods in a year; $\frac{2}{5}$

of the receipts were sales at 20% profit, ½ at 25% profit, and the rest at 33⅓% profit: what was the total cost?

34. Sold a piece of carpeting for $240, and lost 20%: what selling price would have given a gain of 20%?

35. How must cloth, costing $3.50 a yard, be marked that a merchant may deduct 15% from the marked price and still make 15% profit?

36. A merchant marked a lot of goods at 20% above cost, but, in consequence of a rise in the market price, he marked up the goods 10% on the marked price: what per cent was the last selling price of the cost? What would be his gain on sales amounting to $5780.50?

FORMULAS AND RULES.

ART. 224. Formulas.—1. *Gain or loss=cost×rate%.*

2. *Rate%=gain or loss÷cost.*

3. *Cost=gain or loss÷rate%.*

4. *Cost=selling price÷* $\begin{cases} 1+rate\%. \\ 1-rate\%. \end{cases}$

ART. 225. 1. To find the gain or loss, the cost and rate per cent being given:

Rule.—*Multiply the cost by the rate per cent.*

2. To find the rate per cent, the cost and the gain or loss being given:

Rule.—*Divide the gain or loss by the cost, and the quotient expressed in hundredths will be the rate per cent.*

3. To find the cost, the gain or loss and the rate per cent being given:

Rule.—*Divide the gain or loss by the rate per cent.*

4. To find the cost, the selling price and the rate per cent of gain or loss being given:

Rule.—*Divide the selling price by 1 plus or minus the rate per cent.*

COMMISSION AND BROKERAGE.

ART. 226. An **Agent** is a person who transacts business for another.

Agents are called *Factors, Commission Merchants, Brokers, Collectors,* etc. A Factor, or Commission Merchant, buys and sells goods intrusted to his possession and control. A Broker buys and sells bills of exchange, stocks, bonds, etc.; or property in possession of others, as real estate. A Collector collects debts, rents, etc.

When a factor lives in a different country, or part of the country, from his employer (the principal), he is called a *Correspondent,* or *Consignee.* The sender of goods to him is the *Consignor,* and the goods shipped or consigned, a *Consignment.*

ART. 227. Commission is an allowance made to a factor, or other agent, for the transaction of business. The commission allowed a broker is called *Brokerage.*

ART. 228. Commission is computed at a certain per cent of the amount of property bought or sold, or of the amount of business transacted. The rate per cent is called the *Rate of Commission,* and the amount of business transacted is the *Base.*

The rate of commission varies with the amount and nature of the business. A broker's commission is usually less than a factor's.

ART. 229. The **Net Proceeds** of a sale or collection are the proceeds less the commission and other charges.

ORAL PROBLEMS.

1. An auctioneer sold $300 worth of furniture at a commission of 5%: how much did he receive?

2. A peddler bought $500 worth of rags at a commission of 10%: what was his commission?

3. An agent sold $1200 worth of school furniture at a commission of $16\frac{2}{3}\%$: how much did he receive?

4. An attorney collected bad debts to the amount of $800, and charged 20%: what was his commission?

5. A society paid a lad $6 for collecting membership dues to the amount of $100: what rate of commission did he receive?

6. A book-seller received $30 for selling $150 worth of maps: what was his rate of commission?

7. A real estate broker received $40 for selling a house and lot at 5% commission: for how much was the property sold?

8. An attorney received $60 for collecting a note at 10% commission: what was the amount collected?

9. An agent received $108 with which to buy peaches, after deducting his commission at 8%: how much did he expend for peaches?

10. A factor received $309 with which to buy flour, after deducting his commission at 3%: what was the cost of the flour?

WRITTEN PROBLEMS.

11. A commission merchant sold 540 barrels of flour at $6.37\frac{1}{2}$ a barrel: what was his commission at 3%?

12. A real estate broker sold 325 acres of land at $24.50 an acre, and charged a commission of $2\frac{1}{2}\%$: what was his commission?

13. An auctioneer sold $5160.50 worth of dry goods, and $715.25 worth of furniture: what was his commission at $1\frac{1}{2}\%$?

14. A lawyer collected 65% of a note of $950, and charged $6\frac{1}{4}\%$ commission: what was his commission? What was the amount paid over?

15. A factor in New Orleans purchased $75000 worth of cotton for a Lowell manufacturer at $1\frac{3}{4}\%$ commission: what was his bill for cotton and commission?

N. C. A.—17.

16. An architect charged $\frac{1}{4}$% for plans and specifications, and $1\frac{3}{8}$% for superintending the erection of a building costing $120000: how much was his fee?

17. An agent furnished a school-house for $4500, and received $540 commission: what was the rate?

18. An attorney charged $75 for collecting rents to the amount of $1125: what was the rate of commission?

19. A commission merchant charged $2\frac{1}{2}$% for buying produce, and his commission was $750: how much produce did he purchase?

20. An agent received 5% for buying wool, and his commission was $208.50: how much wool did he buy?

21. My agent has bought 3300 barrels of apples at $1.75 a barrel, and I allow him 3% commission: how much money must I remit to pay both the cost of the apples and the commission?

22. A Boston merchant sent his factor in Cincinnati $3529.20 to be invested in bacon, after deducting his commission at 2%: how much did he expend for bacon, and what was his commission?

23. A cotton broker in Charleston received $11774 with which to purchase cotton, after deducting his commission of $1\frac{1}{2}$%: how much did he expend for cotton, and what was his commission?

24. A real estate broker sold a section of land at $7.50 an acre, and invested the proceeds in railroad stock, receiving $1\frac{1}{2}$% for selling the land and $\frac{7}{8}$% for buying the stock: what was his brokerage?

25. What will be the total cost of 750 yards of carpeting at $1.75 a yard, if a merchant pay $2\frac{1}{4}$% commission for purchasing, $\frac{1}{4}$% for a draft covering cost and agent's commission, and $12.50 for freight?

26. A grain dealer in Chicago received $5000, with directions to purchase wheat at $1.10 a bushel, after deducting his commission at $2\frac{1}{2}$%: how many bushels of wheat did he purchase?

ART. 230. **Formulas:**

1. *Commission or brokerage = base × rate %.*
2. *Rate % = commission or brokerage ÷ base.*
3. *Base = commission or brokerage ÷ rate %.*
4. *Base = (base + commission or brokerage) ÷ (1 + rate %).*

ART. 231. 1. To find commission or brokerage:

Rule.—*Multiply the sum of money denoting the amount of business transacted by the rate per cent.*

2. To find the sum to be invested when the amount given includes both the sum to be invested and the commission or brokerage:

Rule.—*Divide the given amount by 1 plus the rate per cent, and the quotient will be the sum invested.*

NOTE.—These two rules cover all the ordinary business transactions in commission or brokerage. Rules corresponding to the second and third formulas can be easily formed by the pupil.

CAPITAL STOCK.

ART. 232. **Capital** is property invested in trade, manufactures, or other business.

The original or nominal value of capital is its *Par Value,* and the sum for which it will sell is its *Market Value.*

When the market value of capital equals its par value, it is said to be *at par;* when the market value is more than the par value, it is *above par,* or *at a premium;* when the market value is less than the par value, it is *below par,* or *at a discount.*

ART. 233. A **Company** is an association of persons united for the transaction of business.

When a company is organized and regulated by law, it is said to be incorporated. An incorporated company is called a *Corporation,* and the law regulating it a *Charter.*

ART. 234. The capital of a corporation is called *Capital Stock*, or, briefly, *Stock*.

Capital Stock is divided into equal parts, called *Shares*. Certificates of these shares are *Stock Certificates*, or *Scrip;* and the holders of such certificates are *Stockholders*.

Stocks are *at par*, *above par*, or *below par*, according as their market value equals, exceeds, or is less than their par value or face.

The market value of stocks is quoted at a certain per cent of the par value. Stocks quoted at 108 are worth 108 % of their face ; that is, are 8 % *above par:* stocks quoted at 92 are worth 92 % of their face ; that is, are 8 % *below par*.

ART. 235. A **Dividend** is the part of the earnings of a company distributed among the stockholders.

The total receipts of a company from its business are called the *Gross Earnings;* and the net profits, found by deducting all expenses and losses from the gross earnings, are the *Net Earnings*. The net earnings are distributed as dividends.

Dividends are usually declared annually or semi-annually, and they are computed as a per cent of the par value of the stock. The rate per cent is called the *Rate of Dividend*. The market value of stocks depends chiefly on the dividends paid and the financial condition of the company.

ART. 236. An **Assessment** is a sum levied upon the stockholders to meet the losses or expenses of the business.

The business of incorporated companies is usually managed by directors, who are elected by the stockholders, each of the latter being entitled to as many votes as he owns shares.

NOTE.—When a business corporation wishes to raise money in addition to that derived from its capital stock, it issues notes or bonds, payable at a specified time with interest, and secured by mortgage on the property of the corporation. The bonds, called *Mortgage Bonds*, are negotiable, and are called Stocks (Art. 301) ; but they should be carefully distinguished from *Capital Stock*.

ORAL PROBLEMS.

1. When stock is 6% premium, what is the market value of $1? Of $100? Of $1000?

2. When stock is 12% discount, what is the market value of $1? Of $100? Of $1000?

3. How much will 5 shares of telegraph stock cost at 4% premium? At 4% discount?

Note.—A share is $100, if no other value is named.

4. What will 10 shares of telephone stock cost at 20% premium? At 15% premium?

5. How is stock quoted when it is 15% premium? When it is 15% discount? 8% discount?

6. When stock is quoted at $107\frac{1}{2}$, what is the value of $1? Of $10? Of $100?

7. When stock is quoted at 87, what is the value of $1? Of $100? Of $10?

8. How much will 10 shares of mining stock cost when quoted at 104? When quoted at 85? At 90?

9. A company declares a dividend of 3%: how much will a stockholder, owning 15 shares, receive?

10. A manufacturing company made an assessment of 5% to repair damages caused by a freshet; how much must a stockholder, owning 20 shares, pay?

WRITTEN PROBLEMS.

11. A man bought 75 shares of railroad stock at $7\frac{1}{2}\%$ discount: how much did they cost?

12. A broker bought 70 shares of insurance stock at $6\frac{1}{2}\%$ premium, and sold them at $\frac{3}{4}\%$ discount: how much did he lose?

13. Bought 100 shares of Little Miami stock at $109\frac{1}{2}$, and sold them at $112\frac{1}{2}$: how much did I gain by the transaction?

14. A man bought 52 shares of Illinois Central at 127; and sold 36 shares at 135, and the rest at $137\frac{1}{2}$: how much did he gain?

15. A broker bought 84 shares, $50 each, of gas stock at 94, and sold them at $100\frac{3}{7}$: how much did he gain?

16. When bank stock is quoted at 105, how many shares can be bought for $525? For $840?

17. How many shares of bank stock at 4% premium can be bought for $8320?

18. When New York Central is quoted at $95\frac{5}{8}$, how much stock can be bought for $6894, brokerage $\frac{1}{8}$%?

SUGGESTION.—Brokerage is computed on the *par value* of stock, and hence the cost of the stock will be $95\frac{5}{8} + \frac{1}{8}$, or $95\frac{6}{8}$ %. This is an exception to the general principle stated in Art. 228.

19. How much railroad stock at $12\frac{1}{4}$ discount can be bought for $8750, brokerage $\frac{1}{4}$%?

20. A broker bought 84 shares of coal stock at $108\frac{1}{2}$, received a dividend of $5\frac{1}{2}$%, and then sold the stock for 106: how much did he gain?

21. A broker bought stock at 4% discount, and, selling the same at 5% premium, gained $450: how many shares did he purchase?

22. A man bought Michigan Central at 120, and sold at 124: what per cent of the investment did he gain?

23. A gas company declares a dividend of $16\frac{2}{8}$%: how much will a man who holds 36 shares receive?

24. A company with a capital of $125000 declares a dividend of 4%, with $3500 surplus: what were the net earnings of the company?

NOTE.—The surplus is a part of the net earnings set apart to meet future demands.

25. The capital of an insurance company is $500000, and it declares a dividend of $4\frac{2}{5}$%, with $2500 surplus:

how much money is distributed among the stockholders? What were the net earnings of the company?

26. The net earnings of a gas company are $22425, and the capital stock is $215000: what rate of dividend can be declared, no surplus being reserved? What will be the dividend on 45 shares?

FORMULAS AND RULES.

Art. 237. **Formulas:**

1. *Dividend or assessment* = *stock* × *rate %.*
2. *Rate %* = *divid. or assess.* ÷ *stock.*

---

3. *Prem. or dis.* = *par value* × *rate %.*
4. *Market val.* = *par val.* × (1 ± *rate %*).
5. *Par val.* = *market val.* ÷ (1 ± *rate %*).

Art. 238. 1. To find the premium or discount on a given amount of stock:

Rule.—*Multiply the amount of stock by the rate per cent of premium or discount.* (Formula 3.)

2. To find the cost or market value of a given amount of stock:

Rule.—*Multiply the amount of stock by 1 plus or minus the rate per cent, or by the quoted price expressed as hundredths.*

3. To find the amount of stock which can be bought for a given amount of money:

Rule.—*Divide the amount of money to be invested by 1 plus or minus the rate per cent, or by the quoted price expressed as hundredths.*

Note.—When brokerage is paid, the rate of brokerage must be added to the quoted price before dividing.

INSURANCE.

ART. 239. **Insurance** is an agreement by one party to indemnify another party for loss or damage.

The act of insuring is called *taking a risk*. The party that insures, or takes the risk, is called an *insurer* or *underwriter;* and the party to be indemnified in case of loss or damage, the *insured* or *policy-holder*.

ART. 240. The **Policy** is the written contract between the insurer and the insured.

ART. 241. The **Premium** is the sum of money paid by the insured for the insurance.

ART. 242. There are two kinds of insurance; viz, *Property Insurance* and *Personal Insurance*.

Property insurance includes indemnity for loss by fire, called *Fire Insurance*, and indemnity for loss of property while transported by water, called *Marine Insurance*. Insurance on the property transported is *Cargo Insurance;* that on the vessel, *Hull Insurance*.

Personal insurance includes *Life Insurance*, *Health Insurance*, and *Accident Insurance*.

NOTE.—The insurance business is chiefly carried on by corporations, called *Insurance Companies*. In *Joint Stock Companies* the profits and losses are shared by the stockholders, but in *Mutual Companies* they are divided among the policy-holders.

ORAL PROBLEMS.

1. A house was insured for $2500, at 1% : what was the premium?

2. A stock of goods was insured for $8000, at $\frac{3}{4}$% : what was the premium?

3. A hotel worth $6000 is insured for $\frac{2}{3}$ of its value, at $1\frac{1}{4}$% : what is the premium?

4. What will it cost to get a house insured for $4000, for 10 years, at ¼% a year?

5. The premium paid for insuring a library for $500, is $5: what is the rate of insurance?

6. An insurance company insures a dwelling-house for $1000, and charges $5 premium: what is the rate?

WRITTEN PROBLEMS.

7. A factory worth $75000 is insured for ⅔ of its value, at 1¼% : how much is the premium?

8. A merchant has his store insured for $7850, at ¾%, and his goods for $12400, at ½% : what premium does he pay?

9. A house worth $5400 was insured for ¾ of its value, at ⅞%, and the cost of the survey and policy was $1.50: what was the cost of the insurance?

NOTE.—When a new risk is taken, a small fee is usually charged for examining the property, called the *Survey*, and for issuing the policy.

10. What will it cost to insure a building valued at $12400 for ⅔ of its value, at ¾%, the cost of survey and policy being $2.25?

11. A block of buildings worth $135000 is insured for ⅘ of its value by three companies; the first taking ⅓ of the risk at ¾% ; the second taking ⅖ of it at ⅞% ; and the third taking the remainder at ⅔% : what was the total premium?

12. Suppose the above block should be damaged by fire to the amount of $60000, how much of the damage would each company be obliged to pay?

13. An insurance company insures a school-house for $10000, and charges $50 premium: what is the rate?

14. The owners of a vessel paid $561 for a hull insurance of $25500: what was the rate of insurance?

15. A merchant paid $100 for an insurance of $12500 on a stock of goods: what was the rate of insurance?

16. The premium for insuring a cargo of goods, at 2%, was $240: what was the amount of goods insured?

17. A school-house is insured at $\frac{2}{5}$%, and the premium was $93.60: for how much is the house insured?

18. A grain shipper paid $525 for the insurance of a cargo of wheat, at $1\frac{1}{2}$% : for how much was the wheat insured?

19. A grain dealer had a cargo of wheat, valued at $31360, insured at 2%, so as to cover both the value of the wheat and the cost of the premium: for how much was the wheat insured?

SUGGESTION.—Since the premium was 2% of the amount insured, the value of the wheat was 100% − 2%, or 98% of the amount insured. Hence, $31360 = .98 of the amount insured.

20. For how much must a cargo of lumber, worth $21825, be insured, at 3%, to cover both the value of the lumber and the cost of the premium?

21. For how much must property worth $11859.40 be insured, at $1\frac{1}{2}$%, to cover both property and premium?

22. For what must a cargo of goods valued at $11520 be insured, at 4%, to cover both goods and premium?

23. To cover both goods and premium, at 1%, a merchant had a cargo of goods insured for $35000: what was the value of the goods?

24. A man 30 years of age has his life insured for $6000, at $23.60 per $1000: what is his annual premium?

NOTE.—In Life Insurance, the premium is a specified sum for each $1000 insured, and hence its computation does not involve the principles of percentage.

25. A man 38 years of age has his life insured for $5000, on the ten-year plan, at $44.50 per $1000: what will be the sum of his premiums should they all be paid?

FORMULAS AND RULES.

ART. 243. **Formulas:**

1. *Premium = amount insured × rate%.*
2. *Rate% = prem. ÷ amount insured.*
3. *Amount insured = prem. ÷ rate%.*
4. *Property and premium = property ÷ (1 — rate%).*

ART. 244. 1. To find the premium:

Rule.—*Multiply the amount insured by the rate per cent.*

2. To find for what sum property must be insured to cover both property and premium:

Rule.—*Divide the value of the property insured by 1 less the rate per cent.*

TAXES.

ART. 245. A **Tax** is a sum of money assessed on the person, or property, or business of a citizen, for the support of the government or for other public purposes.

A tax on the person of a citizen is called a **Poll** or **Capitation Tax**; a tax on property, a **Property Tax**; and a tax on business, an **Excise Tax.**

ART. 246. A tax on property is assessed either at a given rate per cent of the valuation, or at the rate of a given number of mills on the dollar, or a given number of cents on each hundred dollars.

Property is classified as *Real Estate* and *Personal Property*. The taxable value of real estate is appraised by officers called *Appraisers* or *Assessors*, and the value of personal property is fixed by the owner, under oath, or by the assessor.

Excise taxes consist of fees for business licenses, revenue stamps for business papers, postage stamps, taxes on manufactured products, as distilled and malt liquors, tobacco, etc.

WRITTEN PROBLEMS.

1. The valuation of the taxable property of a village was $632000, and a tax of $9480 was assessed to build a school-house: what was the rate of tax?

PROCESS.

$9480 ÷ $632000 = .015
Rate = $1\frac{1}{2}\%$, or 15 mills.

Since the tax was .015 of the property, the rate was $1\frac{1}{2}\%$, or 15 mills on the dollar.

2. The tax levied in a certain city, for all purposes, was $259776, and the taxable property was listed at $21648000: what was the rate % of tax? The rate of tax in mills?

3. The amount of tax to be assessed in a certain township is $19340.20; the taxable property is $1425400; and the number of polls, assessed at $1.50 each, is 540: what amount of tax must be assessed on property? What rate per cent?

4. The cost of the public schools of a certain city for the next school year, is estimated at $36848: what amount of school tax must be assessed, the cost of collecting being 2%, and allowing 6% of the assessed tax to be uncollectible?

PROCESS.

.98)$36848

.94)$37600, *Tax collected.*

$40000, *Tax assessed.*

Since 2% of tax collected is paid for collection, $36848 is 98% or .98 of the tax to be collected. $36848 is .98 of $37600.

Since 6% of the tax assessed is not collectible, the collectible tax, or $37600, is .94 of the tax

to be assessed. $37600 is .94 of $40000, which is the amount to be assessed.

NOTE.—Since the amount of uncollectible tax can only be estimated, the amount to be assessed may be found, with sufficient accuracy for all practical purposes, by adding the percentages for collection and for uncollectible taxes to the amount of money to be raised for the given purpose. In several states, taxes are collected by officers who receive a salary.

5. The net proceeds of a certain tax assessment, after deducting $1\frac{1}{2}\%$ for collection, were $11703.84\frac{1}{2}$, and $7\frac{1}{2}\%$ of the tax was not collected: what was the amount of tax assessed?

6. The amount of tax assessed on the property of a certain city was $145850; the treasurer was allowed a fee of $\frac{3}{4}\%$ for collection, and 10% of the tax was uncollectible: what were the net proceeds of the assessment?

7. The taxable property of a certain city is valued at $87045060, and the rate of tax for school purposes is $5\frac{1}{2}$ mills on the dollar: what is the amount of school tax assessed?

SUGGESTION.—Since $5\frac{1}{2}$ mills $= .005\frac{1}{2}$ of a dollar, the tax assessed $= .005\frac{1}{2}$ of the property.

FORMULAS AND RULES.

ART. 247. **Formulas:**

1. $Tax = property \times rate\%$.
2. $Rate \% = tax \div property$.
3. $Tax\ collected = net\ proceeds \div (1 - rate\ \%\ for\ collection)$.

ART. 248. 1. To find the amount of tax:

Rule.—*Multiply the amount of taxable property by the rate of tax, expressed decimally.*

2. To find the rate of tax in mills:

Rule.—*Divide the amount of tax by the amount of property, and express the quotient as thousandths. The number of thousandths will be the number of mills.*

ART. 249. The labor of making out a tax list may be much lessened by using tables giving the tax on convenient amounts of property, at the given rate.

CUSTOMS OR DUTIES.

ART. 250. Customs, or **duties**, are taxes levied by the government on imported goods.

Ports of Entry for foreign goods are established by law, and at each port of entry there is a *Custom House*, where customs or duties are collected. The officer in charge of the custom house is called the *Collector of Customs*, and a list of the rates of duties to be collected is called a *Tariff*.

ART. 251. Duties are *specific* or *ad valorem*.

Specific Duties are customs assessed on the quantity of goods imported, without reference to their value.

In specific duties certain allowances were formerly made for waste, leakage, breakage, etc., but it is now the custom to count, measure, or weigh imported goods, and to assess the duty on the amounts thus found.

Ad Valorem Duties are customs assessed on the cost of goods in the country from which they are imported.

The cost of imported goods is shown by an *Invoice* or *Manifest*, and when the currency of the country from which goods are imported has a depreciated value, the amount of depreciation is stated in a consular certificate attached to the invoice. When the owner or consignee can not exhibit an invoice of goods at the custom house, their value is determined by appraisement.

The revenue for the support of the United States Government, called *United States Revenue*, is derived from Duties and Internal Revenue, the latter consisting chiefly of excise taxes (Art. 245) and the proceeds of the sales of public lands.

NOTE.—Taxes are classified as *direct* and *indirect*. Property and poll taxes are direct; excise taxes and duties are indirect, since they are paid *indirectly* by the consumer.

WRITTEN PROBLEMS.

1. What is the duty on 650 yards of broadcloth, invoiced at $1.80 per yard, at $33\frac{1}{3}\%$ ad valorem?

2. What is the duty on 1500 yards of lace, invoiced at 62½ cts. per yard, at 40% ad valorem?

3. What is the duty on 850 meters of French silk, invoiced at $1.15 per meter, at 50% ad valorem?

4. A merchant imported 4 cases of Irish linen, each case containing 560 yards: what was the duty, the invoice price being 42 cts. per yard and the duty 45%?

5. A manufacturer imported from Spain 40 bales of wool, 400 lb. each, invoiced at 45 cts. per pound, and 20 bales, 350 lb. each, invoiced at 40 cts.: what was the duty, at 20% ad valorem?

6. A merchant imported 1450 yards of broadcloth, invoiced at $2.15 a yard; 3240 yards of Brussels carpeting, invoiced at $1.60; and 480 yards of silk, invoiced at $2.85: how much was the duty at 35% for the woolen goods, and 50% for the silk?

7. The duty on 1250 yards of silk, at 40% ad valorem, was $1100: what was the invoice price a yard? For how much a yard must the importer sell the silk to clear 20%?

8. What is the duty on 240 tons of bar iron at $17.50 per ton, and 75 tons of steel at $22 per ton?

NOTE.—Since specific duties are levied at a given rate per pound, ton, gallon, yard, etc., their computation does not involve the principles of percentage.

9. A merchant imported from Havana 225 hogsheads of sugar, 475 lb. each, and 120 hogsheads of molasses, 126 gal. each: what was the duty at 3 cts. a pound for the sugar, and 8 cts. a gallon for the molasses?

ART. 252. **Formulas:**

1. *Ad val. duty = net inv. price × rate %.*
2. *Net inv. price = ad val. duty ÷ rate %.*

BANKRUPTCY.

ART. 253. A **Bankrupt** is a person who fails in business and has not property enough to pay all his debts. A bankrupt is also called an *Insolvent*.

ART. 254. An **Assignment** is the transfer of the property of a bankrupt to certain persons, called *Assignees*, whose duty it is to convert the property into money, and divide the net proceeds among the creditors.

ART. 255. The property of a bankrupt is called his **Assets,** and the amount of his indebtedness, his **Liabilities.** The assets less the expenses of settling are the **Net Proceeds.**

WRITTEN PROBLEMS.

1. A merchant failed in business, owing $15750, and his assets amount to $10515: what per cent of his liabilities can he pay, allowing $750 for expense of settling?

PROCESS.

$10515 — $750 = $9765, *net proceeds.*

$9765 ÷ $15750 = .62, or 62%

Since the net proceeds of his assets are but .62 of his liabilities, he can pay but 62%, or 62 cts. on a dollar.

2. In the above case of bankruptcy there are four creditors, whose claims are respectively $3580, $4635, $5300, and $2235: how much will each receive?

3. Smith, Jones & Co. have become insolvent, owing A $3500, B $1250, C $3750, D $1000, and E $2500; their assets amount to $7150, and the expense of settling will be $550: what per cent of their liabilities can they pay? What will each creditor receive?

4. A dry goods merchant has failed, with liabilities amounting to $25000; his assets in goods are $9500, in building and lot $5400, and in bills collectible $2100; and the expense of settling will be 5% of the assets: how many cents on the dollar can he pay?

FORMULAS AND RULE.

ART. 256. **Formulas:**

    1. *Rate % = net proceeds ÷ liabilities.*
    2. *Dividend = claim × rate %.*

ART. 257. To find what per cent of his liabilities a bankrupt can pay:

Rule.—*Divide the net proceeds of his assets by the amount of his liabilities, and the quotient expressed in hundredths will be the rate per cent.*

NOTE.—It is more common to find how many cents on the dollar the net proceeds will pay; the process is the same.

MISCELLANEOUS WRITTEN PROBLEMS.

1. A lawyer collected a bill at 25% commission, and remitted $7.50 as net proceeds: what was the amount collected? What was the lawyer's commission?

2. A book-seller sold a lot of books on commission at 20%, and remitted $160 as net proceeds: for how much were the books sold?

3. A merchant paid a broker $\frac{3}{8}$% for a draft of $1280 on New York: how much was the brokerage?

4. A broker bought $15600 worth of stocks at 80 cts., and charged $\frac{1}{4}$%: what was his fee?

5. Teas costing 70 cts. and 90 cts. are mixed in equal quantities, and sold at 95 cts.: what is the gain per cent?

6. If iron ore yields $65\frac{1}{2}$% of iron, how much ore will be required to yield 524 tons of iron?

7. A grain dealer bought 500 bushels of wheat at 80 cts., 700 bushels at 85 cts., and 800 bushels at 87½ cts.; and then sold the entire lot at 92 cts.: what did he gain per cent?

8. A merchant marked a lot of Brussels carpeting at $1.80 per yard, this being an advance of 25% on the cost: what per cent reduction can he make and still gain 20% on the cost?

9. A factory valued at $24000 was insured at ⅔ of its value at ¾%: what was the annual premium?

10. A company insured a block of buildings for $150000 at ¾%, but, the risk being too great, it re-insured $40000 in another company at ⅞%, and $35000 in another company at ⅘%: how much premium did it receive more than it paid?

11. What amount must be insured to cover property worth $2587, and premium at ½%?

12. A house which has been insured for $3500 for 10 years, at ⅖% a year, was destroyed by fire: how much did the money received from the company exceed the cost of premiums?

13. A steamer burned in 1869 had been insured by a single company 20 years, for $40000, at 2½% a year: what was the actual loss to the company, no allowance being made for interest?

14. A merchant shipped a cargo of flour from New York to Liverpool, and, to cover both the flour and the premium, he took out a policy for $50400, at 3½%: what was the value of the flour?

15. The valuation of taxable property in a certain county is $35460850, and the rate of tax levied is 25 mills: what will be the net proceeds of the tax, the cost of collection being 3%, and 8% of the tax being uncollectible?

16. A merchant imported 90 chests of tea, each containing 65 pounds, and 75 sacks of coffee, each containing 80 pounds, the tea being invoiced at $62\frac{1}{2}$ cts., and the coffee at $18\frac{3}{4}$ cts.; what was the duty, the rate on the tea being 40%, and on the coffee 25%?

17. The entire capital stock of the railroads in Ohio for 1882 was $610728103, and their net earnings for the year were $24414142: what was the average rate of dividend?

18. The capital of a mining company is $450000; the gross receipts are $70680; and the expenses are $40325: what rate of dividend can it declare, reserving a surplus of $6505?

19. A speculator bought 75 shares of Western Union Telegraph stock at $102\frac{1}{2}$, and sold them at $107\frac{1}{4}$: how much did he gain, brokerage paid for buying being $\frac{1}{4}$% and for selling $\frac{1}{8}$%?

20. An agent sold 45 sewing-machines at $75 apiece, and 9 at $125 apiece, and, deducting his commission, remitted $3375 to the manufacturer as proceeds: what was his rate of commission?

21. A factor sold $15000 worth of goods at 10% commission, and invested the proceeds in cotton, first deducting 5% commission for buying: how much money did he invest in cotton?

22. Smith & Jones sell for C. Bell & Co. 3040 pounds of butter at 22 cts. a pound, and 10560 pounds of cheese at 15 cts. a pound, and invest the proceeds in dry goods, first deducting their commission of 5% for selling and 3% for buying: how much did they invest in dry goods? What was their entire commission?

23. A commission merchant sold 1300 barrels of flour at $5.75 a barrel, receiving a commission of $3\frac{1}{2}$%, and invested the net proceeds in coffee at 28 cts. a pound, first deducting 2% commission: how many pounds of coffee did he purchase? What was his entire commission?

INTEREST.

ORAL PROBLEMS.

1. Mr. King borrowed $100 of a neighbor, and paid him $6 for the use of the money for one year: what per cent of the $100 did he pay for its use?

2. If Mr. King had paid $7 for the use of $100 for one year, what per cent of the $100 would he have paid?

3. If Mr. King had paid 8% of the $100 for the use of it one year, what decimal part of $100 would he have paid?

SOLUTION.—Since $8\% = .08$, he would have paid .08 of $100.

4. If Mr. King had paid $7\frac{1}{2}\%$, what decimal part of $100 would he have paid?

ART. 258. The money paid for the use of money is **interest,** and the money for the use of which interest is paid is the **principal.**

5. What is the interest of $100 for one year at 5%? At $4\frac{1}{2}\%$? At $5\frac{1}{2}\%$? At 9%? At 10%? At 15%?

6. What is the interest of $50 for one year at 6%? At 4%? At 5%? At 7%? At 9%? At 10%? .

7. What is the interest of $400 for one year at 5%? At 7%? At $4\frac{1}{2}\%$? At 6%? At 8% At 10%?

8. What is the interest of $120 for one year at 5%? At 6%? At 8%? At 7%? At 3%? At 10%?

9. What is the interest of $250 for 3 years at 6%?

SOLUTION.—The interest of $250 for 1 year, at 6%, is $15, and the interest for 3 years is 3 times $15, which is $45.

10. At 8%, what is the interest of $150 for 2 years? For $4\frac{1}{2}$ years? $5\frac{1}{3}$ years? 8 years? 5 years?

11. At $4\frac{1}{2}\%$, what is the interest of $200 for 3 years? 4 years? $6\frac{1}{2}$ years? $3\frac{1}{5}$ years? $5\frac{1}{2}$ years?

12. What is the interest of $70 for 2 yr. 4 mo. at 5%?

Suggestion.—4 months $= \frac{1}{3}$ of a year, and 2 yr. 4 mo. $= 2\frac{1}{3}$ yr.

13. At 4%, what is the interest of $150 for 3 years 3 months? For 5 yr. 6 mo.? For 2 yr. 4 mo.?

14. What is the interest of $60 for 5 years 6 months, at 4%? At 5%? At 6%? At 8%? At 10%?

WRITTEN PROBLEMS.

15. What is the interest of $145.60 for 5 yr. 10 mo., at 5%?

PROCESS.

$$\begin{array}{ll} \$145.60 & 5 \ yr. \ 10 \ mo. = 5\frac{5}{6} \ yr. \\ \quad .05 & \\ \hline \$7.2800 = Int. \ for \ 1 \ year. & \\ \quad 5\frac{5}{6} & \\ \hline \$42.47 = Int. \ for \ 5 \ yr. \ 10 \ mo. & \end{array}$$

16. What is the interest of $273.45 for 8 yr. 3 mo., at 10%? At 8%?

What is the interest of:

17. $65.30 for 1 yr. 3 mo., at 6%? At 8%?
18. $640.58 for 4 yr. 11 mo., at 5%? At 10%?
19. $1000 for 1 yr. 1 mo., at $3\frac{1}{2}\%$? At 7.3%?
20. $85 for 3 yr. 7 mo., at 7%? At $4\frac{1}{2}\%$?
21. $38.10 for 6 yr. 3 mo., at 6%? At 9%?
22. $84.75 for 2 yr. 5 mo. 21 da., at 8%?

PROCESS.

$$\begin{array}{rl} 21 \ da. = .7 \ mo. & \$84.75 \\ 5 \ mo. \ 21 \ da. = 5.7 \ mo. = .475 \ yr. & \quad .08 \\ 2 \ yr. \ 5 \ mo. \ 21 \ da. = 2.475 \ yr. & \overline{\$6.78 \ 00}, \ Int. \ for \ 1 \ yr. \\ & \quad 2.475 \\ & \overline{\$16.78 +}, \ Int. \ for \ 2 \ yr. \ 5 \ mo. \ 21 \ da. \end{array}$$

23. $208.44 for 7 yr. 8 mo. 15 da., at 6% ? At 5% ?
24. $356.75 for 5 yr. 10 mo. 24 da., at 4% ? At 6% ?
25. $184.80 for 1 yr. 1 mo. 10 da. (1⅒ yr.), at 9% ?
26. $321.70 for 4 yr. 3 mo. 27 da., at 6% ? At 4% ?
27. $356.50 for 3 yr. 9 mo. 25 da., at 8% ?

PROCESS BY ALIQUOT PARTS FOR DAYS.

$$\$356.50$$
$$.08$$

12)$28.5200 × 3 = $85.560, *Int. for 3 yrs.*

(*Int. for 1 mo.*) $2.3766 × 9 = 21.389, *Int. for 9 mo.*
15 da. = ½ mo.   1.188, *Int. for 15 da.*
10 da. = ⅓ mo.   .792, *Int. for 10 da.*

$108.929, *Int. for 3 yr. 9 mo. 25 da.*

What is the interest of:

28. $84.66 for 5 yr. 7 mo. 20 da., at 10% ? At 5% ?
29. $4000 for 10 yr. 10 mo. 10 da., at 7½% ? At 4½% ?
30. $1262.70 for 11 mo. 27 da. at 6% ? At 7¼% ?
31. $504.08 for 3 yr. 1 mo. 1 da. at 4% ? At 10% ?
32. $3084.90 for 7 mo. 22 da., at 5½% ? At 12% ?
33. $2016.05 for 1 yr. 1 mo. 29 da., at 4% ? At 8% ?
34. What is the amount of $80 for 2 yr. 15 da., at 5% ?

NOTE.—The amount is the sum of principal and interest.

What is the amount of:

35. $60.85 for 10 yr. 10 mo. 10 da., at 6% ? At 4% ?
36. $740.10 for 1 yr. 1 mo. 18 da., at 5% ? At 8% ?
37. $1.40 for 7 yr. 11 mo. 21 da., at 8% ? At 7½% ?
38. $121.75 for 3 yr. 18 da., at 10% ? At 12% ?
39. $80.65 for 1 yr. 6 mo. 12 da., at 7% ? At 10½% ?
40. $356.50 for 3 yr. 9 mo. 25 da., at 8% ? At 5% ?
41. $262.75 for 1 yr. 5 mo. 19 da., at 6% ? At 9% ?
42. $192.60 for 2 yr. 2 mo. 2 da., at 5% ? At 12% ?
43. $240 from Feb. 15, 1878, to Apr. 27, 1879, at 8% ?
44. $180 from May 14, 1873, to Aug. 28, 1875, at 7% ?
45. $137.50 from July 3, 1882, to Feb. 3, 1883, at 9% ?

5. What decimal part of the principal is the interest at 6% for 6 days? For 12 da.? 8 da.? 15 da.?

Note.—The interest at 6% for 1 yr. = .06 of the principal.
    "   "   " " " 2 mo.= .01 "   "   "
    "   "   " " " 1 mo. = .005 "   "   "
    "   "   " " " 6 da. = .001 "   "   "
    "   "   " " " 1 da. = .000⅙" "   "

What decimal part of the principal is the interest at 6% for:

6. 1 year 2 months? 2 yr. 4 mo.? 3 yr. 6 mo.?

7. 4 years 5 months? 6 yr. 7 mo.? 5 yr. 9 mo.?

8. 2 years 11 months? 3 yr. 9 mo.? 10 yr. 10 mo.?

9. 2 months 12 days? 4 mo. 18 da.? 5 mo. 6 da.?

10. 6 months 9 days? 8 mo. 15 da.? 10 mo. 21 da.?

11. 5 months 13 days? 3 mo. 22 da.? 7 mo. 25 da.?

12. 4 months 16 days? 6 mo. 29 da.? 10 mo. 10 da.?

13. 6 months 18 days? 9 mo. 28 da.? 11 mo. 11 da.?

14. 1 yr. 2 mo. 12 da.? 2 yr. 8 mo. 9 da.?

15. 3 yr. 3 mo. 3 da.? 1 yr. 1 mo. 1 da.?

WRITTEN PROBLEMS.

16. What is the interest of $245.60 for 2 yr. 7 mo. 18 da., at 6%?

PROCESS.

$245.60
   .158
─────
1964.80
12280 0
24560
─────
$38.80480, *Int.*

Int. for 2 *yr.* = .12 *of prin.*
Int. for 7 *mo.* = .035 *of prin.*
Int. for 18 *da.* = .003 *of prin.*
─────────────────────
Int. 2 *yr.* 7 *mo.* 18 *da.* = .158 *of prin.*

17. What is the interest of $160.80, at 6%, for 1 yr. 7 mo. 12 da.? For 2 yr. 2 mo. 21 da.?

18. What is the interest of $508.09, at 6%, for 3 yr. 3 mo. 15 da.? For 1 yr. 7 mo. 12 da.?

19. What is the interest of $245.60 for 2 yr. 7 mo. 21 da., at 9%? At 11%?

PROCESS (1).

$245.60
.1585

$38.928, *Int. at* 6%.
19.464, *Int. at* 3%.

$58.392, *Int. at* 9%.

PROCESS (2).

$38.928, *Int. at* 6%.
19.464, *Int. at* 3%.
12.976, *Int. at* 2%.

$71.368, *Int. at* 11%.

What is the interest of:

20. $540 for 10 mo. 24 da., at 6%? At 8%?
21. $327.50 for 1 yr. 3 mo. 6 da., at 7%? At 10%?
22. $142.64 for 2 yr. 15 da., at 4%? At $4\frac{1}{2}$%?
23. $3008.75 for 4 yr. 1 mo. 20 da., at 5%? At 9%?
24. $622.40 for 9 mo. 29 da., at 12%? At 5%?

What is the amount of:

25. $804.25 for 1 yr. 5 mo. 10 da., at 8%? At $7\frac{1}{2}$%?
26. $112.40 for 11 mo. 21 da., at $5\frac{1}{2}$%? At $6\frac{1}{2}$%?
27. $2000 for 1 yr. 1 mo. 1 da., at 8%? At 11%?
28. $5.90 for 3 yr. 3 mo. 3 da., at 3%? At 12%?
29. $16.50 for 2 yr. 2 mo. 2 da., at 6%? At $7\frac{1}{2}$%?
30. $50.30 for 3 yr. 3 mo. 3 da., at 8%? At 5%?
31. $200 for 4 yr. 4 mo. 4 da., at 4%? At 10%?
32. What is the interest of $108.60, from Sept. 12, 1876, to May 6, 1880, at 6%? At 8%?
33. What is the interest of $15.80, from Oct. 23, 1875, to Apr. 12, 1879, at 8%? At 9%?
34. A note of $565.80, dated June 3, 1874, was paid Nov. 28, 1879, with interest at 7%: what was the amount paid?
35. A man borrowed $60 May 10, 1874, and paid it March 4, 1876, with interest at 6%: what amount did he pay?
36. A debt of $40.50 was paid May 21, 1880, with interest at 6% from Nov. 9, 1874: what was the amount paid?

37. A note of $350, dated Oct. 17, 1875, was paid Apr. 11, 1878, with interest at 7%: what was the amount paid?

38. A note of $150.75, dated June 15, 1877, was paid Jan. 1, 1880, with interest at 5%: what was the amount paid?

39. A note of $1250, dated July 5, 1878, was paid June 1, 1880, with interest at 8%: what was the amount paid?

40. A note of $87.50, dated Aug. 8, 1877, and bearing interest at 10%, was paid March 25, 1879: what was the amount paid?

41. A note of $65.80, dated Feb. 20, 1878, and bearing interest at 7%, was paid June 25, 1880: what was the amount paid?

ART. 266. To compute interest at 6%:

Rule.—*Take as many times 6 hundredths as there are years, as many times 5 thousandths as there are months, and as many times $\frac{1}{6}$ of a thousandth as there are days, and multiply the principal by the resulting decimal.*

2. To compute interest at any other rate than 6%:

Rule.—*Find the interest at 6%, and then increase or diminish this interest by such a part of itself as will give the interest at the given rate.*

NOTES.—1. Instead of finding the decimal part of the principal as above, interest at 6% may be computed *by taking 6 times as many cents as there are years, $\frac{1}{2}$ as many cents as there are months, and $\frac{1}{6}$ as many mills as there are days; and then multiplying the principal by the abstract decimal which corresponds to the interest of $1 thus found.*

2. The following table denotes the part of the interest to be added or subtracted to give the interest at the given per cent:

7 % = 6% + $\frac{1}{6}$ of 6%	10% = $\frac{1}{6}$ of 6% × 10
7$\frac{1}{2}$% = 6% + $\frac{1}{4}$ of 6%	5 % = 6% − $\frac{1}{6}$ of 6%
8 % = 6% + $\frac{1}{3}$ of 6%	4 % = 6% − $\frac{1}{3}$ of 6%
9 % = 6% + $\frac{1}{2}$ of 6%	4$\frac{1}{2}$% = 6% − $\frac{1}{4}$ of 6%

METHOD BY DAYS.

ART. 267. When the time is short, it is the custom of bankers and other business men to compute interest for the actual number of days included in the time, each day being considered as $\frac{1}{360}$ of a year.

WRITTEN PROBLEMS.

1. What is the interest of $80.60 from March 15th to June 10th, at 6% ?

PROCESS.

In March 16 days. $80.60
In Apr.   30 days.   .014$\frac{1}{2}$
In May   31 days.   32240
In June   10 days.   8060
     6)87 days.   4030
       14$\frac{1}{2}$ $1.16870 *Int.*

Since interest at 6% is $\frac{1}{6}$ as many thousandths of the principal as there are days in the time, the interest of $80.60, for 87 days, is $\frac{1}{6}$ of .087 times $88.60. $\frac{1}{6}$ of .087 = .014$\frac{1}{2}$, and $80.60 × .014$\frac{1}{2}$ = $1.1687, interest.

ANOTHER PROCESS.

$80.60,   *Principal.*
 .806,   *Int. for* 60 *da.*
 .2686$\frac{2}{3}$, *Int. for* 20 *da.* = $\frac{1}{3}$ *of* 60 *da.*
 .0806,   *Int. for* 6 *da.* = $\frac{1}{10}$ *of* 60 *da.*
 .0134$\frac{1}{3}$, *Int. for* 1 *da.* = $\frac{1}{6}$ *of* 6 *da.*
$1.1687 , *Int. for* 87 *da.*

Since 60 days equal 2 months, or $\frac{1}{6}$ of a year, the interest for 60 days is $\frac{1}{6}$ of .06 of the principal, which is .01 of the principal. Hence, the interest for 60 days, at 6%, is

found *by removing the decimal point in the principal two places to the left*, and the interest for 27 days (87 days—60 days) is found by taking convenient parts of the interest for 60 days.

2. What is the interest of $125.80 from July 5th to Oct. 23d, at 6% ?   At 8% ?

3. What is the amount of $25.25 from Oct. 30, 1882, to Feb. 1, 1883, at 6% ?   At 7$\frac{1}{2}$% ?

4. What is the amount of $65.80 from Dec. 28, 1882, to Mch. 15, 1883, at 5% ?   At 10% ?

5. What is the amount of $75.40 from Jan. 13, 1883, to June 15, 1883, at 8%? At 7%?

6. What is the amount of $120 from Mch. 15, 1883, to July 4, 1883, at 7%? At 9%?

7. A note of $420, dated Jan. 25, 1883, was paid Apr 16, 1883, with interest at 8%: what was the amount?

8. A man borrowed $150, June 6th, and paid it, with interest at 7%, Sept. 24th: how much did he pay?

9. A note of $80, dated Jan. 15, 1878, was paid June 21, 1878, with interest at 8%: what was the amount?

10. A note of $150, dated Mch. 30, 1883, was paid July 4, 1883, with interest at 6%: what was the amount? What would have been the amount at $7\frac{1}{2}$%?

Art. 268. **1.** To compute interest for days at 6%:

Rules.—*1. Multiply the principal by one sixth of as many thousandths as there are days in the time.* Or:

2. Find the interest for 60 days by taking .01 of the principal; and then take such multiples or parts of this interest as the given time may require.

Note.—The interest for 60 days is found by removing the decimal point in the principal *two* places to the left, and for 6 days by removing the decimal point *three* places to the left.

2. To compute interest for days at any rate:

Rule.—*Find the interest at 6%, and then increase or diminish this interest by such a part of itself as the given rate is greater or less than 6.*

Notes.—1. Since the common year consists of 365 days, instead of 360, the true interest for 360 days is $\frac{360}{365}$ or $\frac{72}{73}$ of the interest for a year; whereas, by the above method, the interest for 360 days equals the interest for a year. Hence, the true interest for any number of days in a common year is $\frac{1}{73}$ less than the interest found by the above rule; in leap year the true interest is $\frac{1}{61}$ less than the interest thus found. But the convenience of the method which allows 360 days to the year, has secured its very general adoption by the business men of the country, and in several states it is sanctioned by law.

2. An *accurate* rule for computing interest for days is, *to take as many 365ths, and in leap year as many 366ths, of the interest for one year as there are days in the time.* In Great Britain, a day's interest is made $\frac{1}{365}$ of a year's interest, and the same rule is adopted by the United States Government in computing interest upon bonds, etc.

3. There are four methods of finding the time between two dates:

(1) *By compound subtraction*, allowing 30 days to the month.

(2) *By finding the number of calendar months from the first date to the corresponding day of the month of the second date, and then counting the actual number of days left.* This method has been legalized by a number of States.

(3) *By taking the number of whole years and finding the number of days in the part of the year, each day being reckoned as $\frac{1}{365}$ part of a year.* The month unit is thus excluded. This is the method adopted by the United States Government.

(4) *By counting the actual number of days between the two dates, and reckoning each day as $\frac{1}{360}$ part of a year.* This method gives the exact time, and is generally used in finding the time of "short paper."

4. Bankers and other accountants generally use "Time Tables," which give the exact number of days between any two dates less than a year apart, and "Interest Tables" which give the interest of $1 at different rates for years, months, and days. These tables are designed for use in business, and not for pupils in the schools.

BANK DISCOUNT.

ART. 269. When a bank loans money, the borrower gives his note payable at a specified time, *without interest*. This note is then discounted by taking from its face the interest for the actual number of days plus three days, called *days of grace;* and the difference, called the *proceeds*, is paid to the borrower. The interest thus deducted is called *bank discount*.

A note is *payable* at the time mentioned in it, but is *due* on the third day following. The date on which a note is due, or matures, is called the date of *maturity*. The date when payable and the date of maturity are usually written with a line between them, thus: Jan. $\frac{9}{12}$.

When a note *drawing interest* is discounted by a bank, the discount is computed on the *amount* of the note at the time of its maturity.

WRITTEN PROBLEMS.

1. What is the bank discount of a note of $350, payable in 60 days, discounted at 10%? What are the proceeds?

PROCESS (1).   PROCESS (2).

$350.
.0105
―――――
1750   *60 da. + 3 da. = 63 da.* $350
3 50   3.50
―――――   .175
6)$3.6750   6)$3.675

$.6125 × 10 = $6.125, *Bank discount.*   .6125

$350 — $6.125 = $343.875, *Proceeds.* $6.125, *Dis.*

Find the bank discount and proceeds of a note of:

2. $250, payable in 90 days, discounted at 9%.

3. $145, payable in 60 days, discounted at 7%.

4. $80.50, payable in 30 days, discounted at 8%.

5. $1000, payable in 90 days, discounted at 7½%.

6. $750, payable in 45 days, discounted at 9%.

7. $1250, payable in 100 days, discounted at 6%.

8. $56, dated Jan. 1, 1882, payable May 1, 1882, discounted at 6%. At 8%.

9. $120, dated April 3, 1881, payable June 15, 1881, discounted at 8%. At 10%.

10. $500, dated Dec. 15, 1880, payable Feb. 18, 1881, discounted at 8%. At 7%.

11. $8.75, dated Nov. 21, 1880, payable March 12, 1881, discounted at 9%. At 8%.

12. $400, dated March 4, payable July 24, discounted at 5%. At 8%.

13. A note, dated April 10, 1881, is payable in 90 days: what is the time of its maturity?

NOTE.—The date of maturity is found by counting forward the number of days plus three days, when the time is expressed in days; and the number of calendar months plus three days, when the time is expressed in months.

14. A note, dated Feb. 6, 1868, was payable in 60 days: what was the date of its maturity?

15. A note, dated Aug. 9, 1880, is payable 4 months from date: what is the date of its maturity?

16. A note of $460, dated April 3, 1870, and payable in 90 days, with interest at 6%, was discounted May 10, 1870, at 8%: what were the proceeds?

SUGGESTION.—Find the amount of $460 for 93 days, at 6%, and then discount this amount for 56 days, at 8%.

17. A note of $125, dated May 21, 1880, and payable in 60 days, with interest at 6%, was discounted May 25, 1880, at 10%: what were the proceeds?

18. A note of $1000, dated Aug. 15, 1879, and payable in 6 months, with interest at 7%, was discounted Nov. 27, 1879, at 9%: what was the bank discount?

SUGGESTION.—Compute the interest for 6 mo. 3 da., and the discount for 83 days.

19. A note of $90, dated April 12, 1870, and payable in 4 months, with interest at 5%, was discounted June 1, 1870, at 7%: what were the proceeds?

20. A note of $650, dated March 2, 1869, payable Apr. 1, 1870, and indorsed $300 Oct. 1, 1869, was discounted Feb. 3, 1870: what were the proceeds at 6%?

21. For what sum must a note, payable in 60 days, be drawn to produce $493, when discounted at 8%?

PROCESS.

$1 — $.014 = $.986, *Pro. of $1.*
$493 ÷ $.986 = 500
$1 × 500 = $500, *Face of note.*

Since the proceeds of $1 are $.986, it will require as many times $1 to produce $493 as $.986 is contained times in $493, which is 500; 500 times $1 = $500.

22. For what sum must a note, payable in 90 days, be drawn to produce $1969, when discounted at 6%?

23. What must be the face of a note, dated July 5, 1881, and payable in 4 months, to produce $811, when discounted at 9% ?

24. What must be the face of a note, dated Jan. 10, 1870, and payable in 3 months, to produce $1938, when discounted at 12% ?

25. A merchant discounted a bill of $750, payable in 4 months, by deducting the interest for the time without grace, at 10% : what were the cash proceeds of the bill?

NOTE.—Business men often discount notes and bills, not drawing interest, by deducting the interest for the time by months or days, as the time is expressed in the paper discounted, and with or without grace, as per agreement. This is sometimes called *Business Discount.* The rate of interest allowed is usually greater than the current rate.

26. A note of $340, due in 9 months, without interest, was discounted by deducting the interest for the time, at 8% : what was the cash value of the note?

27. A merchant, having sold a bill of goods amounting to $1030, on three months' time, allowed 5% off for cash : what were the cash proceeds of the sale?

NOTE.—Bills due in three, four, or six months are often discounted by deducting 5% or more of their face, without regard to time. This is called *Trade Discount.*

28. A retail dealer, having bought $950 worth of goods, on 6 months' time, cashed the bill for $7\frac{1}{2}$% off: what were the cash proceeds?

29. A merchant bought a bill of goods amounting to $675 on 60 days' credit, but, having obtained the money, cashed the bill at 5% off: what was the cost of the goods?

30. A grocer bought sugars amounting to $725 on 90 days' time, but, being offered 4% off for cash, borrowed the money at a bank for the time (less grace) at 9%, and cashed the bill: what was the face of the note? How much did he gain by the transaction?

31. A merchant bought, March 20, 1870, a bill of goods amounting to $3540, on three months' time, but, being offered 5% off for cash, he borrowed the money at a bank for the time, at 10%, and cashed the bill. How much did he gain by the transaction?

DEFINITIONS AND RULES.

ART. 270. **Bank Discount** is the interest on a note paid in advance. It is also called *Bank Interest.*

ART. 271. The **Proceeds** of a note is the sum discounted, less the discount. The proceeds are also called *Avails* and *Cash Value.*

ART. 272. **Days of Grace** are the three days allowed for the payment of a note after the specified time.

When the third day of grace falls on Sunday, or a legal holiday, a note is due the day before or the day after, according to the special statute of the State in which the note is drawn.

ART. 273. 1. To compute bank discount:

Rule.—*Find the interest on the sum discounted at the given rate per cent and for the actual number of days in the time plus three days. The difference between the sum discounted and the interest thus found will be the proceeds.*

NOTE.—In discounting a note, *bearing interest,* the interest is computed by months or by days, according as the time is expressed in the note, but the discount on the amount of the note is usually computed by days.

2. To find the face of a note that will yield given proceeds:

Rule.—*Divide the given proceeds by the proceeds of $1 for the given time with grace, and multiply $1 by the quotient.*

NOTE.—Bank discount is not only interest paid *in advance,* but the interest is computed on both the proceeds *and the discount.* The borrower pays interest on more money than he receives.

PROMISSORY NOTES.

ART. 274. A **Promissory Note** is a written agreement by one party to pay another a specified sum of money at a specified time.

The sum of money specified is called the *Face* of the note. The person who signs a note is its *Maker;* the person to whom it is payable is the *Payee;* and the owner is the *Holder.* The person who writes his name on the back of a note as security for its payment, is an *Indorser.*

A note signed by two or more persons who are jointly liable for its payment, is a *Joint Note.* A note signed by two or more persons who are jointly and singly liable for its payment, is a *Joint and Several Note.*

A note payable on demand is a *Demand Note;* a note payable at a future specified time is a *Time Note.*

ART. 275. The following are the more common forms of promissory notes :

FORM I.—DEMAND NOTE.

$95 $\frac{50}{100}$.   NASHVILLE, TENN., May 1, 1883.

For value received, I promise to pay to John Purdue, on demand, Ninety-five $\frac{50}{100}$ *Dollars.*

HENRY SMITH.

NOTE.—A demand note may also be drawn payable to "bearer" or "order."

FORM II.—TIME NOTE.

$95 $\frac{50}{100}$ ST. LOUIS, MO., May 1, 1883.

Ninety days after date, I promise to pay to Martin L. Peirce, or bearer, Ninety-five $\frac{50}{100}$ *Dollars, with interest, for value received.*

R. W. STEVENS.

FORM III.—JOINT AND SEVERAL NOTE.

95\frac{50}{100}$.   LOUISVILLE, KY., March 12, 1883.

 *Four months after date, we jointly and severally prom-
ise to pay Henry H. Jones, or order, Ninety-five* $\frac{50}{100}$ *Dollars,
with interest at 8%, for value received.*

        THOMAS HUGHES,
        CHARLES KING.

FORM IV.—NOTE PAYABLE AT A BANK.

$500.   NEW YORK CITY, April 10, 1883.

 *Sixty days after date, we promise to pay to Van Antwerp,
Bragg & Co., or order, at the First National Bank, Five
Hundred Dollars, for value received.*

        CHARLES GREEN & CO.

REMARKS.—1. A note should contain the words "value received," otherwise the holder may be required to prove that the
maker received its value. The sum of money to be paid should
be written in words.

2. When the time for the payment of a note is not specified,
it is due on demand. If the place of payment is not given, it is
payable at the maker's residence or place of business.

3. When a note contains the words "with interest," and no
rate is specified (Form II), interest accrues at the legal rate. If
the words "with interest" are omitted (Form IV), no interest accrues until maturity, when the note draws interest, at the legal
rate, until paid.

ART. 276. A **Negotiable Note** is one which may be
bought and sold.

A note is negotiable when it is made payable "to the bearer"
or to the payee "or bearer," or to the payee "or order." A
note drawn as in Form I. is not negotiable.

A note made payable to the *bearer* is negotiable without indorsement. United States treasury notes and bank notes, used as
money, are payable to the bearer, and are transferred by delivery.

A note payable to *order* must be *indorsed* by the payee before it is negotiable; and each holder in his turn must indorse the note, thus becoming liable for its payment, in case the maker fails to pay it when due. An indorser may free himself from responsibility for payment by accompanying his signature with the words "without recourse."

When the payee indorses a note by simply writing his name on the back, it is called an *indorsement in blank*, and the note is payable to the holder. When the indorser orders the payment to be made to a particular person, as, "Pay to Charles Williams," it is called a *special indorsement.*

ART. 277. When a note in bank is not paid at maturity, a written notice of the fact, made by a notary public, is served on the indorsers, who are responsible for the payment of the note. Such a notice is a *Protest.*

A protest should be made out on the day the note *matures*, and it must be sent on that day or the next, otherwise the indorsers are not responsible.

ART. 278. A **Check** is a written order on a bank by a depositor for money.

The following is the common form of a check:

Lafayette, Ind., *March 3,* 1883.

FIRST NATIONAL BANK,

Pay to   *William M. Bloss,*   or order,

Six hundred   65 Dollars.
                                                    100

$600 65/100.   *Thomas W. Smith.*

NOTE.—Before this check is paid, it must be indorsed by William M. Bloss. He may draw the money from the bank, or he may transfer the check to another party, who must also indorse it, as in the case of the transfer of a promissory note. If the words *or bearer* are used in place of *or order*, no indorsement is necessary, and any one holding the check may draw the money.

PARTIAL PAYMENTS.

ART. 279. When partial payments have been made on notes or other obligations, the interest is computed by the following rule, which, having been adopted by the Supreme Court of the United States, is called the

UNITED STATES RULE.

When partial payments have been made, apply the payment, in the first place, to the discharge of the interest then due. If the payment EXCEEDS *the interest, the surplus goes toward discharging the principal, and the subsequent interest is to be computed on the balance of principal remaining due.*

If the payment be LESS *than the interest, the surplus of interest must not be taken to augment the principal, but interest continues on the former principal until the period when the payments, taken together, exceed the interest due, and then the surplus is to be applied toward discharging the principal, and the interest is to be computed on the balance, as aforesaid.*

ART. 280. This rule is based on the following principles:

1. Payments must first be applied to the discharge of interest then due, and the balance, if any, to the payment of the principal.

2. Unpaid interest must not be added to the principal, and thus draw interest.

3. Interest must accrue only on the principal.

NOTE.—The United States Rule has been adopted by all the states, with few exceptions (including Vermont and Connecticut); and is generally used when the time between the date of a note and its payment exceeds one year.

1. A note of $650, dated May 20, 1866, and drawing interest at 6%, had payments indorsed upon it as follows:

Sept. 2, 1866, $25.   March 2, 1867, $150.

Dec. 20, 1866, $10.   July 8, 1867, $200

What was the amount due Nov. 11, 1867?

PROCESS.

```
                                       $650
                                        .017
                                       ————
                                       4550
     1866    9    2                     650
     1866    5   20                    ——————
                                     $11.050,   1st interest.
          3 mo. 12 da.   .017          650.
                                     ————————
                                     $661.05
               $25.                    25.00,   1st payment.
                                     ————————
                                     $636.05,   2d principal.
                                        .018
     1866   12   20                   508840
     1866    9    2                    63605
                                     ————————
          3 mo. 18 da.   .018   $10  $11.44890,   2d interest.
                                     ————————
               $10                   $636.05,   3d principal.
                                        .012
                                     ————————
                                $150  $7.63260,   3d interest.
     1867    3    2                  11.4489,   2d interest.
     1866   12   20                 636.05
                                    —————————
          2 mo. 12 da.   .012       $655.1315
                                    160.00    2d+3d payment.
               $150.                —————————
                                    $495.1315,   4th principal.
                                        .021
                                    —————————
     1867    7    8                 4951315
     1867    3    2                 9902630
                                    —————————
          4 mo. 6 da.   .021       $10.3977615,   4th interest.
                                    495.1315
               $200.               —————————
                                   $505.5293
                                   200.00    4th payment.
                                   —————————
     1867   11   11                $305.5293,   5th principal.
     1867    7    8                    .0205
                                   —————————
          4 mo. 3 da.   .0205      15276465
                                   6110586
                                   —————————
                                   $6.26335065,   5th interest.
                                   305.5293
                                   —————————
                                   $311.7926,  Am't due Nov. 11, 1867.
```

The first step is to find the difference of time between each two consecutive dates, and form the corresponding decimal multipliers by the six per cent method. The payments may be written below. This preparation will lessen the liability of error in the calculation.

Since the 1st payment is greater than the 1st interest, form the amount and subtract therefrom the payment; the difference is the second principal. Find the 2d interest.

Since the 2d payment is less than the 2d interest, let the interest stand, drawing a double line beneath it, and bringing down the second principal for a 3d principal. Find the 3d interest.

Since the sum of the 2d and 3d payments is greater than the sum of the 2d and 3d interests, form the amount and subtract therefrom the sum of the 2d and 3d payments; the difference is the 4th principal. Find the 4th interest.

Since the 4th payment is greater than the 4th interest, form the amount and subtract therefrom the 4th payment. Compute the interest on the difference, the 5th principal, to the last date, and form the amount, which is the sum then due.

NOTES.—1. Sometimes an estimate of the interest may be made *mentally* with sufficient accuracy to determine whether it is greater or less than the payment. If greater, the *sum* of the two or more decimal multipliers can be used for a multiplier. Instead of multiplying by .018 and .012 above, .03, their sum, might have been used.

2. When the rate is other than 6%, the several interests should be increased or diminished, as the rate may require, before forming the amounts.

2. A note of $600, dated June 10, 1877, had indorsements as follows: Dec. 4, 1877, $50; March 25, 1878, $12; July 9, 1878, $75. How much was due Oct. 15, 1878, at 6% interest?

3. A note of $1000, dated Apr. 10, 1874, was indorsed as follows: Nov. 10, 1875, $80.50; July 5, 1876, $100; Jan. 10, 1877, $450.80; Oct. 1, 1879, $500. What was due Jan. 1, 1880, at 7% interest?

4. A note of $450, dated July 4, 1878, was indorsed as follows: Jan. 20, 1879, $15; June 9, 1879, $200; Oct. 20, 1879, $10. What was due Jan. 10, 1880, at 10% interest?

5. A note of $850, dated March 4, 1875, had indorsements as follows: Sept. 1, 1875, $12; May 4, 1876, $10; Sept. 15, 1876, $250; Jan. 20, 1877, $400. What was due July 1, 1878, at 6% interest?

6. $1250. CINCINNATI, JULY 1, 1878.

On demand, I promise to pay Peter Smith, or order, twelve hundred and fifty dollars, with interest at $7\frac{1}{2}$%, for value received. JOHN COONS.

Indorsements: Sept. 14, 1878, $300; Jan. 20, 1879, $12; Oct. 20, 1879, $20; Nov. 8, 1879, $500.

What was due on the above note Jan. 1, 1880?

7. $1000. SAN FRANCISCO, APR. 10, 1881.

For value received, I promise to pay to Wm. Penn, Jr., or order, thirty days after date, one thousand dollars, with interest at 10%. GOULD DIVES.

Indorsements: July 28, 1881, $500; Dec. 13, 1881, $8: Feb. 25, 1882, $12; July 7, 1882, $125; Oct. 3, 1882, $200; March 15, 1883, $50.

What was due on the above note June 3, 1883?

ART. 281. When partial payments are made on mercantile accounts, past due, and on notes running a *year or less*, the interest is often computed by

THE MERCHANTS' RULE.

Compute the interest on the principal from the time it begins to draw interest to the time of settlement, and also on each payment from the time it was made to the time of settlement.

From the sum of the principal and its interest, subtract the sum of the payments and their interests, and the difference will be the balance due.

N. C. A.—20.

8. A note of $520, dated April 12, 1883, had three indorsements, as follows: May 20, 1883, $120; June 9, 1883, $12; July 21, 1883, $85. What was due Oct. 18, 1883, at 8% interest?

9. A note of $800, dated March 12, 1882, and drawing interest at 8%, was indorsed as follows: May 15, 1882, $200; Aug. 10, 1882, $75; Oct. 20, 1882, $125. What was due Dec. 30, 1882?

10. Payments were made on a debt of $350, due Feb. 1, 1882, as follows: March 20, 1882, $45; May 1, 1882, $60; July 5, 1882, $80; Oct. 1, 1882, $50. What was due Nov. 1, 1882, at 6% interest?

NOTE.—The chief aim of legislative enactments on this subject has been to protect the debtor from paying *interest on interest,* but there is no essential difference between applying payments to the discharge of interest instead of principal, and paying interest on such accrued interest. The debtor loses the use of so much of every payment as is applied to interest, and the creditor gains the use of it. The " Merchants' Rule" is the only one that does not practically allow interest on interest.

ANNUAL INTEREST.

ART. 282. When a note reads "with interest payable annually," or "with interest annually," the interest on the face of the note, due at the close of each year, is called **Annual Interest.**

ART. 283. When annual interest is not paid at the close of the year, when due, it draws *simple interest* until paid.

In several of the states it is not legal to collect interest on unpaid annual interest; and in a few other states unpaid annual interest is added to the principal, and draws annual interest, thus compounding the interest. (Art. 285.)

In Ohio and several other states, the annual interest, if not paid when due, draws simple interest *at the legal rate,* whatever may be the rate of interest prescribed for the principal.

WRITTEN PROBLEMS.

1. A note of $500, dated May 10, 1883, is due in 4 years, with interest at 6%, payable annually: if both interest and principal remain unpaid, what will be the amount due on the note at maturity?

PROCESS.

$500 × .06 = $30, *Interest on principal due annually.*
 $30 × 4 = $120, *Total annual interest.*

$30 × .06 × 3 =   5.40, *Simple interest on 1st annual interest for 3 yr.*
$30 × .06 × 2 =   3.60, *Simple interest on 2d annual interest for 2 yr.*
$30 × .06 × 1 =   1.80, *Simple interest on 3d annual interest for 1 yr.*
      $130.80, *Total interest due at maturity of note.*   6 yr.
      500.00
      $630.80, *Amount due at maturity.*

OR :

3 yr. $500 × .06   = $30,   *Annual interest.*
2 yr. $30 × 4   = $120,   *Total annual interest.*
1 yr. $30 × .06 × 6 =   10.80, *Interest on annual interest for 6 yr.*
6 yr. $130.80, *Total interest due at maturity.*
          500.00
          $630.80, *Amount.*

The first annual interest ($30) due, draws simple interest for 3 years; the second for 2 years; and the third for 1 year; and hence the simple interest on the several annual interests equals the interest on $30 for 3 yrs. + 2 yrs. + 1 yr., or for 6 years. The amount due on the note at maturity consists of (1) *the principal;* (2) *the total annual interest;* and (3) *the simple interest on the annual interests.* Hence, the amount due is $500 + $30 × 4 + $1.80 × 6, or $630.80.

2. A note of $750, with interest payable annually, at 8%, was paid 3 yr. 3 mo. 18 da. after date, and no interest had been previously paid: what was the amount due?

$750 × .08 = $60.   *Annual interest.*
$60 × 3.3 = $198.00, *Total an. interest for 3 yr. 3 mo. 18 da. (3.3 yr.)*
$60 × .312 = $18.72, *Simple interest on $60 for 3 yr. 10 mo. 24 da.*
$750.

$966.72, *Amount.*

The first annual interest draws interest for 2 yr. 3 mo. 18 da.; the second, for 1 yr. 3 mo. 18 da.; and the third, for 3 mo. 18 da. 2 yr. 3 mo. 18 da. + 1 yr. 3 mo. 18 da. + 3 mo. 18 da. = 3 yr. 10 mo. 24 da.

NOTE.—In Ohio and several other states, the interest on the unpaid annual interests would be computed at 6%, the legal rate. $60 × .234 = $14.04, simple interest on annual interests at 6%.

3. A note of $1000, with annual interest at 6%, is due 4 yr. 6 mo. after date: no interest having been paid, what will be due at maturity?

4. A man bought a farm for $3500, to be paid in 4 years, with annual interest at 6%, but failed to pay the interest: what was due at the close of the 4th year?

5.   COLUMBUS, OHIO, July 1, 1881.

On the first day of January, 1884, for value received, I promise to pay John Black, or order, six hundred and fifty dollars, with interest payable annually, at 7%.

                              CHARLES CHURCH.

If no interest be paid on the above note, what will be due at maturity? What will be due if interest on interest be computed at 6%?

6. If the above note and interest be not paid until Sept. 13, 1884, what will be the amount due? What will be due if interest on interest be computed at 6%?

7. A note of $800, dated March 18, 1877, and due in 3 years, with interest at 6%, payable annually, has the following indorsements: Oct. 24, 1878, $150; Nov. 12, 1879, $240. What was due March 18, 1880?

PROCESS.

$800 \times .06 = \$48$,   *First annual interest.*

$48 \times 2 = \$96$,   *Annual interest due Mch. 18, 1879.*

$48 \times .06 = \quad 2.88$,   *Interest on 1st annual interest.*

98.88,   *Interest due Mch. 18, 1879.*

800

898.88,   *Amount due Mch. 18, 1879.*

Payment, $150.   ⎫
Int. on same, 3.60. ⎬ $= \$153.60$,   *Amount of $150, Mch. 18, 1879.*
  ⎭

745.28,   *New principal.*

$745.28 \times .06 = \$44.716$,   *Interest due Mch. 18, 1880.*

789.996,   *Amount due Mch. 18, 1880.*

Payment, $240.   ⎫
Int. on same, 5.04. ⎬ $= \$245.04$,   *Amount $240, Mch. 18, 1880.*
  ⎭

544.956,   *Amount due at maturity.*

NOTE.—The annual interest and the interest on the same are computed to the close of the year in which the first payment is made, and the interest on the payment is computed to the same date. The difference between the amount of the face of the note and the amount of the payment is the new principal for the third year.

8. A note of $500, dated Jan. 15, 1865, and due in 2 years, with interest at 10%, payable annually, is indorsed as follows: May 21, 1866, $100; March 9, 1867, $200. What was the amount due July 15, 1867?

ART. 284. 1. To compute annual interest when not paid until maturity of note:

Rule.—*Compute the interest on the principal for the entire time it is on interest, and the interest on each year's interest for the time it is unpaid. The sum of the principal, the interest on the principal, and the interest on the unpaid interest will be the amount due.*

NOTE.—Instead of computing the interest on the several annual interests separately, *simple interest may be computed on one year's interest for a time equal to the sum of the periods of time the several annual interests are unpaid*, as in the solution of problem 2 above.

2. To compute annual interest when partial payments have been made:

Rule.—1. *Compute the interest on the principal to the end of the first year in which any payment is made, and also the interest on the unpaid annual interest to the same date, and form the amount.*

2. *Compute the interest on the payment or payments to the end of the year, and form the amount.*

3. *Subtract the amount of the payment or payments from the amount of the principal and interest, and, taking the difference for a new principal, proceed as before with succeeding payments, making the date of settlement the last date.*

Note.—This rule is based on the principle that the payments with added interest should be applied first to the discharge of the accrued interest at the end of a year, and then to the discharge of the principal. When the amount of the payment or payments will not cancel all the interest due, the unpaid interest draws *simple interest* to the end of the next year in which a payment is made.

COMPOUND INTEREST.

Art. 285. **Compound Interest** is interest on the principal and also on the interest, which, at regular intervals of time, is added to the principal, forming a new principal.

Interest may be compounded annually, semi-annually, or quarterly. When compounded semi-annually, the rate of interest is one half the yearly rate; and when compounded quarterly, the rate is one fourth of the yearly rate. When compounded annually, each year's interest draws *annual interest*, the same as the principal.

WRITTEN PROBLEMS.

1. A note of $450 is due in 3 years 4 months, with interest at 6%, compounded annually: what will be the amount due at maturity? What will be the compound interest due?

PROCESS.

$450	
.06	
$27.00	*1st year's interest.*
450.	
$477	*2d principal.*
.06	
$28.62	*2d year's interest.*
477.	
$505.62	*3d principal.*
.06	
$30.3372	*3d year's interest.*
505.62	
$535.9572	*Amount due at the end of 3d year.*
.02	
$10.719144	*Interest for 4 months.*
535.9572	
$546.6763	*Amount due at maturity.*
450.0000	
$96.6763	*Compound interest at maturity.*

2. What is the amount of $600 for 4 years at 5%, compounded annually? What is the compound interest?

3. What is the compound interest of $1500 for 3 years at 10%? At 8%?

4. What is the amount of $800 for 2 years at 6%, compounded semi-annually?

SUGGESTION.—Compute the interest at 3% for 4 years.

5. What is the compound interest of $650 for 3 yr. 4 mo. 12 da. at 6% per annum?

ART. 286. To compute compound interest:

Rule.—*Find the amount of the given principal for one interval of time; then, taking this amount as a new principal, find the amount for the second interval, and so continue for the entire time. The difference between the last amount and the principal is the compound interest for the time.*

NOTE.—Compound interest is usually computed by the aid of a table giving the amount of $1 at different rates, and for any given number of years.

THE FIVE PROBLEMS IN SIMPLE INTEREST.

ART. 287. The five numbers considered in interest are the *Principal, Rate %, Time, Interest,* and *Amount.* Such is the relation between these numbers that, if any three of them are given, the other two may be found.

PROBLEM I.

PRINCIPAL, RATE PER CENT, AND TIME GIVEN TO FIND THE INTEREST OR AMOUNT.

NOTE.—This problem has already been considered. The following problems may be solved by the pupil by any one of the preceding methods, but in the last three problems the time should be found by the method by days.

1. What is the interest of $12.50 for 3 yr. 1 mo. 15 da., at 6%?   At 10%?

2. What is the interest of $160.80 for 2 yr. 3 mo. 3 da., at 7%?   At 9%?

3. What is the interest of $1000 from May 13, 1881, to July 8, 1882, at 6%?   At 7½%?

4. What is the amount of $204.50 from Jan. 21, 1879, to Feb. 3, 1880, at 9%?   At 12%?

5. A note of $345.60, dated Feb. 5, 1880, was paid Aug. 20, 1882: what was the amount at 6%?

6. A note of $252, dated March 9, 1879, was paid May 12, 1881: what was the amount at 7%?

7. What is the interest of $80.25 from May 15 to Sept. 24, at 6%?   At 8%?

8. A note of $920, dated Jan. 4, was paid Apr. 3: what was the amount at 9%?

9. A note of $7.50, dated Apr. 20, was due Oct. 12, with interest at 8%: what was the amount?

ART. 288. **Formulas:**

1. *Interest = principal × rate % × time.*
2. *Amount = principal + interest.*

PROBLEM II.

PRINCIPAL, INTEREST, AND TIME GIVEN TO FIND THE RATE.

10. The interest on $540 for 8 mo. 18 da. was $27.09: what was the rate?

PROCESS.

$540
.043
———
1620
2160
———
6)$23.220, *Interest at 6%.*

$3.87, *Interest at 1%.*

$27.09 ÷ $3.87 = 7, *Rate.*

Since the interest on $540 for 8 mo. 18 da., at 1%, is $3.87, the rate which produced $27.09 interest was as many times 1 as $3.87 is contained times in $27.09, which is 7. Hence, the interest accrued at 7%.

The interest at 1% may also be found by multiplying $540 by $\frac{1}{6}$ of .043, which is .007⅙.

11. The interest of $456 for 3 yr. 5 mo. 18 da. is $79.04: what is the rate?

12. The interest of $560 for 2 yr. 4 mo. 15 da. was $106.40: what was the rate?

13. The interest of $95.40 for 3 yr. 9 mo. is $28.62: what is the rate?

14. The interest of $240 from Feb. 15, 1878, to Apr. 27, 1879, was $23.04: what was the rate?

15. The interest of $252 from Aug. 2, 1877, to March 9, 1878, was $12.152: what was the rate?

16. A note of $345.60, dated Feb. 5, 1880, was paid Aug. 20, 1882, and the amount was $407.088: what was the rate?

FORMULA AND RULE.

ART. 289. **Formula:**

$Rate = interest ÷ (principal × 1\% × time).$

ART. 290. To find the rate:

Rule.—*Divide the given interest by the interest of the principal for the given time, at 1 per cent.*

N. C. A.—21.

PROBLEM III.

PRINCIPAL, INTEREST, AND RATE PER CENT GIVEN TO FIND THE TIME.

17. The interest of $300, at 9%, is $60.75: what was the time?

PROCESS.

$300
.09
$\overline{}$
$27.00, *Interest for 1 yr.*
$60.75 ÷ $27 = 2.25
2.25 yr. = 2 yr. 3 mo.

Since the interest of $300 for 1 year, at 9%, is $27, $300 must be on interest as many years to produce $60.75 interest as $27 are contained times in $60.75, which is 2.25. Hence, the time is 2.25 years, or 2 yr. 3 mo.

18. The interest of $908, at $3\frac{1}{2}$%, was $79.45: what was the time?

19. The interest of $56.78 for a certain time, at 10%, was $22.24: what was the time?

20. How long must a note of $300 run to give an amount of $347.25, at 6%?

21. In what time will any principal double itself at 4% interest? At 6%? At 10%?

22. In what time will any principal double itself at 5% interest? At 7%? At 12%?

23. In what time will any principal treble itself at 5% interest? At 10%? At 6%?

FORMULA AND RULE.

ART. 291. **Formula:**

Time = interest ÷ (principal × rate %).

ART. 292. To find the time:

Rule.—*Divide the given interest by the interest of the principal for 1 year, at the given rate per cent.*

NOTE.—Reduce the fraction of a year to months and days. If preferred, the interest may be divided by the interest for 1 month, at the given rate per cent.

PROBLEM IV.

INTEREST, RATE PER CENT, AND TIME GIVEN TO FIND THE PRINCIPAL.

24. What principal will produce $49.20 of interest in 1 yr. 4 mo. 12 da., at 6%?

PROCESS.

$.082 = Interest of $1.

$49.20 ÷ $.082 = 600

$1 × 600 = $600. *Ans.*

Since $1 of principal produces $.082 of interest, it will take as many times $1 of principal to produce $49.20 of interest as $.082 is contained times in $49.20, which is 600. 600 times $1 = $600, the required principal. Or,

OR:

Interest of $1 = .082 of $1.

$49.20 ÷ .082 = $600, *Ans.*

Since the interest of $1 is .082 of itself, $49.20 is .082 of the required principal. $49.20 ÷ .082 = $600.

25. What principal will produce $15.24 interest in 7 mo. 6 da., at 8%?

26. What principal will produce $1000 interest in 5 yr. 6 mo. 20 da., at 5%?

27. What sum invested at 7% will produce $378 interest annually? $252?

28. What sum invested at 5% will yield an annual income of $17,000? $10,200?

29. What sum invested at 4½% will yield an annual income of $900? $1350?

30. What principal will produce $220 interest, from Oct. 25, 1881, to March 7, 1882, at 8%?

31. What principal will produce $17.78 interest, from Jan. 10, 1884, to March 13, 1884, computed *by days*, at 6%? At 4%?

FORMULA AND RULES.

ART. 293. **Formula:**

Principal = interest ÷ (rate % × time).

ART. 294. To find the principal when the interest, rate per cent, and time are given:

Rules.—*1. Divide the given interest by the interest of $1 for the given time and rate per cent, and multiply $1 by the quotient. Or,*

2. Divide the given interest by the decimal corresponding to the interest of $1 for the given time and rate per cent.

PROBLEM V.

AMOUNT, RATE PER CENT, AND TIME GIVEN TO FIND THE PRINCIPAL.

32. What principal on interest, at 8%, for 1 yr. 6 mo. 18 da., will give an amount of $730.60?

PROCESS.

$1.124 = amount of $1.

$730.60 ÷ $1.124 = 650

$1 × 650 = $650, *Ans.*

OR:

Amt. of $1 = 1.124 of $1.

$730.60 ÷ 1.124 = $650, *Ans.*

The interest of $1 for 1 yr. 6 mo. 18 da. is $.124, and the amount is $1.124. If the amount of $1 is $1.124, it will take as many times $1 to yield an amount of $730.60 as $1.124 is contained times in $730.60, which is 650. Or,

Since the amount of $1 is 1.124 of itself, $730.60 is 1.124 of the required principal.

33. What principal on interest, at 5%, for 1 yr. 10 mo. 24 da., will amount to $70.518?

34. What sum of money put at interest, at 7%, for 8 mo. 18 da., will amount to $567.09?

35. What sum of money put at interest, at 8%, for 2 yr. 1 mo. 15 da., will amount to $421.20?

36. What sum of money put at interest March 15, 1880, at 6%, will amount to $2600.40, Aug. 6, 1881?

37. The amount is $843, the time 1 yr. 6 mo. 18 da., and the rate 8: what is the principal?

ART. 295. **Formula:**

Principal = amount ÷ [1 + (rate % × time)].

ART. 296. To find the principal when the amount, rate per cent, and time are given:

Rules.—*1. Divide the given amount by the amount of $1 for the given time and rate per cent, and multiply $1 by the quotient. Or,*

2. Divide the given amount by the decimal corresponding to the amount of $1 for the given time and rate per cent.

NOTE.—The principal thus found is the *present worth* of the amount. See next article.

MISCELLANEOUS WRITTEN PROBLEMS.

1. What is the interest of $205 for 2 yr. 5 mo. 24 da., at 7%?

2. What is the amount of $160, from Jan. 12, 1869, to July 3, 1870, at 8%?

3. At what rate per cent will $512 yield $25.088 interest in 8 mo. 12 da.?

4. The principal is $126.75, the interest $20.956, and the time 2 yr. 24 da.: what is the rate?

5. How long will it take $5000 to produce $1125 interest, at 8%?

6. The principal is $326.50, the interest $2.76, and the rate 8: what is the time?

7. The amount is $1563.75, the interest $63.75, and the rate 7½: what is the time?

8. What principal will yield $1.36 interest in 20 days, at 6%?

9. What principal, at 7%, will amount to $659.40 in 8 months?

10. The interest on a certain principal from Nov. 11, 1877, to Dec. 15, 1879, at 6%, was $4.474: what was the principal?

11. The interest is $12.78, the time 1 yr. 2 mo. 6 da., and the rate 6: what is the amount?

12. What principal will amount to $609.20 in 4 mo. 18 da., at 4%?

13. What principal will amount to $288.85 in 1 yr. 6 mo., at 6%?

14. What principal will produce $20.23 interest from Jan. 1 to Oct. 20, 1883, at 7%?

15. How long will it take any principal to triple itself at 6%? At 4%? At 10%?

16. What is the amount of $420, from June 10, 1879, to Jan. 21, 1880, at 10%?

17. What sum, bearing interest at 5%, will yield an annual income of $1000?

18. What sum, bearing interest at $4\frac{1}{2}$%, will yield an annual income of $900?

PRESENT WORTH.

ART. 297. The **Present Worth** of a debt due at a future time, without interest, is the sum of money which, put at interest, will amount to the debt at the time it is due.

ART. 298. **True Discount** is the difference between a debt, not bearing interest, and its present worth.

It is called true discount to distinguish it from bank discount and business discount. True discount is the interest on the *present worth* of a note or debt, while bank discount is the interest on the *note* or *debt*. The difference is the interest on the true discount for the time. True discount is, however, seldom used in business. (For *Business* and *Trade Discount*, see p. 225.)

WRITTEN PROBLEMS.

1. What is the present worth of a note of $212, due 1 year hence, without interest, the current rate of interest being 6%? What is the true discount?

PROCESS.

$212 ÷ $1.06 = 200

$1 × 200 = $200, *Pres. worth.*

$212 — 200 = $12, *True dis.*

OR:

$212 ÷ 1.06 = $200, *Pres. worth.*

The amount of $1 for 1 year, at 6%, is $1.06, and hence the present worth of $1.06, due 1 year hence, is $1. If the present worth of $1.06 is $1, the present worth of $212 is as many times $1 as $1.06 is contained times in $212, which is 200. Or, since $1.06 is 1.06 of $1, $212 is 1.06 of its present worth. $212 ÷ 1.06 = $200.

NOTE.—This is only an application of Problem V. The debt corresponds to the *amount*; the present worth, to the *principal*; and the true discount, to the *interest*.

2. What is the present worth of a bill of $260 due in 8 months, without interest, the current rate of interest being 6? What is the true discount?

3. What is the present worth of $220 due in 1 yr. 6 mo., without interest, current rate being 7?

4. What is the true discount of $145.60 due in 8 mo. 12 da., without interest, current rate being 8?

5. What is the present worth of $305.75 due in 9 mo. 6 da., without interest, current rate being 9?

6. What is the true discount of $1250 due in 1 yr. 7 mo. 21 da., without interest, current rate being 5?

7. What is the true discount of $1508 due in 90 days, without interest, current rate being 7?

8. What is the true discount of $2040.50 due in 36 days, without interest, current rate being 10?

9. What is the difference between the true discount of $216, due in 2 years, without interest, current rate being 8, and the interest of $216 for 2 years, at 8%?

10. What is the difference between the true discount of $199.80, due in 1 yr. 10 mo., without interest, current rate being 6, and the interest of $199.80 for 1 yr. 10 mo., at 6%?

11. How large a note, due in 1 yr. 6 mo., with interest at 7%, will cancel a debt of $442, due in 1 yr. 6 mo., without interest?

12. What is the difference in the present value of a cash payment of $345, and a note of $371 due in 9 months, without interest, the use of money being worth 8%?

FORMULAS AND RULES.

ART. 299. **Formulas:**

1. *Present worth* = *debt* $\div [1 + (rate \% \times time)]$.
2. *True discount* = *debt* — *present worth.*

ART. 300. To find the present worth of a debt due at a future time, without interest:

Rules.—*1. Divide the debt by the amount of $1 for the given time, at the current rate of interest, and multiply $1 by the quotient. Or,*

2. Divide the debt by the decimal corresponding to the amount of $1 for the given time, at the current rate of interest.

STOCK INVESTMENTS.

To TEACHERS.—It may be desirable to review Capital Stock, pp. 195–199.

ART. 301. A **Bond** is an interest-bearing note issued under seal by a nation, state, city, railroad company, or other corporation.

Bonds are issued in denominations of convenient size, as $100, $1000, etc., with interest payable annually, semi-annually, or quarterly. They are made usually negotiable like certificates of capital stock.

ART. 302. The bonds issued by the United States Government, called United States Securities or Government Securities, are of two classes; viz, *Registered Bonds* and *Coupon Bonds*.

Registered bonds are recorded in the name of the owner in the United States Treasury Department at Washington, and the interest is sent directly to the owner. To effect its transfer from one party to another, a registered bond must be indorsed by the owner and the record changed.

Coupon bonds are transferred by delivery as bank notes. The coupons attached to these bonds are interest certificates, which, as the interest becomes due, are cut off and presented to the United States Treasurer for payment.

ART. 303. The different United States securities are distinguished by the rate of interest and the date at which they are payable. Thus, "U. S. $4\frac{1}{2}$'s, 1891," means United States bonds bearing $4\frac{1}{2}\%$ interest, and payable in 1891.

Most United States bonds are payable in coin. When a bond is payable in currency, this fact is stated in its description. Thus, "U. S. cur. 6's, '99" are bonds bearing interest at 6%, and payable in currency in 1899.

Bonds issued by corporations, and by states, cities, etc., are distinguished in various ways; as, Missouri 6's, Massachusetts 5's, '94; Hartford and Erie 7's, etc.

ART. 304. The market price of bonds, like that of capital stock, is quoted at a specified per cent of their par value. (Art. 234.)

The quoted price of United States securities includes the accrued interest, since all such bonds are sold, with "interest to buyer." Other bonds are sometimes quoted with "interest to seller." The interest on several classes of United States bonds is paid quarterly.

ART. 305. **Stocks** include capital stock, bonds, and other securities bought and sold in the stock market.

The business of buying and selling stocks is called *Stock Jobbing*, and persons engaged in such business are *Stock Brokers* or *Stock Jobbers*.

An association of stock brokers is called a *Stock Exchange.* The transactions of the New York Stock Exchange determine the market price of nearly all the stocks sold in this country. Quotations of the principal stocks are published in the leading daily papers.

ART. 306. The investing of money in stocks, including capital stocks, bonds, and other securities, is called *Stock Investment.*

Since both dividends and interest are computed on the *face* of stocks, the value of an investment will depend on the rate of dividend or interest and *the price paid for the stock.*

WRITTEN PROBLEMS.

1. What will \$50000 new U. S. 4's cost at 119?

SUGGESTION.—The cost of stock is found by *multiplying its face by the quoted price.* (Art. 238, 2.)

2. What will \$3000 U. S. 3's cost at 104? At 102½?

3. What will \$24000 Michigan 7's cost at 112½?

4. How much U. S. 3½'s can be bought for \$10450, at 104½?

PROCESS: \$10450 ÷ 1.045 = \$10000, stock.

5. How much Hartford and Erie 7's can be bought for \$3680 at 115?

6. What annual income will be derived from \$340000 invested in United States 4½'s? In U. S. 4's?

7. How much more stock can be bought for \$11960 at 115, than for \$7680 at 80?

8. What income will be derived from \$8500 United States 4's? Michigan 7's?

9. How large an investment in Massachusetts 5's will give an income of \$1500?

SOLUTION.—Since \$1 gives \$.05, it will require as many times \$1 worth of stock as \$.05 is contained times in \$1500, which is 30000. \$1 × 30000 = \$30000. Or, \$1500 ÷ .05 = \$30000.

10. How much 7% stock will give an income of $2863? Of $3570?

11. How much 5% stock will give a semi-annual income of $1250? Of $1750?

SUGGESTION.—Find the annual income and then proceed as in problem 9.

12. What annual income will $3000 worth of 7% stock and $3500 worth of 6% stock yield?

13. A widow owns $210C0 United States bonds, and receives a quarterly income of $210: what is the rate of interest?

14. A bank owns $50000 Union Pacific bonds, and receives $1500 interest semi-annually: what is the rate of interest?

15. The endowment fund of a college is invested in 5% state bonds, and the quarterly income is $4250: what is the amount invested?

16. A widow invests $10250 in 5% stock at 102½: what income will she receive?

PROCESS: $10250 ÷ 1.025 = $10000, *Stock.*
$10000 × .05 = $500, *Income.*

17. A college invested $616000 in United States currency 6's at 112: what annual income will it receive?

18. What income will be derived from $6900 invested in Michigan 7's at 115?

19. A person invested his property in United States 4½'s at 112½: what rate of interest on the investment will he receive?

SUGGESTION.—At 112½, $100 stock costs $112.50, which pays $4.50 interest. $4.50 ÷ $112.50 = .04, the rate per cent.

20. If 3½% stocks are bought at 87½, what rate of interet will the purchaser receive on his investment?

21. At what price must 5% stock be purchased to yield the buyer 6% interest on his money?

22. At what price must 4% stock be bought to yield the same interest as 5% stock at par?

23. If $8000 worth of 6% stocks be sold at 120, and the proceeds invested in $4\frac{1}{2}$% stock at 96, what will be the change in the income?

24. If $8000 worth of $3\frac{1}{2}$% stocks be sold at $87\frac{1}{2}$, and the proceeds invested in 5% stock at $116\frac{2}{3}$, what will be the change in the income?

25. A college sold $320000 worth of United States currency 6's at $112\frac{1}{2}$, and invested the proceeds in Indiana 5% bonds at par: what was the loss in its income?

26. A widow invested $6550 in gas stock at 110, and the stock paid an average annual dividend of 8%: what was her income?

27. A widow sold £6000 worth of Missouri 6's at 115, and invested the proceeds in gas stock at 120, paying an average annual dividend of 8%: what was the change in her annual income?

28. A guardian sold $7200 worth of Massachusetts 5's at par, and invested the proceeds in Michigan 7's at 120: what was the change in his ward's annual income?

29. A person invested $2760 in bank stock at 115, and received an average annual income of $180: what was the rate of dividend? What was the rate of interest on the money invested?

30. Which is the better investment, United States $4\frac{1}{2}$'s, or Missouri 6's, both at par, when taxes on personal property average 2%? When taxes average $1\frac{1}{2}$%?

NOTE.—United States bonds are not subject to taxation, but other bonds are assessed at their market or par value, as state law may provide.

31. When taxes average $1\frac{1}{2}$%, and taxable bonds are assessed at their market value, which is the better investment, United States $3\frac{1}{2}$'s at par, or Massachusetts 5's at 120? What would be the difference in income from $5000 worth of bonds?

32. Which is the better investment, United States 4's or Missouri 6's, both at same quoted price, when taxes on personal property average 16 mills on the dollar, and Missouri bonds are assessed at par value?

33. Which is the better investment, United States 5's at 115 or Michigan 7's at 120, taxes on personal property being 2%, and Michigan bonds being assessed at par value?

EXCHANGE.

ART. 307. A **Draft** is an order made by one party on another to pay a specified sum to a third party named. It is also called a *Bill of Exchange.*

The person who makes the order is called the *Drawer;* the person to whom it is addressed is called the *Drawee;* and the person to whom the money is payable is the *Payee.*

ART. 308. Bills of Exchange are of two kinds: *Domestic,* or *Inland,* and *Foreign.*

A **Domestic** or **Inland Bill** is a draft which is payable in the country where it is drawn.

A **Foreign Bill** is a draft which is drawn in one country and payable in another.

ART. 309. **Exchange** is the process of making payments at distant places by the remittance of drafts, instead of money.

When a draft can be bought for its face, it is said to be *at par;* when the cost is less than the face, it is *below par,* or at a *discount;* and when the cost is more than the face, it is *above par,* or at a *premium.* The rate per cent which the cost of a draft is more or less than its face, is called the *Rate of Exchange.*

NOTE.—The rate of exchange between two places depends chiefly on their relative trade. If Cincinnati owes New York, drafts on New York are at a premium in Cincinnati; if New York owes Cincinnati, drafts on New York are at a discount; if the trade of the two cities with each other is equal, exchange is at par.

DOMESTIC EXCHANGE.

ART. 310. The following are the common forms of domestic or inland drafts:

FORM I.—SIGHT DRAFT.

$100.   CINCINNATI, O., Oct. 1, 1880.

Pay to the order of Bartlit & Smith, One Hundred Dollars, and place to the account of
                                              CHARLES S. KELLEY.
To GEORGE BROWN, Esq., New York.

FORM II.—TIME DRAFT.

$100.   CINCINNATI, O., Oct. 1, 1880.

Thirty days after sight [or date], pay to the order of Bartlit & Smith, One Hundred Dollars, and place to the account of
                                              CHARLES S. KELLEY.
To GEORGE BROWN, Esq., New York.

When the drawee accepts a draft, he writes the word "Accepted," with the date, across the face, and signs his name, thus: "Accepted, Oct. 3, 1880—George Brown." The draft is then called an *Acceptance*, and the acceptor is responsible for its payment.

A draft made payable to *bearer* or *order* is negotiable, like a promissory note, and is subject to *protest*, in case payment or acceptance is refused.

NOTES.—1. In most of the states both time and sight drafts are entitled to three days of grace. In New York no grace is allowed on sight drafts.

2. When a draft is drawn, "acceptance waived," it is not subject to protest until maturity; and when an indorser writes over his name, "demand and notice waived," a protest in his case is not necessary.

3. The liability of an indorser of a note or draft may be avoided by his writing over his indorsement, "without recourse." (Art. 276.)

1. What is the cost of a draft on New York for $800, exchange being $\frac{3}{4}\%$ premium?

PROCESS: $800 × .00$\frac{3}{4}$ = $6, *Prem.*

$800 + $6 = $806, *Cost.*

2. What is the cost of a draft on New Orleans for $1250, at $\frac{1}{2}\%$ discount?

3. What is the cost of a draft on Philadelphia for $1050, at $\frac{1}{4}\%$ premium?

4. A merchant in St. Louis wishes to remit $2500 by draft to New York: what will be the cost of the draft, exchange being $1\frac{1}{2}\%$ premium?

5. What will be the cost of a draft for $500, payable in 30 days after sight, exchange being 1% premium, and interest 6%?

PROCESS.

$500.

$500 × .0055 = $2.75, *Discount at 6% for 33 days.*

$497.25, *Proceeds of draft (cost at par).*

$500 × .01 = 5.00, *Premium at 1%.*

$502.25, *Cost of draft.*

NOTE.—The face may be multiplied by the cost of $1, which is $1 — $.0055 + $.01, or $1.0045. $500 × 1.0045 = $502.25.

6. What will be the cost of a draft for $650, payable in 60 days after sight, exchange being $\frac{1}{2}\%$ premium, and interest 8%?

7. What will be the cost of a draft for $320, payable in 45 days after sight, exchange being $\frac{3}{4}\%$ discount, and interest 7%?

8. How large a sight draft can be bought for $259.52, exchange being $1\frac{3}{8}\%$ premium?

PROCESS: $259.52 ÷ 1.01$\frac{3}{8}$ = $256, *Face of draft.*

9. How large a sight draft can be bought for $962.85, exchange being $1\frac{3}{4}\%$ discount?

10. A sight draft, bought at $\frac{1}{2}\%$ premium, cost $1256.25: what was its face?

11. A sight draft cost $4681.25 at $1\frac{1}{4}\%$ discount: what was its face?

12. How large a draft, payable 30 days after sight, can be bought for $502.25, exchange being 1%, and interest 6%?

PROCESS.

$1 - $.0055 = $.9945, *Proceeds of $1 discounted for 33 days.*
$.9945 + $.01 = $1.0045, *Cost of $1.*
$502.25 \div 1.0045 = $500, *Face of draft.*

13. How large a draft, payable 60 days after sight, can be bought for $798.80, exchange being $1\frac{1}{4}\%$ premium, and interest 8%?

14. A draft, payable in 30 days after sight, was bought for $352.62, exchange being $1\frac{1}{2}\%$ discount, and interest 6%: what was its face?

15. A commission merchant sold $4750 worth of wheat, and, after deducting his commission at 3%, purchased with the proceeds a 60-day draft at 10% interest, and at $\frac{3}{4}\%$ premium: what was the cost of the draft?

FOREIGN EXCHANGE.

ART. 311. Foreign Bills of Exchange are expressed in the currency of the country on which they are drawn. They are issued in sets of three, of the same tenor and date, called the *First*, *Second*, and *Third* of Exchange, which are sent by different mails to avoid delay in case of miscarriage. When one is paid, the others are void.

Art. 312. The following is the common form of a foreign bill of exchange:

Exchange for *£1000.*　　　*New York, Feb. 1, 1883.*

Sixty days after *sight* of this **First** of Exchange, *Second and Third of the same tenor and date unpaid,* pay to the order of *William A. Brown,*

One thousand pounds sterling,

value received, and place the same to the account of

To *Gilmore & Co.*　　　*Burns, Barret & Co.*

N₀. *1426.*　　　*London.*

Art. 313. The comparative value of the currencies of two countries is called the *Par of Exchange.*

The commercial value of foreign exchange may be higher, equal to, or lower than the par of exchange. A bill payable in sixty days costs less than a bill payable on sight, or in three days, called "short sight."

The commercial or quoted value of exchange is used in finding the cost of a foreign bill.

EXCHANGE ON ENGLAND.

Art. 314. Bills between the United States and England are expressed in sterling money, and are drawn on London. They are called *Sterling Bills.*

The legal or par value of a pound sterling (£) is $4.8665; and this is now the custom house value. The commercial or exchange value is quoted in dollars and cents, gold. The gold coin, whose value is £1, is a *Sovereign.* A pound equals 20 shillings (*s.*), and a shilling 12 pence (*d.*).

N.C. A.—22.

WRITTEN PROBLEMS.

1. What will a bill on London for £448 11s. cost in New York, when sterling exchange is quoted at 4.86⅔?

PROCESS.

£448 11s. = £448.55

$4.86⅔ × 448.55 = $2182.943, *Cost of bill in gold.*

2. What will a sterling bill for £219 10s. 6d. cost in New York, when sterling exchange is quoted at 4.91⅑?

3. What will a bill on London for £200 12s., payable in 60 days, cost in New York, when sterling exchange is quoted at 4.85⅗?

4. What will a sight draft on London for £300 8s. cost, when sterling exchange is quoted at 4.88?

5. What will a sight draft on London for £250 cost a merchant in Cincinnati, when sterling exchange is quoted at 4.86, and the broker's commission is ⅛% of cost of draft in New York?

NOTE.—The broker's commission is sometimes included in the quoted price, but this is not the usual custom.

6. What amount of sterling exchange can be bought for $1080.45 in gold, when sterling exchange is quoted at 4.90?

PROCESS: $1080.45 ÷ $4.90 = 220.5; £220.5 = £220 10s.

7. How large a draft on London can be bought in Chicago for $2195.475, when sterling exchange is quoted at 4.86⅔, including broker's commission?

8. How large a sight draft on London can be bought in New York for $1174.20, when sterling exchange is quoted at 4.89¼?

ART. 315. 1. To find the cost of sterling exchange:

Rule.—*Multiply the cost of £1 by the number of pounds denoting the face of the bill.*

2. To find the amount of sterling exchange that can be bought for a given sum of United States money:

Rule.—*Divide the given sum of money by the cost of £1 of exchange.*

EXCHANGE ON FRANCE.

Art. 316. The New York quotations of exchange on Paris give the number of francs and centimes which are equal in exchange to $1 of United States money (gold). The centimes are usually expressed as *hundredths.*

Quotations on Antwerp and Switzerland are also in francs. Quotations on Amsterdam are in guilders, worth about 41 cents.

The value of a franc (Louis Napoleon) is $.192 nearly, $1 being equal to 5 francs and 14⅜ centimes. The custom house value is $.193.

9. What will be the cost of a bill on Paris for 3870 fr., when Paris exchange is quoted in New York at 5.16?

process: 3870 fr. ÷ 5.16 fr. = 750; $1 × 750 = $750.

Since $1 will buy 5.16 fr., it will take as many times $1 to buy 3870 fr. as 5.16 fr. is contained times in 3870 fr., which is 750.

10. What will a draft on Paris for 6475 fr. cost in New York, when Paris exchange is quoted at 5.18?

11. What will a bill on Paris for 5330 fr. cost in New York, when Paris exchange is quoted at 5.12½?

12. What amount of exchange on Paris can be bought for $1500, when Paris exchange is quoted at 5.14¼?

process: 5.14½ fr. × 1500 = 7717.5 fr., *Ans.*

13. How large a draft on Paris can be bought in New York for $2432, when Paris exchange is quoted at 5.16⅔?

14. What will be the cost of a bill on Antwerp for 6418¾ fr., when exchange is quoted at 5.13½?

15. What amount of exchange on Switzerland can be bought for $650, when exchange is quoted at 5.12½? When quoted at 5.15?

ART. 317.   1. To find the cost of exchange on Paris:

Rule.—*Divide the number of francs in the face of the bill by the number of francs that equal $1 of exchange.*

2. To find the amount of exchange on Paris that can be bought for a given sum of money:

Rule.—*Multiply the number of francs that equal $1 of exchange by the number denoting the given sum of money.*

EXCHANGE ON GERMANY.

ART. 318.   Exchange on Germany is quoted at so many cents per four reichsmarks (marks).

The par value of a reichsmark (mark), the new German coin, is $.243, or about 1¼ francs.

16. What will be the cost of a sight bill on Hamburg for 2240 marks, when exchange is quoted in New York at .96¼?

PROCESS: $.96¼ × 2240 ÷ 4 = $539, *Cost.*

17. What would be the cost of a sight bill on Berlin for 1680 marks, when exchange is quoted at .96½?

18. What would be the cost in St. Louis of a sight draft on Hamburg for 3200 marks, when exchange is quoted at .96⅛?

19. What amount of exchange on Frankfort can be bought for $1752.60, when exchange is quoted at .95¼?

PROCESS: $1752.60 ÷ $.95¼ × 4 = 7360 *marks.*

20. What amount of exchange on Berlin can be bought for $324, when exchange is quoted at .94½?

21. What will a draft for 960 marks cost when exchange is quoted at .95¾? At 95½?

22. How large a draft on Frankfort can be bought for $514.35, when exchange is quoted at .95¼?

23. What amount of exchange on Hamburg can be bought for $240, when exchange is quoted at .96¼?

ART. 319. 1. To find the cost of exchange on Germany:

Rule.—*Multiply the cost of four marks by the number of marks in the face of the bill, and divide the result by 4.*

2. To find the amount of exchange on Germany that can be bought for a given sum of money:

Rules.—*1. Divide the given sum of money by the cost of four marks, and multiply the result by 4. Or,*

2. Divide the given sum of money by the cost of 1 mark.

EQUATION OF PAYMENTS.

ART. 320. **Equation of Payments** is the process of finding an equitable time for the payment of several debts due at different times, without interest. It is also called the *Average of Payments.*

ART. 321. The equitable time sought is called the *Average Time,* or the *Equated Time.* The time between the making of a debt and its payment is called the *Term of Credit,* or *Time of Credit.*

PROBLEMS.

1. A owes B $300, of which $200 is due in 3 months, and $100 in 6 months: when will the payment of $300 equitably discharge the debt?

PROCESS BY PRODUCTS.

$200 × 3 = $600
$100 × 6 = $600
―――――――――――――
$300   )$1200
              4

Ans. 4 *mo.*

A is entitled to the use of $200 for 3 months, which equals the use of $600 for 1 month, and to the use of $100 for 6 months, which equals the use of $600 for 1 month; and, hence, he is entitled to the use of $300 until it equals the use of $600 + $600, or $1200, for 1 month. It will take $300 as many months to equal the use of $1200 for 1 month, as $300 is contained times in $1200, which is 4. Hence, the payment of $300 in 4 months will equitably discharge the debt.

PROOF.—In paying the $200 in 4 months, A *gains* the use of $200 for 1 month, and in paying the $100 in 4 months, he *loses* the use of $100 for 2 months, which equals the use of $200 for 1 month. Hence, his gain and his loss are *equal*.

2. A owes a merchant $200 due in 4 months, and $600 due in 8 months: what is the equated time for the payment of both debts?

3. A owes B $1200, of which $300 is due in 4 months, $400 in 6 months, and the remainder in 12 months: what is the equated time for the payment of the whole?

4. A owes B $800, of which $\frac{1}{8}$ is due in 2 months, $\frac{1}{2}$ in 3 months, and the remainder in 6 months: what is the equated time for the payment of the whole?

5. A man owes $300 due in 4 months, $600 due in 5 months, and $700 due in 10 months: what is the equated time for the payment of the whole?

6. Smith & Jones bought $500 worth of goods on 4 months' credit, $700 worth on 6 months' credit, and $1000 worth on 5 months' credit: what is the equated time for the payment of the whole?

7. A bought $2000 worth of goods, ¼ of which was to be paid down, ⅓ in 3 months, ¼ in 4 months, and the remainder in 8 months: what is the equated time for the payment of the whole?

8. What is the equated time for the payment of $300, due in 30 days; $250, due in 45 days; and $350, due in 60 days?

PROCESS BY INTEREST.

Int. of $300 for 30 days, at 6% = $ 1.50
Int. of $250 for 45 days, at 6% =   1.875
Int. of $350 for 60 days, at 6% =   3.50
$900 $6.875

$9.00 = Int. of $900 for 60 days.
.15 = Int. of $900 for 1 day.

$6.875 ÷ $.15 = 45.9.   *Ans. 46 days.*

The debtor is entitled to the use (1) of $300 for 30 days, which, at 6%, equals $1.50 interest; (2) of $250 for 45 days, which equals $1.875 interest; (3) of $350 for 60 days, which equals $3.50 interest. Hence, he is entitled to the use of $900, the sum of the debts, until the interest thereon, at 6%, equals the sum of $1.50 + $1.875 + $3.50, which is $6.875. The interest of $900 for 1 day is $.15; and since $6.875 ÷ $.15 = 45.9, it will take 45.9 days for $900 to yield $6.875 interest. The equated time for payment is 46 days.

NOTE.—When the fraction of a day in the equated time is more than ½, it is counted as a day; when it is less than ½, it is disregarded.

9. What is the equated time for the payment of $220, due in 30 days; $300, due in 40 days; $250, due in 60 days; and $100, due in 90 days?

10. What is the equated time for the payment of $520, due in 45 days; $340, due in 60 days; and $640, due in 90 days?

11. What is the equated time for the payment of $375, due now; $425, due in 30 days; $500, due in 60 days; and $600, due in 75 days?

12. What is the equated time for the payment of $340, due May 10, 1880; $450, due June 10; $560, due July 15; and $650, due Aug. 10?

NOTE.—Begin with the first date (May 10) and find the exact number of days between it and each succeeding date. The equated time is counted forward from the first date.

13. What is the equated time for the payment of $1000, due June 1, 1880; $850, due July 1; $750, due Sept. 1; and $900, due Oct. 1?

14. What is the equated time for the payment of $75, due May 6, 1880; $115, due May 26; $220, due June 25; $315, due July 16; and $350, due July 30?

15. Solve the first seven problems above by interest, and the last seven by products.

PRINCIPLE AND RULES.

ART. 322. **Principle.**—*The payment of a sum of money* BEFORE *it is due is offset by keeping an equal sum of money an equal time* AFTER *it is due.*

ART. 323.   To equate the time of several debts or payments:

Rules.—*1. Multiply each debt or payment by its time of credit, and divide the sum of the products by the sum of the debts or payments.* Or:

2. Compute the interest of each debt or payment for its time of credit, and divide the sum of the interests by the interest of the sum of the debts or payments for one month or one day.

NOTES.—1. As the result will be the same at any rate, the interest may be computed at that rate which is most convenient.

2. The correctness of each of the above methods may be readily proven.

Art. 324. When partial payments are made on a debt before it is due, the time for the payment of the balance of the debt is proportionately extended.

16. A owes a merchant $200, due in 12 months, without interest; in 4 months he pays $50 on the debt, and in 8 months, $50: when in equity should he pay the balance?

PROCESS.

$$\$50 \times 8 = \$400$$
$$\$50 \times 4 = \$200$$
$$\$200 - \$100 = \$100)\overline{\$600}$$
$$6$$

Ans. 6 *mo.*

In paying $50 in 4 months, A loses its use for 8 months, and in paying $50 in 8 months, he loses its use for 4 months, and hence he loses the use of $400 + $200, or $600, for 1 month. To offset this loss, he is entitled to keep the balance ($100) 6 months *after* its maturity.

17. A owes B $300, due in 8 months: if he pay $200 in 5 months, when should he pay the balance?

18. A man bought a horse, agreeing to pay $150 in 6 months, without interest: if he pay $50 down, when should he pay the balance?

19. A owes B $600, payable in 6 months, but, at the close of 3 months, he proposes to make a payment sufficiently large to extend the time for the payment of the balance 6 months. How large a payment must he make?

20. A owed B $1500, due in 12 months, but in 4 months paid him $400, and in 6 months $300, and in 8 months $200: when in equity ought the balance to be paid?

21. Clark & Brown bought, March 10, 1880, a bill of goods amounting to $2500, on 4 months' credit; but they paid $450 Apr. 7; $200 Apr. 30; $250 May 20; June 10, $350; and June 25, $250. When ought they to pay the balance?

Art. 325. To find the time for the payment of the balance of a debt on which payments have been made:

Rule.—*Multiply each payment by the time it was paid before it was due, and divide the sum of the products by the balance unpaid.*

Art. 326. The process of finding the equated time for the payment of the balance of an account, or the time when the balance was due, is called the *Equation of Accounts.*

When an account contains only debit items, the equated time of maturity is found in the same manner as the equated time for the payment of several debts.

22. A bookseller bought of Van Antwerp, Bragg & Co. the following bills of blank books, each on 4 months' credit:

$$
\begin{aligned}
&\text{Feb.} \quad 3, 1883, \text{ a bill of } \$450. \\
&\text{``} \quad\; 24, \text{ ``} \qquad\text{``} \text{ ``} \quad 500. \\
&\text{Mch.} \; 25, \text{ ``} \qquad\text{``} \text{ ``} \quad 750. \\
&\text{Apr.} \;\; 20, \text{ ``} \qquad\text{``} \text{ ``} \quad 600.
\end{aligned}
$$

What is the equated time of maturity?

PROCESS.

$$
\begin{aligned}
\text{Due June} \quad 3, 1883, \quad \$450 \times 00 &= \\
\text{``} \qquad\text{``} \quad 24, \quad\text{``} \qquad 500 \times 21 &= 10500 \\
\text{``} \quad \text{July } 25, \quad\text{``} \qquad 750 \times 52 &= 39000 \\
\text{``} \quad \text{Aug. } 20, \quad\text{``} \qquad 600 \times 78 &= 46800 \\
\hline
\$2300 \;\;)\; \$96300 \,(41.8 \; days.
\end{aligned}
$$

The equated date of maturity of the above bills is 42 days from June 3, 1883, which is July 15, 1883.

Note.—The date of maturity of each bill is found by counting forward 4 months from the date of purchase. The same result would be obtained by finding the average or equated date of purchase, and counting forward 4 months. The equated time may be found by interest, as in the equation of payments.

23. Murray & Co. bought of Smith & Moore goods as follows:

Apr. 15, 1879, a bill of $400, on 3 mo. credit.
May 20, " " 245, on 4 " "
June 25, " " 375, on 4 " "
Sept. 15, " " 625, on 3 " "

What is the equated time of maturity?

24. A merchant has the following charges against a customer:

May 9, 1880, $340, on 4 mo. credit.
June 6, " 530, on 4 " "
July 8, " 213, on 3 " "
Aug. 30, " 150, on 4 " "

What is the equated time of maturity? How much would settle the account Dec. 6, 1880?

SUGGESTION.—The sum of the items draws interest from the equated date of maturity to the date of payment.

25. J. O. Bates & Co. bought of Smith & Brown several bills of goods, as follows:

March 3, 1883, a bill of $250, on 3 mo. credit.
April 15, " " 180, on 4 " "
June 20, " " 325, on 3 " "
Aug. 10, " " 80, on 3 " "
Sept. 1, " " 100, on 4 " "

What is the equated date of maturity? How much would settle the account Dec. 1, 1883, at 6%?

NOTE.—The method of finding the equated time for the payment of the balance of an account with both debit and credit items is given in the Appendix. It is seldom used in ordinary business.

ANALYSIS.

Art. 327. **Analysis** is the process of separating a problem into its elements to find the value of some number sought.

Note.—The principles and processes of analysis have both been used throughout the preceding pages, and the following problems are here added to afford a *special drill in analytic reasoning*, for which the pupil is well prepared. The drill on each problem should be continued until the analysis is made with requisite accuracy and rapidity. The forms of analysis employed should be simple and concise. The problems in Proportion (pp. 281–285) may also be solved by analysis.

ORAL PROBLEMS.

1. If $\frac{7}{8}$ yd. of silk cost $\$2\frac{1}{25}$, what will $\frac{5}{6}$ yd. cost?

2. If $\frac{3}{4}$ of a barrel of flour cost $\$5\frac{1}{4}$, what will $\frac{5}{7}$ of a barrel cost? $\frac{5}{8}$ of a barrel?

3. If $\frac{3}{4}$ lb. of coffee cost 15 cts., what will $3\frac{1}{2}$ lb. cost? $5\frac{1}{2}$ lb.? $12\frac{1}{2}$ lb.?

4. A man sold a watch for $120, which was $\frac{4}{5}$ of what it cost him: how much did it cost?

5. A farmer sold a horse for $90, which was $\frac{1}{4}$ more than its cost: what was the cost of the horse?

6. A piece of flannel lost $\frac{2}{7}$ of its length by shrinkage in fulling, and then measured 30 yards: what was its length before fulling?

7. $\frac{2}{5}$ of my money is in my purse, $\frac{3}{8}$ in my hand, and the remainder, which is 25 cents, is in my pocket: how much money have I?

8. A boy having $\frac{2}{5}$ of a dollar, gave $\frac{2}{3}$ of his money to John and $\frac{1}{2}$ of the remainder to James: what part of a dollar did James receive?

9. A farmer sold $\frac{2}{3}$ of his sheep and then bought $\frac{2}{5}$ as many as he had left, when he had 40 sheep: how many had he at first?

10. John lost $\frac{2}{5}$ of his money and spent $\frac{1}{3}$ of the remainder, and then had only 10 cents: how much money had he at first?

11. A man sold a horse for $60, which was $\frac{4}{5}$ of $\frac{3}{4}$ of its cost: how much was lost by the bargain?

12. A man sold a horse for $130, which was $\frac{5}{8}$ more than it cost him: what was the cost of the horse?

13. If a staff 5 feet long casts a shadow 2 feet long at 12 o'clock, what is the height of a steeple whose shadow, at the same hour, is 80 feet?

14. If a staff 3 feet long cast a shadow 2 feet in length, how long a shadow will a tree 90 feet high cast at the same time of day?

15. If a steeple 200 feet high casts a shadow 150 feet long, what is the height of a pole which, at the same time of day, casts a shadow 80 feet long?

16. If 5 men can do a piece of work in 12 days, how long will it take 6 men to do it?

17. If 8 men can do a piece of work in 15 days, how many men can do the same work in 10 days?

18. If 9 men can do a piece of work in $4\frac{2}{3}$ days, how long will it take 7 men to do it?

19. If 3 pipes will empty a cistern in 30 minutes, how many pipes will empty it in 10 minutes?

20. If it require 12 days of 10 hours each to do a piece of work, how many days of 8 hours each will be required to do the same work?

21. If a five-cent loaf weigh 10 ounces when flour is $4 a barrel, what ought it to weigh when flour is $5 a barrel?

22. A garrison of 20 men is supplied with provisions for 12 days: if 12 men leave, how long will the provisions serve the remainder?

23. If a horse eat 2 bushels of oats in 6 days, in how many days will 2 horses eat 18 bushels?

24. If 3 men can mow 18 acres of grass in 4 days, how many men can mow 9 acres in 3 days?

25. If a quantity of provisions will supply 15 men 20 days, how long will it supply 50 men?

26. If 5 men can do $\frac{2}{3}$ of a piece of work in a day, how long will it take one man to do the entire work?

27. If 8 men can do $\frac{3}{4}$ of a piece of work in 3 days, how long will it take 4 men to do the entire work?

28. If 20 men earn $120 in 4 days, how much will 5 men earn in 8 days?

29. If 5 horses eat 40 bushels of oats in 3 weeks, how many bushels will supply 12 horses 10 weeks?

30. If 8 men can dig a ditch 40 rods long in 6 days, how long will it take 12 men to dig a ditch 60 rods long?

31. If the interest of $50 for 9 months be $6, what would be the interest of $150 for 1 yr. 6 mo.?

32. A school enrolls 180 pupils, and the number of boys is $\frac{4}{5}$ of the number of girls: how many pupils of each sex are enrolled in the school?

33. A lady paid $130 for a watch and chain, and the cost of the chain was $\frac{5}{8}$ of the cost of the watch: what was the cost of each?

34. A man bought a watch and chain for $80, and the chain cost $\frac{1}{3}$ as much as the watch: how much did each cost?

35. A has $1\frac{1}{2}$ times as many cents as B, and they together have 40 cents: how many has each?

36. A pole 120 feet high fell and broke into two parts, and $\frac{2}{3}$ of the longer part was equal to the shorter: how long was each part?

37. A tree 120 feet in height was broken into two parts by falling, and $\frac{2}{5}$ of the shorter part equaled $\frac{2}{7}$ of the longer: what was the length of each part?

38. A person giving the time of day, said that $\frac{2}{3}$ of the time past noon equaled the time to midnight: what was the hour of day?

39. What is the hour of day when $\frac{3}{4}$ of the time past noon equals $\frac{3}{8}$ of the time to midnight?

40. What is the time of day when $\frac{2}{3}$ of the time to noon is equal to $\frac{2}{5}$ of the time past midnight?

41. A man being asked his age, said 10 years ago my age was $\frac{7}{9}$ of my present age: what was his age?

42. A son's age is $\frac{2}{3}$ of the age of his father, and the sum of their ages is 80 years: what is the age of each?

43. If to my age you add its half, its third, and 28 years, the sum will be three times my age: what is my age?

44. $\frac{3}{4}$ of A's age equals $\frac{4}{7}$ of B's, and the difference between their ages is 10 years: how old is each?

45. A horse cost $90, and $\frac{3}{10}$ of the price of the horse equals $\frac{2}{3}$ of 3 times the cost of the saddle: what did the saddle cost?

46. A man bought a horse and carriage for $280, and $\frac{2}{9}$ of the cost of the carriage was equal to $\frac{2}{3}$ of the cost of the horse: what was the cost of each?

47. A man bought a horse, saddle, and bridle for $150; the cost of the bridle was $\frac{1}{2}$ of the cost of the saddle, and the cost of the saddle was $\frac{1}{6}$ of the cost of the horse: what was the cost of each?

48. A man and his two sons earned $140 in a month; the man earned twice as much as the elder son, and the elder son earned twice as much as the younger: how much did each earn?

49. Two men hired a pasture for $40, and one put in 3 cows and the other 5 cows: how much ought each to pay?

50. A and B rented a pasture for $72; A puts in 40 sheep and B 8 cows; if 4 sheep eat as much as one cow, how much ought each to pay?

51. A and B together own 824 sheep, and A has $1\frac{2}{3}$ times as many as B: how many has each?

52. A, B, and C rent a pasture for $42; B pays half as much as A, and C half as much as B: what does each pay?

53. A and B own a farm; A owns $\frac{3}{4}$ as much as B, and B owns 40 acres more than A: how many acres does each own?

54. $\frac{3}{4}$ of A's money is $\frac{2}{3}$ of B's, and $\frac{3}{4}$ of B's is $\frac{2}{3}$ of C's, which is $81: how much have A and B each?

55. If a man can reap $\frac{3}{4}$ of an acre of wheat in a day, how much can 6 men reap in 10 days?

56. A makes a shoe in $\frac{2}{3}$ of a day; B makes one in $\frac{2}{5}$ of a day: how many shoes can both make in 2 days?

57. A can mow an acre of grass in $\frac{3}{4}$ of a day, and B in $\frac{2}{5}$ of a day: how long will it take both together to mow an acre?

58. Two men, A and B, agreed to build a wall for $300; A sent 5 men for 4 days, and B 5 men for 6 days: how much ought each to receive?

59. A man can do $\frac{1}{5}$ of a piece of work in a day, and a boy can do $\frac{1}{8}$ of it in a day: in how many days can both of them, working together, do it?

60. A and B together can build a wall in 8 days, and A can build it alone in 12 days: how long will it take B to build it?

61. A can do a piece of work in 6 days, and B in 8 days: if they both work together, how long will it take them to do the work?

62. John can saw a pile of wood in 6 days, and, with the assistance of Charles, he can saw it in 4 days: how long will it take Charles to saw it alone?

63. A and B can do $\frac{1}{3}$ of a piece of work in a day, and A can do $\frac{1}{5}$ of it in a day: how long will it take B alone to do it?

64. A can do a piece of work in 4 days, B in 5 days, and C in 6 days: in what time can they together do it?

65. A and B can do a piece of work in 10 days, and A, B, and C in 8 days: how long will it take C alone to do the work?

66. A, B, and C can do a job in 20 days; A and B can do it in 40 days; and A and C in 30 days: in how many days can each do it alone?

67. Two men start from two places 495 miles apart, and travel toward each other; one travels 20 miles a day, and the other 25 miles a day: in how many days will they meet?

68. A owes $\frac{2}{3}$ of B's income, but, by saving $\frac{7}{45}$ of B's income annually, he can pay his debt in 5 years, and have $50 left: what is B's income? *450*

69. If a man traveling 14 hours a day, perform half a journey in 5 days, how long will it take to perform the other half, if he travel 10 hours a day? *7*

70. If a man can do a piece of work in $9\frac{1}{5}$ days, working 8 hours a day, how long will it take, if he work 6 hours a day?

71. A hare is 30 rods before a hound, but the hound runs 7 rods while the hare runs 5: how far must the hound run to catch the hare? *105*

72. A hare starts 50 leaps before a hound, and leaps 4 times while the hound leaps 3 times; but 2 of the hound's leaps equal 4 of the hare's: how many leaps must the hound take to catch the hare? *75*

73. If a steamer sails 9 miles an hour down stream, and 5 miles an hour up stream, how far can it go down stream and back again in 14 hours. *45*

74. A steamer sails a mile down stream in 5 minutes, and a mile up stream in 7 minutes: how far down stream can it go and return again in one hour? *5*

75. A and B did a piece of work, and $\frac{2}{3}$ of what A did equaled $\frac{4}{5}$ of what B did: if B received $18, how much did A receive? ⟍6

76. A man spent $\frac{3}{4}$ of his money and then earned $\frac{1}{2}$ as much as he had spent, and then had $21 less than he had at first: how much money did he have at first? 56

77. A father bequeathed $17000 to two sons, giving the younger $\frac{7}{10}$ as much as the elder: what was the share of each?

78. A man paid $8100 for 2 farms, and $\frac{2}{5}$ of the cost of the larger farm was equal to $\frac{9}{10}$ of the cost of the smaller: what was the cost of each?

79. A pipe will fill a cistern in 4 hours, and another will empty it in 6 hours: how long will it take to fill it when both pipes run?

80. An estate was so divided between two heirs that $\frac{2}{3}$ of the share of the elder was equal to $\frac{3}{4}$ of the share of the younger, and the difference between their shares was $200: what was the share of each?

81. A and B are partners in business; A's capital is equal to $\frac{3}{4}$ of B's, and their profits are $2100, which are divided on the basis of the capital invested: what is the share of each?

82. A and B are partners; $\frac{2}{5}$ of A's capital is equal to $\frac{2}{3}$ of B's, and their loss in business is $2600: what is each partner's share of the loss?

83. A, B, and C are partners, and B has invested $\frac{3}{4}$ as much capital as A, and C $\frac{2}{3}$ as much as B: if their profits amount to $6300, what will be each partner's share?

84. A sold B a horse for $\frac{1}{5}$ more than its cost, and B sold it for $80, losing $\frac{1}{6}$ of its cost: how much did A pay for the horse?

85. How much grain must a farmer take to mill to bring away 120 lb. after the miller has taken 10% for toll?

RATIO AND PROPORTION.

RATIO.

ORAL EXERCISES.

ART. 328. The ratio of 6 to 2 is $6 \div 2$, or 3; the ratio of 2 to 6 is $2 \div 6$, or $\frac{1}{3}$; the ratio of 6 to 9 is $6 \div 9$, or $\frac{2}{3}$; and the ratio between any two numbers is expressed by their quotient.

1. What is the ratio of 8 to 4? 4 to 8?

2. What is the ratio of 6 to 12? 12 to 6?

3. What is the ratio of 15 to 50? 50 to 15?

4. What is the ratio of \$5 to \$15? \$20 to \$50?

5. What is the ratio of 16 lb. to 40 lb.?

6. What is the ratio of $\frac{9}{10}$ to $\frac{3}{10}$? $\frac{3}{10}$ to $\frac{9}{10}$?

7. What is the ratio of $\frac{1}{2}$ to $\frac{1}{4}$? $\frac{1}{3}$ to $\frac{1}{6}$? $\frac{1}{5}$ to $\frac{1}{4}$?

8. What is the ratio of $\frac{2}{3}$ to $\frac{3}{4}$? $\frac{3}{5}$ to $\frac{5}{8}$? $\frac{5}{6}$ to $\frac{2}{3}$?

9. What is the ratio of 5 to $\frac{1}{3}$? $\frac{1}{3}$ to 4? $\frac{1}{4}$ to $2\frac{1}{2}$?

The ratio of two numbers may be expressed by writing a colon (:) between them; as, $6:3$, which is read *the ratio of 6 to 3.*

10. Read $7:12$; $6:9$; $5:3$; $\frac{1}{2}:\frac{2}{3}$; $.3:.7$

11. Read $3°:16°$; 4 oz. : 10 oz.; $\frac{3}{5}$ ft. : $1\frac{1}{2}$ ft.; \$3 : \$2$\frac{1}{2}$.

WRITTEN EXERCISES.

12. What is the value of the ratio of 112 to 35?

PROCESS: $112 : 35 = 112 \div 35 = 3\frac{1}{5}$, *Ans.*

What is the value of:

13. $216:81$?

14. $129:215$?

15. $14.3:6.5$?

16. $1.44:3.2$?

17. $\frac{4}{16}:\frac{5}{8}$?

18. $150:16\frac{2}{3}$?

19. $12\frac{1}{2}:30\frac{1}{4}$?

20. $34\frac{1}{2}:5\frac{3}{4}$?

21. 6 qt. : 3 pk.?

22. 5 lb. 12 oz. : 17 lb. 4 oz.?

23. 2 ft. 6 in. : 12 ft. 6 in.?

24. 15 pk. : 12 bu. 2 pk.?

Which is the greater ratio:

25. 3 : 4 or 2 : 3?　　**29.** $4 or 3 ft. : 4 ft.?

26. 5 : 7 or 9 : 12?　　**30.** 5 yd. : 6 yd. or 5 in. : 6 in.?

27. .3 : .8 or 5 : 30?　　**31.** 6 lb. : 9 lb. or 9 oz. : 6 oz.?

28. $\frac{1}{2} : \frac{2}{3}$ or $\frac{1}{5} : \frac{1}{2}$?　　**32.** $\frac{2}{3}$ lb. : $\frac{3}{4}$ lb. or $\frac{3}{5}$ yr. : $\frac{2}{3}$ yr.?

33. Multiply the ratio 10 : 21 by the ratio 14 : 15.

PROCESS: $\begin{cases} 10:21 = \frac{10}{21}. \quad 14:15 = \frac{14}{15}. \\ \frac{10}{21} \times \frac{14}{15} = \frac{4}{9}, \textit{ Ans.} \end{cases}$

34. Multiply 9 : 10 by 24 : 23; 7 : 15 by 25 : 14.

35. What is the product of 12 : 25, 15 : 24, and 16 : 21?

36. What is the product of $\frac{2}{3} : \frac{1}{2}$, $\frac{1}{4} : \frac{1}{3}$, and $\frac{2}{5} : \frac{3}{4}$?

37. Reduce the product of 20 : 80, 4 : 3, and 6 : 8 to a simple ratio in its lowest terms.

1ST PROCESS.　　　　　2D PROCESS.

$\begin{array}{r} 20:80 \\ 4:3 \\ 6:8 \\ \hline 20 \times 4 \times 6 : 80 \times 3 \times 8 \\ 480:1920 \\ 1:4, \textit{ Ans.} \end{array}$

$\frac{20}{80} \times \frac{4}{3} \times \frac{6}{8} = \frac{\overset{}{\cancel{20}} \times 4 \times \overset{2}{\cancel{6}}}{\underset{4}{\cancel{80}} \times \cancel{3} \times \underset{4}{\cancel{8}}} = \frac{1}{4}$

$\frac{1}{4} = 1:4, \textit{ Ans.}$

The product of the three ratios by the first process is 480 : 1920, which is reduced to its lowest terms (1 : 4) by dividing both terms by 480.

38. Reduce the product of 6 : 8, 10 : 12, and 16 : 15 to a simple ratio in its lowest terms.

DEFINITIONS, PRINCIPLES, AND RULE.

ART. 329. Ratio is the relation between two like numbers expressed by their quotient.

The two numbers thus compared are the **Terms** of the ratio, the first term being the **Antecedent,** and the second term the **Consequent.** The two terms form a **Couplet.**

When the antecedent is greater than the consequent, the value of the ratio is greater than 1; when the antecedent is less than the consequent, the value is less than 1.

ART. 330. The ratio between two numbers may be expressed by writing a colon between them; as, $5 : 12$; or in the form of a fraction, the antecedent being the numerator and the consequent the denominator; as, $\frac{5}{12}$.

The colon, called the *sign of ratio*, is the sign of division ($\div$) with the horizontal line omitted.

ART. 331. Ratios are either *Simple* or *Compound*.

A **Simple Ratio** is the ratio of two numbers; as, $5 : 8$, or $\frac{3}{5} : \frac{4}{5}$.

A **Compound Ratio** is the product of two or more simple ratios.

A compound ratio may be expressed in three ways, as follows: $(5 : 6) \times (7 : 10)$; or, $\frac{5}{6} \times \frac{7}{10}$; or, $\begin{cases} 5 : 6 \\ 7 : 10 \end{cases}$

The ratio resulting from the inversion of the terms of a given ratio is called an *Inverse Ratio*, also a *Reciprocal Ratio*. Thus, $5 : 7$ is the *inverse* or *reciprocal* of $7 : 5$.

ART. 332. **Principles.**—1. *The two terms of a ratio must be like numbers.*

2. *If the product of the two terms of a ratio be divided by either term, the quotient will be the other term.*

3. *The value of a ratio is not changed by multiplying or dividing both of its terms by the same number.*

4. *The product of two or more ratios equals the ratio of the product of their antecedents to the product of their consequents.* Thus, $(4 : 6) \times (5 : 8) = 4 \times 5 : 6 \times 8$.

ART. 333. To reduce a compound ratio to a simple ratio:

Rule.—*Multiply the antecedents together for an antecedent, and the consequents for a consequent.*

SIMPLE PROPORTION.

ORAL EXERCISES.

1. What two numbers have a ratio to each other equal to the ratio of 15 to 5? 24 to 12? 7:21?

2. What two numbers have a ratio to each other equal to 45:15? 12:60? 72:24? 11 to 44?

3. To what number has 10 a ratio equal to the ratio of 3 to 6? 8 to 4? 3 to 9? 2 to 3?

4. To what number has 12 a ratio equal to 6:30?

5. 12 is to 60 as 5 is to what number?

6. 13 is to 39 as 15 is to what number?

7. 14:42 = 25: what number?

Art. 334. The equality of two ratios is expressed by placing a double colon (::) between them. Thus, $5:10 = 7:14$ is written $5:10::7:14$, and is read 5 *is to* 10 *as* 7 *is to* 14.

8. Read 8:40 :: 12:60, and show that the two ratios are equal.

9. Read 27:9 :: 63:21, and show that the two ratios are equal.

10. Read $5:2\frac{1}{2} :: 25:12\frac{1}{2}$, and show that the two ratios are equal.

WRITTEN EXERCISES.

Find the missing term in the following:

11. 21:7 :: 36: —

12. 15:40 :: 18: —

13. —:24 :: 8:32

14. —:9 :: 60:18

15. 45:30 :: —:24

16. 2.5:62.5 :: —:3.25

17. 7.2:— :: 4.7:9.4

18. .25:— :: 2.5:7.5

19. $\frac{2}{3}:\frac{3}{4} :: \frac{5}{6}:$ —

20. $\frac{3}{5}:\frac{2}{3} :: - :\frac{7}{8}$

21. $- :2\frac{1}{3} :: \frac{1}{4}:\frac{3}{7}$

22. $\frac{1}{3}:- :: \frac{1}{5}:\frac{1}{6}$

23. \$5:\$45 :: 6 lb. : —

24. \$.75:\$3 :: — :56 oz.

25. 6 men:96 men :: 15 da. : —

26. 8 horses:14 horses :: $\frac{4}{5}$: —

DEFINITIONS, PRINCIPLES, AND RULES.

ART. 335. A **Proportion** is an equality of ratios.

The first ratio of a proportion is called the *First Couplet*, and the second ratio the *Second Couplet*. The two terms of each couplet are *like numbers*. (Art. 332, Pr. 1.)

ART. 336. The first and third terms of a proportion are the **Antecedents,** and the second and fourth terms, the **Consequents;** the first and fourth terms are the **Extremes,** and the second and third terms, the **Means**.

The antecedents of a proportion are the antecedents of its ratios, and the consequents are the consequents of its ratios.

The four terms of a proportion are *Proportionals*, and the last is the *fourth* proportional to the other three in their order.

Three numbers are in proportion when the ratio of the first to the second equals the ratio of the second to the third; as, $8:12::12:18$. The second number is called a *mean proportional*.

ART. 337. Proportions are either *Simple* or *Compound*.

A **Simple Proportion** is an equality of two simple ratios.

A **Compound Proportion** is an equality of two ratios, one or both of which are compound.

ART. 338. **Principles.**—The proportion $4:8::6:12$ may be written $\frac{4}{8} = \frac{6}{12}$, and multiplying the two equal fractions by 8 and 12, their denominators, gives $4 \times 12 = 6 \times 8$. Hence,

1. *The product of the extremes of a proportion equals the product of the means.* Hence,

2. *If the product of the extremes of a proportion be divided by either mean, the quotient will be the other mean.*

3. *If the product of the two means of a proportion be divided by either extreme, the quotient will be the other extreme.*

4. *If three of the four terms of a proportion are given, the fourth term may be found.*

Art. 339. 1. To find either extreme of a simple proportion:

Rule.—*Divide the product of the two means by the other extreme.*

2. To find either mean of a simple proportion:

Rule.—*Divide the product of the two extremes by the other mean.*

Art. 340. The solution of a problem by proportion involves:

1. The arranging of the three given terms, called the *Statement.*

2. The finding of the fourth term.

Art. 341. Since the two terms of each couplet or ratio of a proportion must be like numbers and the two ratios equal, a problem involving a proportion may be solved by the following rule:

Rule.—1. *Take for the third term the number which is of the same kind as the answer sought, and make the other two numbers the first couplet, placing the* GREATER *for the second term, when the answer is to be* GREATER *than the third term; and the* LESS *for the second term, when the answer is to be* LESS *than the third term.*

2. *Divide the product of the second and third terms by the first term, and the quotient will be the fourth term.*

Notes.—1. When the terms of the first couplet are denominate numbers, they must be reduced to the same denomination before forming the proportion.

2. The process of finding the fourth term may be shortened by cancellation. The proportion $15 : 45 :: 27.5 :$ — may be completed thus:

$$\frac{\overset{3}{\cancel{45}} \times 27.5}{\cancel{15}} = 82.5 \qquad \text{or}: \quad \cancel{15}\ \Big|\ \frac{\overset{3}{\cancel{45}}}{27.5}$$

$$27.5 \times 3 = 82.5$$

3. The process of solving problems by simple proportion is sometimes called "*The Rule of Three.*"

27. If 15 yards of cloth cost $24, what will 40 yards cost?

STATEMENT.

15 yd. : 40 yd. : : $24 : Ans.

$$\frac{40}{15)\overline{\$960}}$$

$64, *Ans.*

Since the cost of 40 yards is to be the answer, make $24, the cost of 15 yards, the third term of a proportion.

Since 40 yards will cost more than 15 yards, the fourth term is to be *greater* than the third, and hence the second term must be *greater* than the first; make 40 yards the second term and 15 yards the first, giving the proportion 15 yd. : 40 yd. : : $24 : cost of 40 yards.

Multiply $24 by 40 and divide the result (product of the means) by 15; the quotient ($64) is the fourth term sought.

28. If 45 sheep cost $265, what will 140 sheep cost?

29. If 70 acres of land cost $1875, what will 320 acres cost? 640 acres?

30. If 120 acres of land cost $3000, how many acres can be bought for $4500?

31. If 4 lb. 6 oz. of butter cost $1.75, what will 15 pounds cost? 17¼ pounds?

32. If a man's pulse beat 75 times in a minute, how many times will it beat in 8 hours?

33. If a clock tick 120 times in a minute, how many times will it tick in 9¼ hours?

34. If a comet move 4° 20′ in 15 hours, how far will it move in 5 days? In 7½ days?

35. If 24 barrels of flour will supply 160 men 6 weeks, how many barrels will supply 360 men the same time?

36. If a vertical staff 3 feet high cast a shadow 5 feet long, how long a shadow will a pole 120 feet high cast at the same time?

37. If a pole 20 feet high casts a shadow 12 feet long, how high is the tree whose shadow, at the same time, is 90 feet long?

38. If $\frac{5}{9}$ of a farm is worth $4500, what is $\frac{3}{4}$ of it worth? $\frac{2}{3}$ of it?

39. If $\frac{7}{8}$ of a yard of silk cost $2.10, what will $16\frac{1}{2}$ yards cost? $33\frac{1}{3}$ yards?

40. If $6\frac{1}{4}$ tons of hay cost $58.75, how many tons can be bought for $173.90?

41. If a garrison of 160 men consume 24 barrels of flour in 6 weeks, how many barrels will supply it 21 weeks? 52 weeks?

42. If 12 men can mow 20 acres of grass in a day, how many acres can 25 men mow?

Art. 342. A proportion may be regarded as a comparison of two *causes* and their corresponding *effects*, as follows: *1st cause : 2d cause :: 1st effect : 2d effect.*

The principles involved may be thus stated:

1. *The ratio of two like causes equals the ratio of their effects; and, conversely, the ratio of two like effects equals the ratio of their causes.*

2. *The ratio of two like causes equals the* INVERSE *ratio of their times; and, conversely, the ratio of the times of two like causes equals the* INVERSE *ratio of the causes.*

Note.—The second principle may be thus stated: *The greater the cause, the less the time required to produce a given effect; and, conversely, the greater the time, the less the cause required.*

43. If 9 men can build a wall in 15 days, how long will it take 5 men to build it?

STATEMENT.

5 men : 9 men :: 15 days : Ans.

$$5)\overline{135}$$

27 days, *Ans.*

The 15 days is the third term, since the answer is to be in days.

If it take 9 men 15 days to build a wall, it will take 5 men (less cause) more than 15 days; and hence the answer, or fourth term, is greater than the third term, and consequently the second term must be greater than the first term. The proportion is 5 men : 9 men :: 15 days : —.

44. If 12 men can dig a ditch in 6 days, how long will it take 5 men to dig it?

45. If 15 men can harvest a field of wheat in 12 days, how many men can harvest it in 5 days?

46. Divide 90 into two parts whose ratio is equal to the ratio of 4 and 5.

PROPORTIONS: $\begin{cases} (4+5):90::4:\text{smaller part.} \\ (4+5):90::5:\text{greater part.} \end{cases}$

NOTE.—These proportions are based on the principle that when four numbers are in proportion, *the sum of the first and second terms is to the sum of the third and fourth terms as the first term is to the third, or as the second term is to the fourth.*

47. Divide 640 into two parts proportional to 8 and 12. To 9 and 11. 7 and 9. 7 and 25.

48. An estate worth $9600 was divided between two heirs in proportion to their ages, which were 15 years and 17 years respectively: how much did each receive?

49. Two men are 150 miles apart, and approach each other, one traveling 2 miles while the other travels 3: how far will each travel before they meet?

COMPOUND PROPORTION.

WRITTEN PROBLEMS.

1. What is the fourth term of the compound proportion $(5:8) \times (10:9) \times (12:25) :: 13: —$?

1ST PROCESS.

$$\begin{array}{r} 5:8 \\ 10:9 :: 13:— \\ 12:25 \\ \hline 1:3 :: 13:— \\ 3 \times 13 = 39, \ Ans. \end{array}$$

2D PROCESS.

$$\frac{8 \times 9 \times 25 \times 13}{5 \times 10 \times 12}$$

$$3 \times 13 = 39, \ Ans.$$

An inspection of the second process shows that the four numbers above the horizontal line are *the factors of the product of the means*, and that the three numbers below the line are *the factors of the first extreme.* By canceling the factors common to dividend and divisor, the fourth term is found directly.

Find the fourth term of these compound proportions:

2. $\left.\begin{array}{l} 20:48 \\ 36:15 \\ 10:4 \end{array}\right\} :: 25 : -$ **4.** $\left.\begin{array}{l} 5:9 \\ 2.5:7.5 \\ 4:10 \end{array}\right\} :: 6 : -$

3. $\left.\begin{array}{l} 16:35 \\ 21:8 \\ 9:6 \\ 12:45 \end{array}\right\} :: 16 : -$ **5.** $\left.\begin{array}{l} 2\frac{1}{2}:7 \\ 25:10 \\ 4:6\frac{1}{4} \\ 15:12 \end{array}\right\} :: 35 : -$

6. If 2 men can mow 16 acres of grass in 10 days, working 8 hours a day, how many men can mow 27 acres in 9 days, working 10 hours a day?

STATEMENT.

16 acres : 27 acres $\left.\right\}$
9 days : 10 days $\left.\right\} :: 2$ men : —.
10 hours : 8 hours $\left.\right\}$

Since the answer required is to be a number of *men*, make 2 *men* the third term.

If the mowing of 16 acres require 2 men, the mowing of 27 acres will require *more* than 2 men, and hence the first ratio is 16 acres : 27 acres, the *greater* number being the second term.

PROCESS.

$$\frac{\overset{3}{\cancel{27}} \times \cancel{10} \times \cancel{8} \times \cancel{2}}{\cancel{16} \times \cancel{9} \times \cancel{10}} = 3, \; Ans.$$
$$\underset{2}{}$$

If 10 days require 2 men, 9 days will require *more* than 2 men, and hence the second ratio is 9 days : 10 days, the *greater* number being the second term.

If working 8 hours a day require 2 men, working 10 hours a day will require *less* than 2 men, and hence the third ratio is 10 hours : 8 hours, the *less* number being the second term.

This statement gives 3 men for the fourth term.

NOTE.—In determining which number of each ratio of the compound ratio is to be the second term, *reason* FROM *the number in the* CONDITION. See Art. 343, note 2.

7. If 12 men can build 50 rods of wall in 15 days, how many men can build 80 rods in 16 days?

8. If it cost $30 to make a walk 10 feet wide and 90 feet long, how much will it cost to make a walk 8 feet wide and 225 feet long?

9. If 6 men can excavate 576 cubic feet of earth in 8 days of 9 hours each, how much can 8 men excavate in 9 days of 10 hours each?

10. If 7 horses eat 35 bushels of oats in 25 days, how many bushels will 15 horses eat in 21 days?

11. If a man walk 120 miles in 6 days of 10 hours each, how many miles will he walk in 16 days of 8 hours each?

12. If 1500 bricks, each 8 in. long and 4 in. wide, will make a walk, how many slabs of stone, each 2 ft. long and 1 ft. 4 in. wide, will be required for the same purpose?

13. If it cost $84 to shingle a roof 36 ft. long and 21 ft. wide, what will it cost to shingle a roof 33 ft. long and 27 ft. wide?

14. If 4 men dig a trench in 15 days of 10 hours each, in how many days of 8 hours each can 5 men perform the same work?

15. If it cost $120 to build a wall 40 ft. long, 14 ft. high, and 1 ft. 6 in. thick, what will it cost to build a wall 180 ft. long, 21 ft. high, and 1 ft. 3 in. thick?

16. If 4 men can dig a ditch 72 rd. long, 5 ft. wide, and 2 ft. deep in 12 days, how many men can dig a ditch 120 rd. long, 6 ft. wide, and 1 ft. 6 in. deep in 9 days?

17. If 16 men can excavate a cellar 50 ft. long, 36 ft. wide, and 8 ft. deep in 10 days of 8 hours each, in how many days of 10 hours each can 6 men excavate a cellar 45 ft. long, 25 ft. wide, and 6 ft. deep?

18. If 32 men can dig a ditch 40 rd. long, 6 ft. wide, and 3 ft. deep in 9 days, working 8 hours a day, how many men can dig a ditch 15 rd. long, 4½ ft. wide, and 2 ft. deep in 12 days, working 6 hours a day?

ART. 343. To solve a problem by compound proportion:

Rule.—1. *Take for the third term the number which is of the same kind as the answer sought, and arrange the first and second terms of each ratio composing the compound ratio as in simple proportion.*

2. *Divide the product of all the factors of the second and third terms of the compound proportion by the product of the factors of the first term, shortening the process by cancellation.*

NOTES.—1. All compound proportions used in the solution of problems have each one compound and one simple ratio.

2. The terms of each ratio composing the compound ratio are arranged precisely as they would be if the answer depended wholly on them and the third term. They may be arranged on the principle of "cause and effect."

3. The fourth term may be found *by first reducing the compound ratio to a simple ratio* (Art. 333), *and then dividing the product of the second and third terms of the resulting simple proportion by the first term.*

4. The process of solving problems by compound proportion is also called "*The Double Rule of Three.*"

PARTNERSHIP.

ART. 344. A **Partnership** is an association of two or more persons for the transaction of business.

A partnership association is called a *Company*, *Firm*, or *House*, and the members of it are called *Partners*.

ART. 345. The property invested in the business by the partners is called *Capital*, *Joint Stock*, or *Stock in Trade*, according to the nature of the business.

The manner of conducting the business, including the sharing of profits and losses, is usually determined by a written agreement, called a *partnership contract*.

In the absence of a special agreement, or contract, profits and losses are shared by the partners in proportion to the use or value of the capital invested.

Art. 346. When the capital of the several partners is invested an *equal* time, the partnership is called *Simple;* when their capital is invested an *unequal* time, the partnership is called *Compound.*

WRITTEN PROBLEMS.

1. A, B, and C entered into partnership in business for 2 years; A put in $3600, B $2400, and C $2000, and their net profits were $3000: what was each partner's share?

I. PROCESS BY PROPORTION

$3600, *A's capital.*	$8000 : $3600 :: $3000 : $1350, *A's share of profits.*
2400, *B's capital.*	$8000 : $2400 :: $3000 : $900, *B's* " "
2000, *C's capital.*	$8000 : $2000 :: $3000 : $750, *C's* " "
$8000, *Entire capital.*	$3000, *Entire profits.*

Since the capital of the several partners was employed an equal time, their shares of the profits are proportional to their capitals. Hence, the entire capital is to each partner's capital as the entire profits are to his share of the profits.

II. PROCESS BY FRACTIONAL PARTS.

$3600 ÷ $8000 = $\frac{9}{20}$, *A's part of capital.*　　Since A owned $\frac{9}{20}$,
$2400 ÷ $8000 = $\frac{3}{10}$, *B's* " "　　B $\frac{3}{10}$, and C $\frac{1}{4}$ of
$2000 ÷ $8000 = $\frac{1}{4}$, *C's* " "　　the capital, A was
$\frac{9}{20}$ of $3000 = $1350, *A's share of profits.*　　entitled to $\frac{9}{20}$, B $\frac{3}{10}$,
$\frac{3}{10}$ of $3000 = $900, *B's* " "　　and C $\frac{1}{4}$ of the
$\frac{1}{4}$ of $3000 = $750, *C's* " "　　profits.

NOTE.—It is shorter to find what part the profits are of the entire capital (in this problem, $\frac{3}{8}$), and then take the same part of each partner's capital for his share of the profits. The fraction may be expressed *decimally*, if this be preferred.

2. A and B were partners in business; A put in $5000 and B $4000, and their profits in three years were $4500: what was each partner's share of the profits?

3. A, B, and C formed a partnership in business; A put in $8000, B $4500, and C $3500, and their loss the first year was $3200: what was each partner's share?

4. The capital of two partners is proportional to 4 and 3; their profits are $7700: what is each partner's share?

5. A, B, and C form a partnership, A's capital being $4000, B's $6400, and C's $5600; they make a net gain of $3200, and then sell out for $20000: what is each partner's share of the gain? Of the proceeds of the sale?

6. A and B traded in partnership 2 years, making an annual profit of $5460; during the first year A owned $\frac{2}{3}$ of the stock, and during the second year B owned $\frac{3}{4}$ of it: what is each partner's share of the total profits?

7. A and B formed a partnership; A put in $3000, and, at the close of the first year, added $2000; B put in $4000, and, at the close of the second year, took out $2000; at the close of the third year, the profits amounted to $3450: what was each partner's share?

I. PROCESS BY PRODUCTS.

$3000 \times 1 = $3000
$5000 \times 2 = \underline{$10000}

$13000, *A's capital for* 1 *year.*

$4000 \times 2 = $8000
$2000 \times 1 = \underline{$2000}

$10000, *B's capital for* 1 *year.*

$13000 + $10000 = $23000, *Entire capital for* 1 *year.*

$23000 : $13000 :: $3450 : $1950, *A's share of profits.*

$23000 : $10000 :: $3450 : $1500, *B's share of profits.*

Since A had $3000 invested for 1 year and $5000 for 2 years, the use of his capital was equivalent to the use of $13000 for 1 year. Since B had $4000 invested for 2 years and $2000 for 1 year, the use of his capital was equivalent to the use of $10000 for 1 year. Hence the profits, amounting to $3450, should be shared by them in proportion to $13000 and $10000. A's share = $\frac{13}{23}$; B's share = $\frac{10}{23}$.

Interest of $3000 for 1 yr. at 6% = $180
Interest of $5000 for 2 yr. at 6% = $600

$780, *Interest of A's capital.*

Interest of $4000 for 2 yr. at 6% = $480
Interest of $2000 for 1 yr. at 6% = $120

$600, *Interest of B's capital.*

$780 + 600 = $1380, *Interest of entire capital.*

$1380 : $780 : : $3450 : $1950, *A's share.*

$1380 : $600 : : $3450 : $1500, *B's share.*

Since the use of capital is represented by its interest for the time, the use of A's capital is represented by $780, and the use of B's by $600. Hence, the profits ($3450) should be shared by them in proportion to $780 and $600. A's share = $\frac{13}{23}$; B's = $\frac{10}{23}$.

NOTE.—The ratio of the interests will be the same whatever be the rate per cent.

8. A, B, and C entered into business as partners, each putting in $5000 as capital; at the end of 2 years, A took out $1000, B $2000, and C $3000, and, at the end of the fourth year, they closed the business with a loss of $3600: what was the loss of each?

ART. 347. **Principles.**—1. *When the time is equal, the partnership value of the capital of the several partners is in proportion to its amount.* Hence,

2. *In simple partnership, the gain or loss is shared by the partners in proportion to the amounts of their capital.*

3. *When the time is not equal, the partnership value of the capital of the several partners depends jointly on its amount and time of investment.* Hence,

4. *In compound partnership, the gain or loss is shared by the several partners in proportion to the products of the amounts of their capital by the time of investment; or in proportion to the interests of their capital for the time of investment.*

NOTE.—The above principles are applicable only when the several partners devote equal time or otherwise render equal service in carrying on the business.

N. C. A.—25.

INVOLUTION AND EVOLUTION.

Art. 348. The first power of 4 is 4; the second power of 4 is 4×4, which is 16; the third power is $4 \times 4 \times 4$, which is 64; the fourth power is $4 \times 4 \times 4 \times 4$, which is 256; etc.

1. What is the second power of 5? Of 6? 8? 10?

2. What is the third power of 3? Of 5? 6? $\frac{2}{5}$?

3. What is the fourth power of 2? Of 3? $\frac{1}{2}$? $\frac{2}{3}$?

Art. 349. The power to which a number is to be raised may be denoted by a figure, called an *exponent*, placed at the right of the upper part of the figure or figures which express the number.

Thus, 24^2 denotes the 2d power of 24; 16^3 denotes the 3d power of 16, etc.

4. How much is 12^2? 6^3? 10^4? 16^2? 20^3?

5. How much is $(\frac{5}{8})^2$? $(\frac{3}{4})^3$? $(\frac{2}{3})^4$? $(\frac{1}{2})^5$? $(3\frac{1}{3})^2$?

Art. 350. One of the *two* equal factors of a number is called its *second* or square *root;* one of its *three* equal factors, its *third* or cube *root;* one of its *four* equal factors, its *fourth root*, etc.

6. What is the second root of 25? 49? 64? 81?

7. What is the third root of 8? 27? 64? 125?

8. What is the fourth root of 16? Of 81? 256?

9. What is the third root of $\frac{8}{27}$? $\frac{27}{64}$? $\frac{27}{125}$? $\frac{64}{216}$?

Art. 351. The root of a number may be indicated by writing the number under the character called the *radical sign* ($\sqrt{}$), and placing a figure, called the *index*, at the left and above it, to show what root is required.

Thus, $\sqrt[3]{64}$ denotes the third root of 64; $\sqrt[4]{216}$ denotes the fourth root of 216, etc. The second root is denoted by $\sqrt[2]{}$, or by $\sqrt{}$ without the index.

10. How much is $\sqrt[2]{144}$? $\sqrt[3]{125}$? $\sqrt[4]{81}$? $\sqrt[3]{\frac{27}{125}}$?

11. How much is $(\frac{3}{4})^3$? $\sqrt[3]{\frac{27}{64}}$? $(\frac{2}{3})^4$? $\sqrt[4]{\frac{16}{81}}$?

The root of a number may also be indicated by a fractional exponent, the index of the root being the denominator. Thus, $16^{\frac{1}{2}}$ denotes the square root of 16; $16^{\frac{1}{3}}$, the cube root of 16; and $16^{\frac{2}{3}}$ denotes the cube root of the square of 16.

12. How much is $81^{\frac{1}{2}}$? $125^{\frac{1}{3}}$? $256^{\frac{1}{4}}$? $243^{\frac{1}{5}}$? $(\frac{16}{49})^{\frac{1}{2}}$?

13. How much is 15^2? $225^{\frac{1}{2}}$? 6^3? $216^{\frac{1}{3}}$? $625^{\frac{1}{4}}$?

14. What integers between 1 and 100 are perfect squares?

15. What integers between 1 and 1000 are perfect cubes?

DEFINITIONS.

ART. 352. The **Power** of a number is the product obtained by taking the number one or more times as a factor.

The *First Power* of a number is the number itself; the *Second Power*, or *Square*, is the product obtained by taking the number twice as a factor; the *Third Power*, or *Cube*, is the product obtained by taking the number three times as a factor, etc.

ART. 353. An **Exponent** is a figure that denotes the degree of the power to which the number is to be raised.

ART. 354. The **Root** of a number is one of the equal factors which produce it.

The *First Root* is the number itself; the *Second*, or *Square Root*, is one of the two equal factors which produce it; the *Third*, or *Cube Root*, is one of the three equal factors, etc.

ART. 355. The **Index** is a figure placed above the radical sign ($\sqrt{}$) to denote what root is to be taken.

A number which is the product of equal factors is a *perfect power*, and has an exact root. A number which is not the product of equal factors is an *imperfect power*, and its root is called a *surd*.

ART. 356. **Involution** is the process of finding the powers of numbers.

ART. 357. **Evolution** is the process of finding the roots of numbers. It is also called the *extraction of the roots of numbers*.

Involution and evolution are converse processes. The process for finding the root of a number is derived from the process by which the power is formed.

SQUARE ROOT.

ART. 358. The second power, or square, of a number is the product of the number by itself; and the process of finding the square root of this product, or square, is readily derived from the process by which the square is formed.

ILLUSTRATIVE EXAMPLES.

1. What is the square of 53?

PROCESS.

$$53 = 50 + 3; \text{ hence, } 53^2 = (50 + 3)^2$$

$$
\begin{array}{ll}
\begin{array}{r}
50 + 3 \\
50 + 3 \\
\hline
50 \times 3 + 3^2 \\
50^2 + 50 \times 3 \\
\hline
50^2 + 2(50 \times 3) + 3^2 =
\end{array}
&
\begin{array}{l}
\text{PARTS ADDED.} \\
50^2 = 2500 \\
2(50 \times 3) = 300 \\
3^2 = 9 \\
\hline
2809
\end{array}
\end{array}
$$

An inspection of the preceding process will show that the square of 53 is equal to the square of the 5 tens, plus twice the product of the 5 tens by the 3 units, plus the square of the 3 units.

In like manner, it may be shown that the square of any number, composed of tens and units, is equal to (1) *the square of the tens*, (2) *plus twice the product of the tens by the units*, (3) *plus the square of the units*.

2. What is the square of 45?

$$\text{PROCESS: } 45^2 = \begin{cases} 40^2 & = 1600 \\ 2\,(40 \times 5) & = 400 \\ 5^2 & = 25 \\ \hline & 2025, \textit{Ans.} \end{cases}$$

What is the square of:

3. 64?	**5.** 75?	**7.** 38?	**9.** 93?	**11.** 78?
4. 56?	**6.** 82?	**8.** 83?	**10.** 39?	**12.** 85?

DIVISION INTO PERIODS.

Art. 359. The smallest integer composed of one order of figures is 1, and the greatest is 9; the smallest integer composed of two orders is 10, and the greatest is 99, and so on.

Hence, the squares of the smallest and the greatest integers composed of one, two, three, and four orders, are as follows:

$$
\begin{array}{ll}
1^2 = \quad\quad 1 & 9^2 = \quad\quad 81 \\
10^2 = \quad\quad 100 & 99^2 = \quad\quad 9801 \\
100^2 = \quad 10000 & 999^2 = \quad 998001 \\
1000^2 = 1000000 & 9999^2 = 99980001
\end{array}
$$

A comparison of the above numbers with their squares shows that the square of a number contains twice as many orders as the number, or twice as many orders less one. Hence, if a number be separated into periods of two orders each, beginning at the right, *there will be as many orders in its square root as there are periods in the number.*

13. How many orders in the square root of 2809?

SUGGESTION.—Divide the number into periods of 2 orders each, thus: 2̇80̇9. There are 2 periods, and hence there are 2 orders in the square root—*tens and units.*

How many orders in the square root of:
   14. 36864?   **16.** 871616?   **18.** 5475600?
   15. 345744?   **17.** 5308416?   **19.** 144400000?

FINDING THE TERMS OF THE ROOT.

ART. 360.   The squares of the smallest and the greatest number of units, tens, and hundreds are as follows:

$$1^2 = 1 \qquad\qquad 9^2 = 81$$
$$10^2 = 100 \qquad\qquad 90^2 = 8100$$
$$100^2 = 10000 \qquad 900^2 = 810000$$

A comparison of the above numbers with their squares shows that the square of units gives no order higher than tens; that the square of tens gives no order lower than hundreds, nor higher than thousands; that the square of hundreds gives no order lower than ten-thousands, nor higher than hundred-thousands, etc.

Hence, if a number be separated into periods of two orders each, *the left-hand period will contain the square of the left-hand or first term of the square root; the first two left-hand periods will contain the square of the first two terms of the square root,* etc.

20. What is the tens' term of the square root of 2025?

SUGGESTION.—The left-hand period of 2025 is 20; the greatest square in 20 is 16, and the square root of 16 is 4. Hence, the tens' term of the square root of 2025 is 4.

21. What is the tens' term of $\sqrt{4225}$? $\sqrt{1764}$?

22. What is the left-hand term of $\sqrt{6561}$? $390625^{\frac{1}{2}}$?

EXTRACTION OF THE SQUARE ROOT.

23. What is the square root of 3364?

PROCESS.

$$3364 | 58$$
$$5^2 = 25$$
$$5 \times 2 = 10) \; 864$$
$$108 \times 8 = 864$$

Since 3364 is composed of two periods, its square root will be composed of two orders—tens and units. (Art. 359.)

The left-hand period 33 contains the square of the tens' term of the root. The greatest square in 33 is 25, and the square root of 25 is 5. Hence, 5 is the tens' term of the root.

Since the square of a number composed of tens and units is equal to (1) the square of the tens, (2) plus twice the product of the tens by the units, (3) plus the square of the units, the difference between 3364 and the square of the 5 tens of its root, is composed of *twice the product of the tens of the root by the units, plus the square of the units.*

But the product of tens by units contains no order lower than tens, and hence the 86 tens in 864, the difference, contains *twice the product of the tens by the units;* and hence, if the 86 tens be divided by twice the 5 tens of the root, the quotient, which is 8, will be *the units' term of the root,* or one more than the units' term.

If the 8 units be annexed to the 10 tens, used as a trial divisor, and the result, 108, be multiplied by 8, the product, if it be not greater than 864, will be twice the product of the tens by the units, plus the square of the units. $108 \times 8 = 864$, and hence 8 is the units' term, and the square root of 3364 is 58. Proof: $58 \times 58 = 3364$.

What is the square root of:

24. 625?	**31.** 1444?	**38.** 6241?
25. 676?	**32.** 3025?	**39.** 7569?
26. 576?	**33.** 7744?	**40.** 6724?
27. 784?	**34.** 5184?	**41.** 2809?
28. 841?	**35.** 4225?	**42.** 5625?
29. 529?	**36.** 4356?	**43.** 1441?
30. 961?	**37.** 5929?	**44.** 5329?

45. What is the square root of 133225? Of 10.4976?

PROCESS (1).   PROCESS (2).

$$
\begin{array}{rl}
\overset{\cdot\ \cdot\ \cdot}{133225} | 365 \\
9 \\
3 \times 2 = 6)\ \ 432 \\
66 \times 6 =\ \ 396 \\
36 \times 2 = 72)\ \ 3625 \\
725 \times 5 =\ \ 3625
\end{array}
$$

$$
\begin{array}{rl}
10.4976 | 3.24 \\
9 \\
3 \times 2 = 6)\ \ 1.49 \\
6.2 \times 2 =\ \ 1.24 \\
3.2 \times 2 = 6.4)\ \ .2576 \\
6.44 \times .04 =\ \ .2576
\end{array}
$$

What is the square root of:

46. 210681?	**56.** 176.89?	**66.** $\frac{625}{2304}$?
47. 419904?	**57.** .000625?	**67.** $\frac{289}{324}$?
48. 94249?	**58.** 45.1584?	**68.** $272\frac{1}{4}$?
49. 492804?	**59.** .008836?	**69.** $1040\frac{1}{16}$?
50. 57600?	**60.** 75.364?	**70.** 2?
51. 409600?	**61.** 263.85?	**71.** 3?
52. 68425?	**62.** 134.67?	**72.** 5?
53. 522729?	**63.** 586.7?	**73.** 4.2436?
54. 173056?	**64.** 106.75?	**74.** 1.1449?
55. 390625?	**65.** 566.44?	**75.** 4.1209?

PRINCIPLE AND RULE.

ART. 361.   **Principle.**—*The square of a number, composed of tens and units, is equal to the square of the tens, plus twice the product of the tens by the units, plus the square of the units.*

ART. 362.   To extract the square root of a number:

Rule.—1. *Begin at the units' order and separate the number into periods of two orders each.*

2. *Find the greatest perfect square in the left-hand period, and place its square root at the right for the first or highest term of the root.*

3. *Subtract the square of the term of the root found from the left-hand period, and to the difference annex the second period for a dividend.*

4. *Take twice the term of the root found for a trial divisor, and the dividend, exclusive of its right-hand figure, for a trial dividend. The quotient (or the quotient reduced one) will be the next term of the root.*

5. *Annex the second term of the root to the trial divisor, and multiply the result by the second term, and subtract the product from the dividend. If the product is greater than the dividend, reduce the second term of the root, and multiply and subtract as before.*

6. *Annex the third period to the remainder for the next dividend, and divide the same, exclusive of the right-hand figure, by twice the terms of the root found; and continue in like manner until all the periods are used.*

Notes.—1. The left-hand period may contain but one order.

2. Twice the term or terms of the root, as the case may be, is called a *trial divisor*, since the next term of the root sought is sometimes less than the quotient, the dividend containing, when this is true, a part of the square of the next term of the root.

3. If the number be not a perfect square, the exact root can not be found, but it may be approximated by annexing periods of decimal ciphers. Since the square of no one of the nine digits ends with a cipher, the operation may be continued indefinitely, but sufficient accuracy is secured when continued to three decimal places.

4. In pointing off a decimal, or a mixed decimal number, begin with the order of units. If there be an odd number of decimal places, annex a decimal cipher.

5. When both terms of a common fraction are not perfect squares, the exact square root can not be found. An approximate root may be obtained by multiplying both terms of the fraction by the denominator, and extracting the root of the resulting fraction. Thus:

$$\sqrt{\frac{21}{40}} = \sqrt{\frac{21 \times 40}{40^2}} = \frac{29}{40}, \text{ nearly.}$$

6. The square root of a perfect square may be found by resolving it into its prime factors.

GEOMETRICAL EXPLANATION OF SQUARE ROOT.

ART. 363. The area of a square surface is found by squaring the length of one side; and, conversely, the length of the side is found by extracting the square root of the number denoting the area.

Let the annexed diagram represent a square surface whose area

is 625; required the length of one side.

Since the number denoting the area contains two periods, there are two terms in the square root; and since the greatest square in the left-hand period is 4, the tens' term of the root is 2. (Art. 360.) Hence, the length of the side of the square is 20 plus the units' term of the root. What is the units' term?

Taking from the given surface a square whose side is 20 and whose area is 400, there remains a surface whose area is

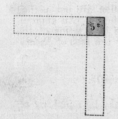

625—400, or 225. This surface consists of two equal rectangles, each 20 in length, and a small square, the length of whose side equals the width of each rectangle. What is the width of each rectangle?

Since the two rectangles contain most of the surface whose area is 225, their width may be found by dividing 225 by their joint length, which is twice 20, or 40. The quotient is 5, and hence the width of each rectangle is 5, and their joint area is 40×5, or 200.

Removing the two rectangles, there remains the small square, whose side is 5 and whose area is 25, the difference between

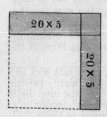

225 and 200. Hence, 5 is the units' term of the root, and the length of the side of the square is $20 + 5$, or 25.

Adding the area of the several parts, we have $20^2 + 2(20 \times 5) + 5^2 = 400 + 200 + 25 = 625$.

It is seen that the square whose side is 20, represents *the square of the tens of the root;* the two rectangles, *twice the product of the tens by the units;* and the smaller square, *the square of the units.*

NOTE.—The entire length of the surface whose area is 225, is twice the side of the square removed, plus the side of the smaller square $(20 \times 2 + 5 = 45)$, and this multiplied by 5 gives an area of 225.

CUBE ROOT.

ART. 364. The third power or cube of a number is the product obtained by taking the number three times as a factor; and the process of finding the third or cube root of this product or cube may be derived from the process by which the product or cube is formed.

ILLUSTRATIVE EXAMPLES.

1. What is the cube of 45?

$$45^3 = (40+5)^3 = 40^3 + 3 \times (40^2 \times 5) + 3 \times (40 \times 5^2) + 5^3.$$

$$
\text{PROOF:} \begin{cases}
40^3 & = 64000 \\
3\,(40^2 \times 5) & = 24000 \\
3\,(40 \times 5^2) & = 3000 \\
5^3 & = 125 \\
\hline
45^3 = & 91125, \textit{Ans.}
\end{cases}
$$

In like manner, it may be shown that the cube of any number, composed of tens and units, is equal to (1) *the cube of the tens,* (2) *plus three times the product of the square of the tens by the units,* (3) *plus three times the product of the tens by the square of the units,* (4) *plus the cube of the units.*

What is the cube of:

2. 23 ?   **8.** 51 ?   **14.** 63 ?

3. 32 ?   **9.** 52 ?   **15.** 77 ?

4. 24 ?   **10.** 55 ?   **16.** 74 ?

5. 54 ?   **11.** 75 ?   **17.** 82 ?

6. 43 ?   **12.** 80 ?   **18.** 85 ?

7. 35 ?   **13.** 64 ?   **19.** 68 ?

DIVISION INTO PERIODS.

ART. 365. The cubes of the smallest, greatest, and an intermediate number, composed of one, two, and three orders, are as follows:

$1^3 =$	1	$9^3 =$	729	$4^3 =$	64
$10^3 =$	1000	$99^3 =$	970299	$44^3 =$	85184
$100^3 =$	1000000	$999^3 =$	997002999	$444^3 =$	87528384

A comparison of the above numbers with their cubes shows that the cube of a number contains three times as many orders as the number, or three times as many orders less two or less one. Hence, if a number be separated into periods of three orders each, *there will be as many orders in its cube root as there are periods in the number.*

20. How many orders in the cube root of 91125?

SUGGESTION.—Point off the number into periods of three orders each; thus, 91125. There are two periods, and hence two orders or terms in the root.

How many orders in the cube root of:

21. 912673? **23.** 84604519? **25.** 3048625?

22. 117649? **24.** 48228544? **26.** 41063625?

FINDING THE TERMS OF THE ROOT.

ART. 366. The cubes of the smallest and greatest number of units, tens, and hundreds are as follows:

$1^3 =$	1	$9^3 =$	729
$10^3 =$	1000	$90^3 =$	729000
$100^3 =$	1000000	$900^3 =$	729000000

A comparison of the above numbers with their cubes shows that the cube of units gives no order higher than hundreds; that the cube of tens gives no order lower than thousands nor higher than hundred-thousands; and that the cube of hundreds gives no order lower than millions nor higher than hundred-millions.

Hence, if a number be separated into periods of three orders each, *the left-hand period will contain the cube of the first term of the cube root; the first two left-hand periods will contain the cube of the first two terms of the cube root*, etc.

27. What is the tens' term of the cube root of 91125?

SUGGESTION.—The left-hand period is 91; the greatest cube in 91 is 64, and the cube root of 64 is 4. Hence 4 is the tens' term of the cube root of 91125.

28. What is the tens' term of $\sqrt[3]{157464}$? Of $\sqrt[3]{110592}$?

29. What is the hundreds' term of $\sqrt[3]{13312053}$?

EXTRACTION OF THE CUBE ROOT.

WRITTEN PROBLEMS.

30. What is the cube root of 262144?

1ST PROCESS.

$$262144 | 64$$
$$6^3 = 216 \quad 4$$
$$6^2 \times 3 = 108) \overline{461\ 44}$$

$$60^2 \times 4 \times 3 = 43200$$
$$60 \times 4^2 \times 3 = 2880$$
$$4^3 = 64$$
$$\overline{46144}$$

2D PROCESS.

$$262144 | 64$$
$$6^3 = 216 \quad 4$$
$$6^2 \times 3 = 108) \overline{46144}$$
$$64^3 = 262144$$

Since 262144 is composed of two periods, its cube root will be composed of two orders.

The left-hand period, 262, contains the cube of the tens' term of the root, and the greatest cube in 262 is 216, the cube root of which is 6; hence, 6 is the tens' term of the root. How is the units' term to be found?

The cube of a number, composed of tens and units, is equal to (1) the cube of the tens, (2) plus three times the product of the square of the tens by the units, (3) plus three times the product of the tens by the square of the units, (4) plus the cube of the units (Art. 364). Hence, the difference between 262144 and the cube of the 6 tens of its cube root is composed of *three times the product of the square of the tens of its root by the units, plus three times the product of the tens by the square of the units, plus the cube of the units.*

But since the square of tens gives no order lower than hundreds (Art. 360), the 461 hundreds of the difference (46144) contains *three times the product of the square of the tens by the units.* Hence, if the 461 hundreds (rejecting the two right-hand figures) be divided by three times the square of the 6 tens of the root, the quotient, which is 4, will be *the units' term of the root,* or more than the units' term.

NOTE.—Instead of forming the parts that compose the difference, 46144, as in 1st process, the 64 may be cubed, and the result subtracted from 262144, as in 2d process.

What is the cube root of:

31. 42875 ?   **33.** 117649 ?   **35.** 274625 ?

32. 91125 ?   **34.** 185193 ?   **36.** 405224 ?

37. What is the cube root of 48228544?

PROCESS.

$$48228\overset{\cdot}{5}\overset{\cdot}{4}\overset{\cdot}{4}\,|\,\underline{364,}\ \textit{Cube root.}$$

$$3^3 = \underline{27} \qquad\qquad 7,4,\ \textit{Trial quotients.}$$

$$3^2 \times 3 = 27)\overline{212}$$

$$36^3 = \overline{46656}$$

$$36^2 \times 3 = 3888)\ \overline{15725}$$

$$364^3 = \overline{48228544}$$

Since the two right-hand figures of each dividend are rejected, only the first figure of each period need be brought down and annexed to the difference.

The quotient obtained by dividing 212 by 27 is 7, which is too large for the second term of the root, the cube of 37 being more than 48228, the first two periods.

The second difference is found by subtracting the cube of 36, the first two terms of the root, from 48228, the first two periods of the number.

NOTE.—Instead of taking the 36^3 from the two left-hand periods, and 364^3 from the number, the parts may be formed as in the 1st process above. *Use only one process.*

What is the cube root of:

38. 3048625 ?	**45.** 15.625 ?	**52.** $\frac{216}{1728}$?
39. 34328125 ?	**46.** 97.336 ?	**53.** $\frac{1331}{42875}$?
40. 43614208 ?	**47.** .074256 ?	**54.** $\frac{2744}{6859}$?
41. 27270901 ?	**48.** .015625 ?	**55.** $5\frac{104}{125}$?
42. 1225043 ?	**49.** 1953.125 ?	**56.** $37\frac{1}{27}$?
43. 421875 ?	**50.** 13312.053 ?	**57.** 2 ?
44. 14348907 ?	**51.** 28.094464 ?	**58.** 3 ?

59. A cubical box contains 19683 cubic inches: what is the length of its edge?

60. A cubical bin holds 100 bushels: what is the length of its edge?

61. A block of granite in the form of a cube contains 41063.625 cubic inches: what is the length of its edge?

PRINCIPLE AND RULE.

ART. 367. **Principle.**—*The cube of a number, composed of tens and units, is equal to the cube of the tens, plus three times the product of the square of the tens by the units, plus three times the product of the tens by the square of the units, plus the cube of the units.*

ART. 368. To extract the cube root of a number:

Rule.—1. *Begin at the units' order and separate the number into periods of three orders each.*

2. *Find the greatest cube in the left-hand period, and place its cube root at the right for the first term of the root.*

3. *Subtract the cube of the first term of the root from the*

left-hand period, and to the difference annex the first figure of the next period for a dividend.

4. *Take three times the square of the first term of the root for a trial divisor, and the quotient for the second term of the root. Cube the root now found, and, if the result is not greater than the two left-hand periods, subtract, and to the difference annex the first figure of the next period for a second dividend. If the cube of the root found is greater than the two left-hand periods, diminish the second term of the root.*

5. *Take three times the square of the two terms of the root found for a second trial divisor, and the quotient for the third term of the root. Cube the three terms of the root found, and subtract the result from the three left-hand periods, and continue the operation in like manner until all the terms of the root are found.*

NOTES.—1. The quotient obtained by dividing the dividend by the trial divisor may be too large, since *three times the square of the next figure of the root* may be a part of the dividend. Usually the term of the root sought is the quotient, or one less than the quotient.

2. When a dividend does not contain the trial divisor, write a cipher for the next term of the root. Take three times the square of the root thus formed for a trial divisor, and to the dividend annex the two remaining figures of the period, and the first figure of the next period for a new dividend.

3. If the number is not a perfect cube, the root may be approximated by annexing periods of decimal ciphers, thus adding decimal terms to the root. Sufficient accuracy is usually secured by continuing the root to two or three decimal places.

4. When both terms of a common fraction are not perfect cubes, the cube root may be found approximately by multiplying both terms of the fraction by the square of the denominator, and extracting the root of the resulting fraction. The error will be less than one divided by the denominator of the root.

5. The above method of extracting the cube root of numbers involves the general principle by which any root may be extracted. The fourth root, for example, is found by dividing the number into periods of *four* figures each, then taking the fourth root of the left-hand period for the first term of the root, four times the cube of this first term for a trial divisor, and the remainder with the first term of the next period annexed, for a dividend, etc.

6. The cube root of a perfect cube may be found by resolving it into its prime factors.

GEOMETRICAL EXPLANATION OF CUBE ROOT.

ART. 369. The solid contents of a cube are found by cubing the length of its edge; and, conversely, the length of the edge is found by extracting the cube root of the number denoting the solid contents.

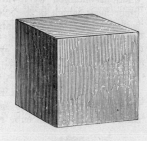

Let the annexed cut represent a cube whose solid contents are 15625; required the length of the edge.

Since the number denoting the solid contents contains two periods, there will be two terms in the cube root; and since the greatest cube in the left-hand period is 8, the tens' term of the root is 2. Hence, the length of the edge of the cube is 20 plus the units' term of the root. What is the units' term?

PROCESS.

$$
\begin{array}{r}
15625\,|\,25 \\
2^3 = 8 \quad\ \underline{6} \\
20^2 \times 3 = 1200)\ \overline{7625} \\
20^2 \times 5 \times 3 =\ \ 6000 \\
20 \times 5^2 \times 3 =\ \ 1500 \\
5^3 =\ \ \ \ \underline{\ 125} \\
\overline{7625}
\end{array}
$$

Taking from the given cube a cube whose edge is 20 and whose volume is 8000, there remains a solid whose volume is 15625 — 8000, which is 7625. An inspection of the annexed

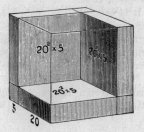

cut shows that this solid contains *three* equal rectangular solids, whose inner face (20²) is equal to the face of the removed

N. C. A.—26.

cube, and whose thickness equals the units' term of the root. What is the thickness of each of these rectangular solids?

Since they compose only a part of the solid whose solid contents are 7625, their thickness can not be greater than the quotient obtained by dividing 7625 by the area of their joint inner faces, which is $20^2 \times 3$, or 1200. The quotient is 6, which is at least one greater than the thickness of each of the three rectangular solids, since 26^3 is greater than 15625, the solid contents of the given cube. Try 5 for the thickness; $25^3 = 15625$, and hence 5 is the required thickness. The length of the edge of the given cube is $20 + 5$, or 25.

The correctness of this result may also be shown by finding the solid contents of the several parts of the given cube. The solid contents of the cube removed are, as shown above, $20^3 =$

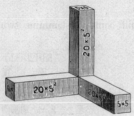

8000. The joint solid contents of the three adjacent rectangular solids are $20^2 \times 5 \times 3 = 6000$.

Removing these three rectangular solids, there remain three other rectangular solids, whose solid contents are 20×5^2, or 500 each, and whose combined solid contents are 500×3, or 1500.

Removing these three rectangular solids, there remains the small cube, whose solid contents are $5^3 = 125$.

Adding the solid contents of the several parts, we have 8000

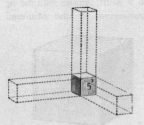

$+ 6000 + 1500 + 125 = 15625$, which represents the solid contents of the given cube.

It is seen that the cube whose edge is 20, represents *the cube of the tens of the root;* the three adjacent rectangular solids represent *three times the product of the square of tens by the units;* the three smaller rectangular solids, *three times the product of the tens by the square of the units;* and the smaller cube, *the cube of the units.*

Note.—The geometrical explanations of square root and cube root, above presented, are the reverse of those usually given.

APPLICATIONS OF POWERS AND ROOTS.

NOTE.—The propositions stated below in the form of *principles*, may be proven by geometry. The rules are readily derived from the principles.

I. THE RIGHT-ANGLED TRIANGLE.

ART. 370. The side of a right-angled triangle opposite the right angle is the *hypotenuse*, and the other two sides are the *base* and the *perpendicular*. (Art. 189.)

ART. 371. **Principles.**—1. *The square of the hypotenuse of a right-angled triangle is equal to the sum of the squares of the other two sides.*

This principle is illustrated by the annexed diagram.

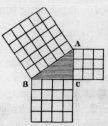

2. *The square of the base or the perpendicular of a right-angled triangle is equal to the square of the hypotenuse, less the square of the other side.*

WRITTEN PROBLEMS.

1. The base of a right-angled triangle is 8 in., and the perpendicular 6 in.: what is the length of the hypotenuse?

SOLUTION.—$\sqrt{8^2 + 6^2} = \sqrt{100} = 10$. 10 in. = length of hypot.

2. The hypotenuse of a right-angled triangle is 20 inches, and the base is 16 inches: what is the perpendicular?

3. The hypotenuse of a right-angled triangle is 45 feet, and the perpendicular is 27 feet: what is the base?

4. A rectangular field is 192 yards long and 144 yards wide: what is the length of the diagonal?

5. The foot of a ladder is 18 feet from the base of a building, and the top reaches a window 24 feet from the base: what is the length of the ladder?

6. Two boys start from the same point, and one walks 96 rods due north, and the other 72 rods due east: how far are they apart?

7. A flag pole 180 feet high casts a shadow 135 feet in length: what is the distance from the top of the pole to the end of the shadow?

8. A boy in flying his kite let out 240 feet of string, and the distance from where he stood to a point directly under the kite was 208 feet: how high was the kite, supposing the string to be straight?

II. The Circle.

Art. 372. Principles.—1. *The area of a circle is equal to the square of its diameter multiplied by .7854* (Art. 192, note 3.). Conversely,

2. *The diameter equals the square root of the quotient obtained by dividing the area by .7854.*

3. *The areas of two circles are to each other as the squares of their diameters.*

Note.—The area of an ellipse equals *the product of its two diameters as factors multiplied by .7854.*

9. A circular pond is 100 feet in diameter: how many square yards does it contain?

10. A circular room has an area of 78.54 square yards: what is its diameter?

11. How many circles, each 3 inches in diameter, will equal in area a circle whose diameter is 2 feet?

12. How many circles, each 15 inches in diameter, will equal in area a circle whose diameter is 5 feet?

13. A horse tied to a stake can graze on $218\frac{1}{6}$ square yards of surface: to what distance from the stake can it graze?

14. How many circles, each 3 inches in diameter, contain the same area as a surface 2.5 feet square?

III. The Sphere.

ART. 373. **Principles.**—1. *The surface of a sphere is equal to the square of the diameter multiplied by 3.1416.*

2. *The solid contents of a sphere are equal to the cube of the diameter multiplied by .5236.*

3. *Two spheres are to each other as the cubes of their diameters.*

NOTE.—The surface of a sphere may also be found *by multiplying the circumference by the diameter;* and the solid contents, *by multiplying the surface by one sixth of the diameter.*

15. What is the surface of a sphere whose diameter is 10 inches? 15 inches?

16. How many square miles on the surface of the earth, its mean diameter being 7912 miles?

17. How many cubic miles in the solid contents of the earth?

18. How many cubic inches in a cannon ball whose diameter is 7 inches? 9 inches?

19. How many balls 2 inches in diameter, equal in solid contents a ball whose diameter is 8 inches?

20. The surface of the planet Mercury contains about 28274400 square miles: what is its diameter?

21. The diameter of the earth is about 4 times the diameter of the moon: how many times larger than the moon is the earth? How does the moon's surface compare with the earth's surface?

22. The diameter of Jupiter, the largest planet, is about 85000 miles, and the diameter of the sun is about 850000 miles: how many times larger than Jupiter is the sun? How does Jupiter's surface compare with the sun's surface?

23. The planet Uranus contains about 18816613200000 cubic miles: what is its diameter?

SUGGESTION.—Divide the solid contents by .5236, and extract the cube root of the quotient.

24. A brass ball contains 904.7808 cubic inches: what is its diameter?

25. The spherical volume of one of the asteroids is 7238246.4 cubic miles: what is its diameter?

IV. CONES AND PYRAMIDS.

ART. 374. **Principles.**—1. *The convex surface of a cone or pyramid equals the product of the circumference or perimeter of the base by one half of the slant height.*

2. *The solid contents of a cone or pyramid equal the area of the base multiplied by one third of the altitude.*

NOTE.—The solid contents of the frustum of a cone or pyramid are found *by adding to the sum of the area of two bases the square root of their product, and multiplying the result by one third of the altitude.*

26. What is the convex surface of a cone whose base is 10 inches in diameter and whose slant height is 12 inches?

27. What is the entire surface of a pyramid whose base is 20 inches square, and whose slant height is 30 inches?

28. The base of a pyramid is 12 inches square and its height 15 inches, and the base of a cone is 12 inches in diameter and its height 15 inches: what is the difference in their solid contents?

29. Find the solid contents of the frustum of a cone the diameters of whose bases are 10 in. and 6 in., and altitude 12 inches.

30. Find the solid contents of a frustum of a pyramid whose two bases are 10 in. and 6 in. square, and whose altitude is 15 inches.

GENERAL REVIEW.

NOTE.—The following problems are chiefly selected from sets used in the examination of pupils for promotion to high schools, and in the examination of teachers.

WRITTEN PROBLEMS.

1. The minuend is 1250, and the remainder 592: what is the subtrahend?

2. The quotient is 71, the divisor 42, and the remainder 15: what is the dividend?

3. What will be the cost of 3760 lb. of hay at $12.50 a ton? At $8.50 a ton?

4. A man paid $36 for a stack of hay containing $4\frac{1}{2}$ tons, and sold it at 50 cts. a hundred: how much did he gain?

5. At $24.50 per acre, how many acres of land can be bought for $3560.75?

6. Add $\frac{2}{3}$, $\frac{5}{6}$, $\frac{1}{2}$ of $\frac{7}{8}$, and $\frac{2}{5}$ of $2\frac{1}{2}$.

7. From $17\frac{1}{2}$ take $\frac{2}{5}$ of $6\frac{1}{4}$, and multiply the remainder by $\frac{1}{5}$ of $3\frac{1}{3}$.

8. Multiply $\frac{3}{4}$ of $\frac{2}{3}$ by $\frac{7}{8}$ of $\frac{5}{7}$, and divide the product by $\frac{2}{3}$ of $\frac{9}{20}$.

9. Divide $\frac{2}{3}$ of $6\frac{1}{4}$ by $\frac{2}{3}$ of $7\frac{1}{2}$.

10. What number multiplied by $28\frac{5}{7}$ will produce 145?

11. From the sum of $215\frac{2}{3}$ and $125\frac{3}{4}$ take their difference.

12. Multiply $\frac{5}{8} + \frac{2}{3}$ of $\frac{3}{4}$ by $\frac{5}{8} - \frac{2}{3}$ of $\frac{3}{4}$.

13. Divide $2\frac{1}{2}$ by $3\frac{1}{3}$, and multiply the quotient by $3\frac{1}{5}$.

14. By what number must $8\frac{13}{16}$ be multiplied that the product may be 3?

15. A man bought $\frac{9}{16}$ of a section of land for $2880, and sold $\frac{2}{3}$ of it at $10 an acre, and the rest at $12 an acre: how much did he gain?

16. A merchant owning $\frac{7}{8}$ of a ship sells $\frac{2}{3}$ of his share for $16800: what is the value of the whole ship, at this rate, and what part of the ship has he left?

17. Add 9 thousandths, 3 hundredths, and 7 units.

18. From 15 ten-thousandths take 27 millionths, and multiply the difference by 205 tenths.

19. Multiply 160 by 16 thousandths, and divide the product by 25 ten-thousandths.

20. Multiply 15 thousandths by 15 hundredths, and from the product take 15 millionths.

21. Divide 256 thousandths by 16 millionths.

22. Multiply 625 by .003, and divide the result by 2.5.

23. Change $\frac{3}{400}$ to a decimal, and divide result by $2\frac{1}{2}$.

24. Change $\frac{8}{125}$ to a decimal, and divide result by 5000.

25. Reduce .625 of a pound troy to lower integers.

26. What decimal of a rod is .165 of a foot?

27. What will 63 thousandths of a cord of wood cost, at $2.25 per cord?

28. How many minutes will there be in the month of February, 1885? In February, 1884?

29. How many seconds in the three summer months?

30. How many steps, 2 ft. 4 in. each, will a person take in walking $2\frac{1}{4}$ miles?

31. How many times will a wheel, 12 ft. 6 in. in circumference, turn round in rolling one mile?

32. How many acres in a street 4 rd. wide and $2\frac{1}{4}$ mi. long?

33. An octavo book contains 480 pages: how many reams of paper will it take to print an edition of 1200 copies, making no allowance for waste?

34. How many grains in 14 ingots of silver, each ~hing 27 oz. 10 pwt.?

35. How many gold rings, each weighing 3.2 pwt., can be made from a bar of gold weighing .75 of a pound?

36. How many square feet of lumber in 40 inch boards, each 12 feet long and $7\frac{1}{2}$ inches wide?

37. What will a board 20 ft. long, 9 in. wide, and $1\frac{1}{2}$ in. thick cost, at $30 a thousand?

38. What will it cost to lay a pavement 36 ft. long and 9 ft. 6 in. wide, at 40 cents a square yard?

39. How many steps, 2 ft. 6 in. each, will a man take in walking round a field 45 rods square?

40. How many lengths of fence, each 14 ft. long, will inclose a field 28 rods square?

41. A rectangular field is 60 rods long and $37\frac{1}{2}$ rods wide: how many boards, each 12 feet long, will inclose it with a fence 5 boards high?

42. How many bricks, 4 by 8 in., will it take to pave a walk 16 ft. wide and $6\frac{1}{2}$ rods long, with no allowance for edges or waste?

43. A tract of land is 4 mi. long and $2\frac{1}{4}$ mi. wide: how many sections does it contain? How many acres?

44. A speculator bought $3\frac{1}{4}$ sections of land at $4.50 an acre, and sold the land at $6.25 an acre: how much did he gain?

45. A man sold a farm containing a quarter of a section of land, for $3280: what did he receive per acre?

46. What will it cost to excavate a cellar 40 ft. long, 21 ft. 6 in. wide, and 4 ft. deep, at $.75 a cubic yard?

47. How many cubic yards of earth must be removed to make a reservoir 120 ft. long, 54 ft. wide, and 9 ft. deep below the surface?

48. How many perches of stone in the walls of a fort 120 ft. square, the walls being $33\frac{1}{3}$ ft. high and, on an average, 11 ft. thick?

49. What will it cost to dig a ditch 80 ^{Dm} long, 1.4 ^{m} wide, and 8 ^{dm} deep, at 35 cts. a cubic meter? At $33\frac{1}{3}$ cts. a cubic yard?

50. How many cubic meters of stone in a wall 32^m long, 2.5^m high, and .65^m thick?

51. At $4.50 a cord, what is the value of a pile of three-foot wood 40 ft. long and 6½ ft. high?

52. A man bought a pile of four-foot wood 36 ft. long and 8 ft. high, at $5.50 a cord: what did it cost?

53. At $2.62½ a cord, what will be the cost of a pile of stove wood 85 ft. 6 in. long and 6 ft. high?

54. Three men, A, B, and C, bought a hogshead of sugar, weighing 13 cwt. 60 lb.; A received ½ of it, B ⅔ of the remainder, and C what was left: how much sugar did each receive?

55. How many sacks, holding 2 bu. 3 pk. 2 qt. each, can be filled from a bin containing 366 bu. 3 pk. 4 qt. of wheat?

56. A lady bought 6 silver spoons, each weighing 3 oz. 3 pwt. 8 gr., at $2.25 an ounce, and a gold chain, weighing 14 pwt., at $1.25 a pwt.: what was the cost of both spoons and chain?

57. How many bricks will it require to build a wall 2 rods long, 6 feet high, and 18 inches thick, each brick being 8 inches long, 4 inches wide, and 2½ inches thick, with no allowance for mortar?

58. Cincinnati is 7° 49′ west of Baltimore: when it is noon at Baltimore, what is the hour at Cincinnati?

59. New York is 75 degrees of longitude west of London: when it is noon at New York, what is the hour at London?

60. Boston is 71° 4′ 9″ W. longitude, and Cleveland is 81° 47′ W.: when it is 4 P. M. at Cleveland, what is the hour at Boston?

1. What part of a rod is 2 ft. 9 in.?

Reduce 208 rods to the decimal of a mile.

...duce ⅝ sq. yd. to the fraction of an acre?

...n ⅞ of a pound troy take ⅘ of an ounce.

...e ⅔ of a quart to the fraction of a bushel.

66. A regiment lost 8% of its men in battle, 25% of those that remained died from sickness, and it then mustered 621 men: how many men in the regiment at first?

67. A quantity of sugar was bought for $150, and sold for $167.50: what was the gain per cent?

68. A merchant bought 500 yards of cloth for $1800: for how much a yard must he sell it to gain 25%?

69. A man sold a piece of cloth for $24, and thereby lost 25%: if he had sold it for $34, would he have gained or lost, and what per cent?

70. I sold goods at 20% gain, and, investing the proceeds, sold at 20% loss: did I gain or lose by the operation, and what per cent?

71. Sold 2 carriages, at $240 a piece, and gained 20% on one and lost 20% on the other: how much did I gain or lose in the transaction?

72. A man bought a horse for $72, and sold it for 25% more than cost, and 10% less than he asked for it: what did he ask for it?

73. A merchant marked a lot of goods, costing $5800, at 30% above cost, but sold them at 10% less than the marked price: how much did he gain? What per cent?

74. What must I ask for cloth, costing $4 a yard, that I may deduct 20% from my asking price and still make 20%?

75. A man bought stock at 25% below par and sold it at 20% above par: what per cent did he make?

76. A fruit dealer lost 33⅓ per cent of a lot of apples, and sold the remainder at a gain of 50 per cent: required the per cent of gain or loss.

77. I bought 63 kegs of nails, each keg containing 100 lb., at 4½ cents a pound, and sold ⅔ of them for what ½ of them cost: what per cent did I lose on the part sold?

78. I bought $128.25 worth of goods; kept them on hand 6 months when money was worth 8% interest, and then sold them at a net gain of 6%: for how much were they sold?

79. When money was worth 9% interest, I bought $800 worth of goods, kept them 4 months, and then sold them for $959.10: what per cent on the cost did I gain?

80. A speculator borrowed the money at 8% and bought 2560 bushels of wheat at 95 cts. a bushel, Sept. 10, 1882, and on June 4, 1883, sold the lot at $1.15 a bushel: how much did he gain, no allowance for grace?

81. A house valued at $3240 is insured for $\frac{2}{3}$ of its value, at $\frac{3}{4}$%: what is the premium?

82. I pay $19.20 premium for insuring my house for $\frac{5}{8}$ of its value, at $1\frac{1}{2}$%: what is the value of my house?

83. A capitalist sent a broker $25000 to invest in cotton, after deducting his commission of $2\frac{1}{2}$%: how much cotton, at 5 cents a pound, did the broker purchase? What was his commission?

84. An agent received $502.50 to purchase cloth, after deducting $\frac{1}{2}$% commission: how many yards did he buy at $1.25 a yard?

85. What is the interest of $125.50 for 7 months 10 days, at 7%?

86. What is the interest of $50000 for 1 day, at 8%? For 2 mo. 2 da.?

87. What is the interest of $75.50 from June 12, 1879, to Aug. 6, 1880, at $7\frac{1}{2}$%?

88. A man loaned $800 for 2 years 6 months, and received $90 interest: what was the rate per cent?

89. At what rate per cent will $311.50 amount to $337.40 in 1 yr. 4 mo.?

90. What sum of money will yield as much interest in 3 yr., at $4\frac{1}{2}$%, as $540 yields in 1 yr. 8 mo., at 7%?

91. The amount of a certain principal for 3 years, at   in rate per cent, is $750, and the interest is $\frac{1}{4}$

of the principal: what is the principal, and what is the rate per cent?

92. A note for $500, dated Oct. 8, 1882, and bearing interest at 9%, is indorsed as follows: Nov. 4, 1883, $30; Jan. 30, 1884, $250. What was due July 1, 1884?

93. What is the bank discount on $125, payable in 90 days, at 8%? What the proceeds?

94. What is the bank discount of $359.50, for 60 days, at 7%? For 90 days at 8%?

95. For what sum must I give my note at a bank, payable in 4 months, at 10%, to obtain $300?

96. What is the present worth of a note of $1320, due in 3 years and 4 months, without interest, money being worth 6%? What is the discount?

97. If $75 yield $10.80 interest, what principal will yield $89.28 interest in the same time?

98. If the interest of $475 is $118.75, what would be the interest of $850 for the same time, at the same rate?

99. If the interest of a certain principal for a certain time at 5% is $120.50, what would be the interest of the same principal for the same time at 12%?

100. When exchange on London is quoted at 4.90, what will be the cost in New York of a bill of exchange for £250?

101. When exchange on Paris is quoted at 5.16½, how large a bill of exchange in francs can be bought for $2400?

102. When exchange on Berlin is quoted at 96¾, what will be the cost in New York of a bill of exchange for 19350 marks?

103. I borrow of A $150 for 6 months, and I afterward lend him $100: how long may he keep it to balance the use of the sum he lent me?

104. A owes B $300, of which $50 is due in 2 months, $100 in 5 months, and the remainder in 8 months: what is the equated time for the whole sum?

105. A man owes $300 due in 5 months, and $700 due in 3 months, and $200 due in 8 months: if he pays $\frac{1}{2}$ of the whole in 2 months, when ought the other half to be paid?

106. I have sold 50 bushels of wheat for A, and 60 bushels for B, receiving $150 for both lots: if A's wheat is worth 20% more than B's, how much ought I to pay each?

107. Two men divided a lot of wood, which they purchased together for $27; one took $5\frac{1}{2}$ cords, the other 8 cords: what ought each to pay?

108. If 8 men cut 84 cords of wood in 12 days, working 7 hours a day, how many men will cut 150 cords in 10 days, working 5 hours a day?

109. If 16 horses consume 84 bushels of grain in 24 days, how many bushels will supply 36 horses 16 days?

110. If the wages of 24 men for 4 days are $192, what will be the wages of 36 men for 3 days?

111. If 4 men in $7\frac{2}{3}$ days earn $53\frac{2}{3}$, how much will 7 men earn in $30\frac{2}{3}$ days?

112. A and B traded in company and gained $750, of which B's share was $600; A's stock was $1200: what was B's stock?

113. A and B formed a partnership for one year, and A put in $2000 and B $800: how much more must B put in at the close of 6 months to receive one half of the profits?

114. A and B engage in trade; A puts in $200 for 5 months, B $300 for 2 months; they draw out capital and profits to the amount of $1389: what is each man's share?

115. What is the square root of 41616? Of 420.25?

116. What is the cube root of 46656? Of 42.875?

117. A certain window is 30 feet from the ground: how far from the base of the building must the foot of a ladder 50 feet long be placed to reach the window?

118. Two men start from the same point; one travels 52 miles north, and the other 39 miles west: how far are they apart?

119. A house is 40 feet high from the ground to the eaves: how long a ladder will reach the eaves, supposing the foot of the ladder be placed 30 feet from the house?

120. How many rods of fence will inclose 10 acres in the form of a square?

121. A floor is 24 ft. long and 15 ft. wide: what is the distance between two opposite corners?

122. A room is 20 ft. long, 16 ft. wide, and 12 ft. high: what is the distance from one of the lower corners to the upper opposite corner?

123. How many cubic feet in a stone 8 ft. long, $5\frac{1}{2}$ ft. wide, and $3\frac{1}{2}$ ft. thick?

124. How many square feet on the surface of a stone 6 ft. long, 4 ft. wide, and $1\frac{1}{2}$ ft. thick?

125. A circular field is 40 rods in diameter: what is its circumference? How many acres does it contain?

126. The area of a circle is $470.8\frac{3}{4}$ square inches: what is the length of its diameter?

127. How many iron balls 2 in. in diameter will weigh as much as an iron ball 8 in. in diameter?

128. How many cubical blocks, each edge of which is $\frac{1}{3}$ of a foot, are equivalent to a block of wood 8 ft. long, 4 ft. wide, and 2 ft. thick?

129. How many two-inch cubical blocks can be packed in a box 12 in. long, 10 in. wide, and 8 in. deep, inside measurement?

130. How many bars of soap, each 4 in. long, $2\frac{1}{2}$ in. wide, and $1\frac{1}{2}$ in. thick, can be packed in a box 12 in. long, 10 in. wide, and 6 in. deep?

131. How many bushels of wheat will fill a bin 8 feet long, 5 feet wide, and 4 feet deep?

132. How many gallons in a round cistern 6 ft. in diameter and 7 ft. deep? How many barrels?

133. How many barrels in a round cistern 6 ft. in diameter and 9 ft. deep?

134. How many barrels of water will a tank contain which is 7 ft. long, 6 ft. wide, and $5\frac{1}{2}$ ft. deep?

135. How many gallons of water will fill a circular cistern 6 ft. deep and 4 ft. in diameter?

136. A square and a triangle contain an equivalent area, and the base of the triangle is 36.1 inches, and its altitude is 5 inches: what is the side of the square?

137. One of the mammoth pines of California is 110 feet in circumference: what is its diameter?

138. How many cubic feet in a portion of the above tree 100 feet in length, supposing its mean circumference to be $94\frac{1}{4}$ feet?

139. The mean distance of the earth from the sun (new value) is about 91400000 miles: if the earth revolves in its orbit in $365\frac{1}{4}$ days, what is its mean hourly motion?

140. The mean distance of Mercury from the sun (new value) is about 35400000 miles, and the planet revolves in its orbit in 87.9 days: what is its mean hourly motion?

141. A man steps 2 ft. 8 in., and a boy 1 ft. 10 in.; but the boy takes 8 steps while the man takes 5: how far will the boy walk while the man walks $3\frac{3}{4}$ miles?

142. Two trees stand on opposite sides of a stream 40 feet wide; the height of one tree is to the width of the stream as 8 is to 4, and the width of the stream is to the height of the other as 4 is to 5: what is the distance between their tops?

143. A cistern is filled by two pipes, one of which will fill it in 2 hours, and the other in 3 hours; it is emptied by three pipes, the first of which will empty it in 5 hours, the second in 6 hours, and the third in $7\frac{1}{2}$ hours: if all the pipes be left open, in what time will it be filled?

REVIEW QUESTIONS.

1. What is a unit? A number? An integer? In how many ways may numbers be represented? Express twenty-five by each method.

2. What is the difference between numeration and notation? Between the Arabic notation and the Roman?

3. How is the value of a figure affected by its removal one order to the left? One order to the right? How is the value of a number affected by annexing a cipher? Why?

4. How many units are there in the sum of two or more integers? Why in addition are like orders of figures written in the same column?

5. Show that the adding of 10 to a term of the minuend, and 1 to the next higher term of the subtrahend, increases the minuend and subtrahend equally. Show that the adding of 10 to a term of the minuend and subtracting 1 from its next higher term does not change the value of the minuend.

6. Why must the multiplier be an abstract number? When the multiplicand is concrete, what is true of the product? Why?

7. What kind of number is the quotient when both divisor and dividend are like numbers? How is the quotient affected by multiplying or dividing both dividend and divisor by the same number? What is the difference between short division and long division?

8. Name all the prime numbers from 1 to 20 inclusive. Show that two composite numbers may be prime with respect to each other.

9. What is meant by the factors of a number? The prime factors? Show that the common factor of two or more numbers is a factor of their sum.

10. How is a number affected by the canceling of a factor? On what principle may the common factors of a dividend and a divisor be canceled?

11. When is a divisor a *common* divisor? What is the greatest common divisor of two or more numbers? Show that the common divisor of two numbers is a divisor of their sum and also of their difference.

12. How many multiples has every number? What is a *common* multiple? What is the least common multiple of two or more numbers?

13. What is the difference between a divisor and a multiple of a number? Between the terms factor and divisor? Divisor and measure?

14. What is a fraction? In what two ways may a fraction be expressed? What is the numerator of a fraction? The denominator?

15. What is the difference between *the unit of a fraction* and *a fractional unit?* Which term of a fraction denotes the size of the fractional unit? When is the value of a fraction equal to 1? Greater than 1? Less than 1?

16. Show that the division or multiplication of both terms of a fraction by the same number, does not change its value. How is the value of a *proper* fraction affected by adding the same number to both of its terms? By subtracting the same number from both of its terms?

17. On what principle is a fraction reduced to lower terms? To higher terms? On what principle are two or more fractions reduced to a common denominator?

18. In what two ways may a fraction be multiplied by an integer? Why? In what two ways may a fraction be divided by an integer? In what three ways may a fraction be divided by a fraction?

19. What is a decimal fraction? Is the fraction *fifteen-hundredths* a decimal fraction? Why? In what two ways may it be expressed by figures? Which is called the *decimal* form? What is the denominator of a decimal fraction?

20. What is meant by decimal places? What is the name of the third decimal order from units? How is a decimal read?

21. How is the value of a decimal affected by annexing decimal ciphers? Why? By prefixing decimal ciphers? Why?

22. How is a decimal reduced to a common fraction? A common fraction to a decimal? Why can decimals be added and subtracted like integers?

23. Why does the product contain as many decimal places as both multiplicand and multiplier? Why does the dividend contain as many decimal places as both divisor and quotient?

24. How is a decimal divided by 10, 100, etc.? How is a decimal multiplied by 10, 100, etc.? Why are numbers denoting sums of money added and subtracted like decimals?

25. Is every concrete number denominate? Give illustrations. What is the difference between a simple denominate number and a compound number? Give examples.

26. How are denominate fractions reduced from a higher to a lower denomination? From a lower to a higher?

27. How is a denominate number reduced to the fraction of a higher denomination? Give an example.

28. What is the difference between simple addition and compound addition? In what respect are the processes alike?

29. When are compound numbers of the same kind? Give examples. How is a compound number divided by another of the same kind?

30. What part of the equator passes beneath the vertical rays of the sun every hour? What part of the tropic of Cancer? What part of any parallel situated between the polar circles?

31. Why is the time of day earlier at New York than at St. Louis? When the difference in longitude between two places is given, how is the difference in time found?

32. What is the Metric System? What is the primary unit of the system? Its length? What is a liter? What is a gram?

33. How are the multiples of the meter, liter, and gram named? How are the subdivisions named? Why are metric numbers added and subtracted like integers or decimals?

34. What is a rectangle? How is its area found?

35. What is a circle? When the diameter is given, how is the circumference found? How is its area found?

36. What is a right-angled triangle? How is its area found?

37. What is a rectangular solid? What is the difference between an edge and a face of a rectangular solid?

38. Show that the product of the three dimensions of a rectangular solid represents its volume or solid contents. How are the contents of a cylinder found?

39. How is the capacity of a bin in bushels found? How is the capacity of a vessel in liquid gallons found?

40. What is meant by 5 per cent of a number? What is the difference between the terms *rate per cent* and *rate?*

41. What three numbers are considered in percentage? Define each. In what two senses is the term *percentage* used? Give the three cases of percentage and the formula for each.

42. What is the distinction between the cost of an article and its selling price? When is an article sold at a profit? When at a loss or discount?

43. What is meant by commission? How is it computed? What is the difference between a factor and a broker? Define net proceeds.

44. What is capital? What is the distinction between the market value and the par value of capital? When is capital at par? At a premium? At a discount?

45. What is insurance? What is the premium? What is the distinction between property insurance and personal insurance?

46. What is a property tax? A poll tax? An excise tax? How is a property tax assessed? How is the rate of tax determined?

47. What are customs or duties? What is the difference between *specific* duties and *ad valorem* duties? What is a tariff? From what kind of taxes is the internal revenue of the United States derived?

48. What is interest? What is the rate of interest?

49. How is the interest of any principal for one year, at any rate per cent, found? Give the rule for the general method of computing interest. Give the rule for the six per cent method.

50. How many methods are there of finding the time between two dates? Which is called the method by days?

51. What is meant by days of grace? When is a note with grace payable? When is it due?

52. How is a note not drawing interest discounted by a bank? What are the proceeds? What is the discount? What is the difference between bank discount and interest?

53. What is a promissory note? What is its face? Who is an indorser? When is a note negotiable? When is a note not negotiable? What is a check?

54. On what principles is the United States Rule for partial payments based? What rule is generally used when a note runs less than a year?

55. What five quantities or numbers are considered in interest? State the five problems in interest, and give the formula for each.

56. What is the present worth of a note due at a future time without interest? Why is the difference between the present worth of a note and its face called the *true* discount? What is the difference between true discount and interest?

57. What is annual interest? When annual interest is not paid when due, what kind of interest does it draw until paid?

58. What is compound interest? In what respect does compound interest differ from annual interest?

59. What is meant by a stock investment? What are stocks? What is the distinction between capital stock and other stock?

60. What is a bond? A United States bond? What is the difference between a coupon bond and a registered bond? When bonds are quoted at 108, what are they worth?

61. What is a draft? What are the names of the three parties named in a draft? What is meant by the acceptance of a draft? By its protest? What is the distinction between a sight draft and a time draft?

62. What is exchange? What is the rate of exchange? The par of exchange? What is domestic exchange?

63. What is foreign exchange? Why is a foreign bill issued in sets of three? How is exchange on England quoted? On France? On Germany?

64. What is the equation of payments? What is meant by the equated time? On what principle is the process of finding the equated time based? What is the equation of accounts?

65. Define ratio. What are the two terms of a ratio called? Which is the dividend? When is the value of a ratio less than one? When is it greater than one?

66. Why must the two terms of a ratio be like numbers? Why is the value of a ratio not changed by multiplying or dividing both of its terms by the same number?

67. What is a compound ratio? How is a compound ratio reduced to a simple ratio?

68. What is a proportion? How many ratios in a proportion? When is a proportion called simple? When is it compound? How many terms in a simple proportion?

69. Which terms are called the extremes, and which the means? To what is the product of the extremes equal?

70. How can a missing mean be found? Why? A missing extreme? Why? If the second term of a proportion is greater than the first term, how will the fourth term compare with the third?

71. In stating a problem in proportion, which number is made the third term? Why? What is the relation between the ratio of like causes and the ratio of their effects?

72. How may a compound proportion be reduced to a simple proportion? How may the fourth term of a compound proportion be found?

73. What is the difference between a simple partnership and a compound partnership? On what does the partnership value of capital depend when the time is equal? When the time is not equal?

74. What is the difference between the power of a number and its root? Give examples. What is the difference between involution and evolution?

75. What is the difference between a perfect power and an imperfect power? Give examples. When is a root called a *surd?*

76. To what is the square of a number composed of tens and units equal? To what is the cube of a number composed of tens and units equal?

77. How many orders in the square of any number? How many orders in the square root of any number? How many orders in the cube of any number? How many orders in the cube root of any number?

78. How is the first term of the square root of any number found? The second term? How is the first term of the cube root of any number found? The second term?

79. To what is the square of the hypotenuse of a right-angled triangle equal? The square of the base or perpendicular?

80. How is the surface of a sphere found? Its volume? What is the relation between the solid contents of two spheres?

81. How is the convex surface of a cone found? The area of the base? The solid contents?

82. How is the surface of a pyramid found? Its solid contents?

83. How are the solid contents of the frustum of a cone found? The frustum of a pyramid?

APPENDIX.

PROOF OF SIMPLE RULES BY "CASTING OUT THE 9's."

ART. 375. The method of proving the elementary operations of arithmetic by "casting out the 9's" is based on the principle, that *the excess of 9's in any number is equal to the excess of 9's in the sum of its digits.*

Take, for example, 2345. Dividing it by 9, we have the remainder 5, for the excess of 9's; and adding the digits $(2 + 3 + 4 + 5 = 14)$, and dividing the sum by 9, we have the same remainder.

This principle may be thus explained:

$$2345 \begin{cases} 2000 = 222 \times 9 + 2 \\ 300 = 33 \times 9 + 3 \\ 40 = 4 \times 9 + 4 \\ 5 = \qquad\quad 5 \end{cases}$$

It is seen that the remainders obtained by dividing the several parts of a number, denoted by its several digits, by 9, are respectively the digits of the number; and the remainder obtained by dividing the number itself by 9, equals the remainder obtained by dividing the sum of its digits by 9.

PROOF OF ADDITION.

PROCESS.

325	*Excess*	1
256	"	4
358	"	7
939	"	3

The excess of 9's in the first number, found by adding its digits, is 1; in the second number, 4; in the third, 7. The excess of 9's in the sum of these excesses is 3, which equals the excess of 9's in 939, the amount. Hence, *The excess of 9's in the sum of several numbers is equal to the excess of 9's in the sum of their excesses.*

PROOF OF SUBTRACTION.

PROCESS.

3676	Excess	4
1508	"	5
2168	"	8
	"	4

Since the minuend is equal to the sum of the subtrahend and remainder, *the excess of 9's in the minuend equals the excess of 9's in the* SUM *of the excesses in the subtrahend and remainder.*

PROOF OF MULTIPLICATION.

PROCESS.

347	Excess	5
53	"	8
1041		40
1735		
18391	Excess	4

Since 347 contains a certain number of 9's with an excess of 5, and 53 contains a certain number of 9's with an excess of 8, the product of 347 and 53 consists of the product of a certain number of 9's, plus the product of 5 and 8, the excesses of 9's. Hence,

The excess of 9's in the product of two numbers is equal to the excess of 9's in the product of the excesses in these numbers.

PROOF OF DIVISION.

PROCESS.

$$347)18496(53$$
$$1735$$
$$\overline{1146}$$
$$1041$$
$$\overline{105}$$

18496	Excess	1
347	"	5
53	"	8
105	"	6
$5 \times 8 + 6 = 46$	"	1

Since the dividend equals the product of divisor and quotient, plus the remainder, the excess of 9's in the dividend is equal to the excess of 9's in the product of divisor and quotient, plus the excess in the remainder. Hence,

The excess of 9's in the dividend is equal to the excess of 9's in the product of the excesses in divisor and quotient, plus the excess in the remainder.

CIRCULATING DECIMALS.

ART. 376. A **Circulating Decimal** is an interminate decimal, containing the same figure or set of figures, repeated in the same order indefinitely. (Art. 119.)

The figure or set of figures repeated is called a *Repetend*. A repetend is denoted by a dot placed over the first and last of its figures; as, $.\dot{5}$ $.\dot{1}\dot{6}$ $.\dot{3}2\dot{5}$.

When a circulating decimal has no term but the repetend, as $.\dot{3}2\dot{5}$, it is a *Pure Circulate;* when it has one or more terms before the repetend, as $.45\dot{2}\dot{6}$, it is a *Mixed Circulate*.

A pure circulate is reduced to a common fraction *by taking the repetend for the numerator, and as many 9's for the denominator as there are figures in the repetend.*

Take, for example, the pure circulate $.\dot{6}\dot{3}$.

$$63.\dot{6}\dot{3} = 100 \text{ } times \text{ } the \text{ } pure \text{ } circulate.$$

$$.\dot{6}\dot{3} = \quad 1 \text{ } time \quad " \quad " \quad "$$

Subtracting, $63. \quad = 99 \text{ } times \quad " \quad " \quad "$

Hence, $\quad \frac{63}{99} \quad = the \text{ } value \text{ } of \text{ } .\dot{6}\dot{3}$

A mixed circulate is reduced to a common fraction *by subtracting the terms which precede the repetend from the whole circulate, and taking the difference for the numerator; and, for the denominator, taking as many 9's as there are figures in the repetend, with as many ciphers annexed as there are decimal figures before the repetend.*

Take, for example, the mixed circulate $.45\dot{1}2\dot{4}$

$$45124.\dot{1}2\dot{4} = 100000 \text{ } times \text{ } the \text{ } mixed \text{ } circulate.$$

$$45.\dot{1}2\dot{4} = \quad 100 \quad " \quad " \quad " \quad "$$

Subtracting, $45079 \quad = 99900 \quad " \quad " \quad " \quad "$

Hence, $\quad \frac{45079}{99900} \quad = the \text{ } value \text{ } of \text{ } .45\dot{1}2\dot{4}$

Pure or mixed circulates may be added, subtracted, multiplied, or divided *by first reducing them to common fractions.*

NOTE.—Circulates may be added, subtracted, multiplied, or divided without first reducing them to common fractions. In all computations, circulates may be carried to enough places to avoid any appreciable error in the result, and then treated as other decimals.

N.C. A.—28.

DUODECIMALS.

ART. 377. Artificers sometimes use a scale of twelfths, called a *duodecimal* scale, in measuring surfaces and solids.

The foot or unit is divided into *primes* ($'$); the primes into *seconds* ($''$); the seconds into *thirds* ($'''$), etc., the accents, $'$, $''$, $'''$, etc., being called *indices*.

When the unit is a *linear foot*, the prime is 1 inch, or $\frac{1}{12}$ ft.; the second, $\frac{1}{12}$ of $\frac{1}{12}$ ft., etc. When the unit is a *square foot*, the prime is $\frac{1}{12}$ sq. ft.; the second, $\frac{1}{12}$ of $\frac{1}{12}$ sq. ft., etc. When the unit is a *cubic foot*, the prime is $\frac{1}{12}$ cu. ft.; the second, $\frac{1}{12}$ of $\frac{1}{12}$ cu. ft., etc.

Hence, $12'''' = 1'''$; $12''' = 1''$; $12'' = 1'$; $12' = 1$ ft. or unit.

The following problems and solutions respectively show the method of adding, subtracting, multiplying, and dividing duodecimals:

1. Add 12 ft. 8$'$ 11$''$, 16 ft. 10$'$ 9$''$, and 24 ft. 6$''$.

$$\text{PROCESS:} \begin{cases} 12 \text{ ft.} & 8' & 11'' \\ 16 \text{ ft.} & 10' & 9'' \\ 24 \text{ ft.} & 0' & 6'' \end{cases}$$

$$\overline{\quad 53 \text{ ft.} \quad 8' \quad 2'' \; \textit{Ans.}}$$

2. From 21 ft. 7$'$ 10$''$ take 15 ft. 9$'$ 4$''$.

$$\text{PROCESS:} \begin{cases} 21 \text{ ft.} & 7' & 10'' \\ 15 \text{ ft.} & 9' & 4'' \end{cases}$$

$$\overline{\quad 5 \text{ ft.} \quad 10' \quad 6'' \; \textit{Ans.}}$$

3. Multiply 13 ft. 7$'$ 8$''$ long and 6 ft. 5$'$ wide.

PROCESS.

13 ft.	7$'$	8$''$	
	6 ft.	5$'$	

5 ft.	8$'$	2$''$	4$'''$
81 ft.	10$'$	0$''$	
87 ft.	6$'$	2$''$	4$'''$ *Ans.*

Multiply first by 5$'$ and then by 6 ft., and add the partial products.

Since $1 \times \frac{1}{12} = \frac{1}{12}$, $\frac{1}{12} \times \frac{1}{12} = \frac{1}{144}$, $\frac{1}{144} \times \frac{1}{12} = \frac{1}{1728}$, etc., feet$\times$primes or (twelfths) must produce *primes*; primes by primes, *seconds;* seconds by primes, *thirds;* and, generally, the denomination of the product of any two denominations is denoted by the *sum of their indices.*

4. Divide 87 ft. 6′ 2″ 4‴ by 13 ft. 7′ 8″.

PROCESS.

Dividend.	Divisor.
87 ft. 6′ 2″ 4‴	13 ft. 7′ 8″
81 ft. 10′	6 ft. 5′, *Quot.*
5 ft. 8′ 2″ 4‴	
5 ft. 8′ 2″ 4‴	

The process is the reverse of that in multiplication. For convenience in multiplying, place the divisor at the right of the dividend, and the terms of the quotient below those of the divisor.

EQUATION OF ACCOUNTS.

ART. 378. When an account contains both debits and credits, the equated time for the payment of the balance may be found by the following

Rule.—1. *Find the equated time for each side of the account.*

2. *Multiply the side of the account which falls due* FIRST *by the number of days between the dates of the equated time of the two sides, and divide the product by the balance of the account.*

3. *The quotient will be the number of days to the maturity of the balance, to be counted* FORWARD *from the later equated date when the* SMALLER *side of the account falls due first, and* BACKWARD *when the* LARGER *side falls due first.*

PROBLEMS.

1. Find the equated date of maturity of each side of the following account:

DR.	JOHN SMITH, *in account with* JOHN JONES.					CR.
1878.			TIME OF CREDIT.	1878.		
Apr. 3,	To Mdse.	$220	3 mo.	July 1,	By Cash	$200
June 1,	"	125	4 "	Oct. 3,	"	150
July 15,	"	200	4 "	Dec. 20,	"	300
Aug. 24,	"	140	6 "			
Oct. 1,	"	190	6 "			

PROCESS.

Debits.		*Credits.*	
DUE.		DUE.	
July 3, 1878, $220 × 00 =		July 1, 1878, $200 × 00 =	
Oct. 1, " 125 × 90 = 11250		Oct. 3, " 150 × 94 = 14100	
Nov. 15, " 200 × 135 = 27000		Dec. 20, " 300 × 172 = 51600	
Feb. 24, 1879, 140 × 236 = 33040		$650)$65700	
Apr. 1, " 190 × 272 = 51680		101	
$875)$122970			
141			

Debits are due 141 days from
July 3, 1878, which is Nov. 21.

Credits are due 101 days from
July 1, 1878, which is Oct. 10.

NOTE.—Each side of the account may be equated without reference to the other, as is done above, or the first or last date of the account may be made a common *starting-point* for both sides.

2. The above account, as equated, stands thus:

Dr.	Cr.
Due Nov. 21, 1878 . . . $875	Due Oct. 10, 1878 . . . $650

When is the *balance* of the account due?

PROCESS.

Debits $875		$650
Credits 650		42
Balance . . . $225		$225)$27300

Difference in time, 42 days.   121

Balance is due 121 days from Nov. 21, 1878, which is March 22, 1879.

Suppose the account settled Nov. 21, the *later* date. Since the credit side of the account has been due since Oct. 10, it has been drawing interest for 42 days. To increase the debit side of the account by an equal amount of interest, the balance must remain unpaid 121 days. Counting *forward* 121 days from Nov. 21, the balance is found to be due March 22, 1879.

3. Suppose that the debit and credit sides of an account when equated stand as follows:

Dr.	Cr.
Due Nov. 21, 1883 . . . $650	Due Oct. 10, 1883 . . . $875

What would be the equated time of payment for the balance?

PROCESS.

Credits	$875	$875
Debits	650	42
Balance . . .	$225	$225)$36750
Difference in time, 42 days.		163

Balance is due 163 days *prior* to Nov. 21, 1883, which is June 11, 1883.

Suppose the account settled Nov. 21, as before. The credit side, having been due since Oct. 10, has been drawing interest for 42 days. That the debit side of the account may be increased by an equal amount of interest, the balance must be regarded as due 163 days prior to Nov. 21.

4. The debit and credit sides of an account when equated stand as follows:

Dr.	*Cr.*
Due June 5, 1883 . . $1285	Due July 1, 1883 . . . $1000

What is the equated time of payment for the balance?

Ans. March 6, 1883.

5. Find the time when the balance of the following equated account began to draw interest:

Dr.	*Cr.*
Due July 12, 1882 . . . $450	Due Sept. 1, 1882 . . . $800

Ans. Nov. 6, 1882.

NOTES.—1. When an account is settled by *cash*, each side of the account is increased by its interest from maturity to the date of settlement, and the difference between the two sides thus increased by interest, is called the *Cash Balance*. Instead of adding the accrued interest to each side, the *balance of interest* may be found and added to or subtracted from the balance of items, according as the two balances fall upon the same or upon opposite sides of the account. Thus, in problem 2 above, the balance of interest, which is the interest of $650 for 42 days, falls on the credit side, and the balance of items on the debit side. The cash balance is $225—$3.90, which is $221.10.

2. The cash balance may be found directly, without equating the account, by finding the interest of each item from its maturity to the date of settlement, and taking the difference between the sums of the debit interests and credit interests for *the balance of interest*. When the balance of interest and the balance of items fall on the *same* side, the cash balance is their *sum;* when they fall on opposite sides, the cash balance is their *difference.*

ARITHMETICAL PROGRESSION.

ART. 379. An **Arithmetical Progression** is a series of numbers which so increases or decreases that the difference between the consecutive numbers is constant.

The numbers which form the series are called *Terms*, the first and last terms being the *Extremes*, and the intervening terms the *Means*. The difference between the consecutive terms is called the *Common Difference*.

In an *Ascending Series* the terms increase; as, 2, 5, 8, 11, 14, etc.; and in a *Descending Series* the terms decrease; as, 20, 17, 14, 11, 8, etc.

In an arithmetical progression five quantities are considered, as follows:

    1. The first term.
    2. The last term.
    3. The common difference.
    4. The number of terms.
    5. The sum of all the terms.

Such is the relation between these five quantities that, if any three of them are given, the other two may be found.

The ascending series, 2, 5, 8, 11, 14, having 5 terms, may be expressed in three forms, as follows:

(1)   2   5   8   11   14
(2)   2   2+3   2+(3+3)   2+(3+3+3)   2+(3+3+3+3)
(3)   2   2+3 $2+3\times2$ $2+3\times3$ $2+3\times4$

A comparison of these three forms of the same series shows that each term is composed of two parts, viz: (1) the first term; (2) the common difference taken as many times as there are *preceding* terms. Hence:

  1. The last term of an ascending series is equal to the first term plus the common difference, taken as many times as there are terms in the series less one. Conversely,

  2. The first term of an ascending series is equal to the last term minus the common difference, taken as many times as there are terms in the series less one.

3. The common difference is equal to the difference between the first and last terms, divided by the number of terms less one.

4. The number of terms less one is equal to the difference between the first and last terms, divided by the common difference.

Let   3   5   7   9   11   13   be an arithmetical series,

and,   13   11   9   7   5   3   be the series reversed.

Then, $16 + 16 + 16 + 16 + 16 + 16 = $ *twice* the sum of the terms,

and $8 + 8 + 8 + 8 + 8 + 8 = $ the sum of the terms.

An inspection of the above shows that the sum of the first and last terms of an arithmetical series, multiplied by the number of terms, is equal to *twice* the sum of all the terms. Hence,

5. The sum of all the terms of an arithmetical series is equal to the product of one half the sum of the first and last terms, multiplied by the number of terms.

NOTE.—One half of the sum of the first and last terms is equal to the *average* of the several terms of the series.

From the above principles may be deduced the following formulas:

1. Last term = first term $\pm$ (common difference $\times$ number terms less 1).

2. First term = last term $\mp$ (common difference $\times$ number terms less 1).

3. Common difference = $\left\{ \begin{array}{l} \textit{last term—first term} \\ \textit{first term—last term} \end{array} \right\} \div$ *number terms less 1.*

4. Number terms less 1 = $\left\{ \begin{array}{l} \textit{last term—first term} \\ \textit{first term—last term} \end{array} \right\} \div$ *common difference.*

5. Sum of terms = $\frac{1}{2}$ (first term + last term) $\times$ number terms.

NOTE.—The first term of an ascending series corresponds to the last term of a like descending series, and the last term of a descending series corresponds to the first term of a like ascending series.

PROBLEMS.

1. The first term of an ascending series is 4, the common difference 3, and the number of terms 8: what is the last term?

Ans. 25.

2. The last term of a descending series is 1, the common difference 4, and the number of terms 12: what is the first term?

Ans. 45.

3. The extremes of an arithmetical series are 47 and 3, and the number of terms 12: what is the common difference?

Ans. 4.

4. The two extremes of a series are 12 and 177, and the common difference 5: what is the number of terms?   *Ans.* 34.

5. The two extremes of a series are 20 and 152, and the number of terms 45: what is the sum of all the terms?   *Ans.* 3870.

GEOMETRICAL PROGRESSION.

ART. 380.   A **Geometrical Progression** is a series of numbers which so increases or decreases that the ratio between the consecutive terms is constant.

The first and last terms are called the *Extremes*, and the intervening terms are the *Means*. The constant ratio is called the *Common Ratio*.

In a geometrical progression five quantities are considered, and these (as in arithmetical progression) are so related to each other that, any three being given, the other two may be found. These five quantities are:

1. *The first term.*
2. *The last term.*
3. *The common ratio.*
4. *The number of terms.*
5. *The sum of all the terms.*

The ascending series, 2, 6, 18, 54, 162, 486, has 6 terms, and the first term is 2, and the common ratio or multiplier is 3. This series may be expressed in three forms, as follows:

(1)	2	6	18	54	162	486
(2)	2	2×3	$2\times3\times3$	$2\times3\times3\times3$	$2\times3\times3\times3\times3$	$2\times3\times3\times3\times3\times3$
(3)	2	2×3	2×3^2	2×3^3	2×3^4	2×3^5

A comparison of the corresponding terms of the three forms shows that each term of the series is composed of two factors; viz, (1) the first term, and (2) the common ratio raised to a power whose exponent or degree is equal to the number of *preceding* terms.   Hence:

1. *The last term of a geometrical series is equal to the first term, multiplied by the common ratio raised to a power whose degree is one less than the number of terms.*   Conversely,

2. The first term is equal to the last term, divided by the common ratio raised to a power whose degree is one less than the number of terms.

3. The common ratio is equal to that root of the quotient of the last term divided by the first term whose index is one less than the number of terms.

By an algebraic process it may be shown that:

4. The sum of an ascending geometrical series is equal to the product of the last term, and the common ratio less the first term, divided by the common ratio less one.

From the above principles may be deduced the following formulas:

1. Last term $=$ first term $\times$ ratio^{n-1}.
2. First term $=$ last term $\div$ ratio^{n-1}.
3. Ratio $= \sqrt[n-1]{\text{last term} \div \text{first term}}$.
4. Sum $= \begin{cases} (\text{last term} \times \text{ratio} - \text{first term}) \div (\text{ratio} - 1). \\ (\text{first term} - \text{last term} \times \text{ratio}) \div (1 - \text{ratio}). \end{cases}$

NOTES.—1. By "ratio $^{n-1}$," in 1st and 2d formulas, is meant the ratio raised to a power whose degree is the *number of terms less* 1. The index of the root, in the 3d formula $(n-1)$, is the number of terms less 1.

2. In an ascending series the ratio is greater than 1, and in a descending series the ratio is less than 1.

3. When the number of terms in a descending geometrical series is infinite, the last term is 0, and *the sum of the series is equal to the first term divided by one less the ratio.*

PROBLEMS.

1. The first term of a geometrical series is 5, the ratio is 3, and the number of terms 7: what is the last term? *Ans.* 3645.

2. The last term of a series is 64, the ratio 2, and the number of terms 10: what is the first term? *Ans.* $\frac{1}{8}$.

3. The first term of a series is 5, and the sixth term is 1215: what is the ratio? *Ans.* 3.

4. The first term of a series is 10, the sixth term 2430, and the ratio 3: what is the sum of the six terms? *Ans.* 3640.

5. A man worked 15 days on condition that he should receive 1 cent the first day, 5 cents the second day, and so on, the wages of each day being 5 times the wages of the previous day: how much did he receive? *Ans.* $76293945.31

N. C. A.—29

ANSWERS TO WRITTEN PROBLEMS.

N. B.—When a problem has two or more answers, with few exceptions, only the *last* answer is given.

Page 13.

11. 108657.
12. 442555.
13. 63077833.
14. 74467648.
15. 12369 bushels.
16. $652.658.
17. 457820 sq. mi.
18. 15780436 pop.

Page 14.

19. 3602990 sq. mi.
21. 383.
22. 502.
23. 462.
24. 649.

Page 15.

25. 598.
26. 732.
27. 803.
28. 631.
29. 867.
30. 636.
31. 633.
32. 156 sheep.
33. 145 students.
34. $156.
35. $117.

Page 17.

14. $4075.
15. 49894136 mi.
16. 936361 pop.
17. 516054 pop.

Page 18.

18. 950112 sq. mi.
19. (1) 325262 sq. mi.; (2) 624850 sq. mi.
20. 215115849 bu.
21. $467.
22. $2330.
23. $1032.
24. $800.
25. 6890 bu.
26. 26956.

Page 21.

11. 2499120.
12. 230668800.
13. 503232000.
14. 364800000000.
15. 17424000 ft.
16. 1572480 mi.
17. 26278400 acres.
18. 28500 soldiers.
19. $798 gain.

20. 1428 mi.
21. 60 mi.
22. 648000.
23. 4560000.
24. 305000000.

Page 24.

1. 120 sheets.
2. 1000 minutes.
3. $500.
4. $12.00, or 1200 cents.
5. $6.00, or 600 c.
6. 162000.
7. 880000.
8. 422000.
9. $135493333\frac{1}{3}$.

Page 25.

11. 5660656.
12. 40822137.
13. 8652963.
14. 617496532.

Page 26.

16. 652919.
17. 94240.
18. 25629438.
19. 4432246.
20. 613566.

Page 27.

11. 54.
12. 233; rem. 20.
13. 536.
14. 526.
15. 365.
16. 485.
17. 18; rem. 3600.
18. 54; rem. 7304.
19. 3464.
20. 8743.
21. 4567.
22. 41.
23. $45\frac{60}{100}$.
24. 356.
25. $4\frac{6035}{10000}$.

Page 28.

26. $38\frac{4602}{10000}$.
27. 95.
29. $9\frac{200}{7000}$.
30. $24\frac{800}{4800}$.
31. $9\frac{10800}{18000}$.
32. $2\frac{1600}{64000}$.
33. 2400 acres.
34. 160 mi.
35. 820 hours.

Page 31.

1. 72 lemons.
2. 20 yards.
3. 42 acres.
4. 45 cows.
7. 50.
8. 13; 95 rem.
9. 61; 50 rem.

Page 32.

11. $761\frac{39}{77}$.
12. $190\frac{28}{70}$.

Page 33.

14. $387\frac{18}{81}$.
15. $480\frac{7}{72}$.
16. $1487\frac{26}{81}$.
17. $5203\frac{49}{77}$.
18. $3604\frac{16}{96}$.
19. $433\frac{3}{110}$.

Page 34.

21. 7.
22. 18.
23. 12.
24. 55.
26. $\frac{1}{6}$.
27. 8.
28. $\frac{5}{21}$.
29. 2.
30. 10.
31. 1.
32. 1.
33. $1\frac{3}{4}$.
34. 3.

Page 37.

8. 5, 5, 2, 3.
9. 2, 2, 2, 2, 2, 2, 5.
10. 2, 2, 2, 5, 7.
11. 2, 2, 3, 5, 7.
12. 2, 2, 2, 2, 2, 3, 3.

Page 38.

14. 2, 3, 7.
16. 42.

17. 48.
18. 5.
19. 189.
20. 275.
21. 15.
22. 3.
23. 35.
24. 63.
25. 21.

Page 40.

11. 12.
12. 63.
13. 48.
14. 28.
15. 42.
16. 128

Page 41.

18. 4.
19. 48.
20. 37.
21. 1.
22. 252.
23. 14.
24. 192.
25. 57.
26. $52.
27. $165.
28. 39 lb.
29. 25.
30. 120.
31. 72.
32. 7.
33. 8.
34. 39.
35. 1

36. 101.
37. 16.
38. 84.
39. 80.

Page 44.

11. 120.
12. 126.
13. 480.
14. 108.
15. 144.
16. 210.
17. 300.
18. $720.

Page 45.

20. 180.
21. 280.
22. 180.
23. 600.
24. 756.
25. 720.
26. 1200.
27. 1890.
28. 3360.
29. 2520
30. 60.
31. 108.
32. 90.
33. 210.
34. 5040.
35. 720.
36. 630.
37. 756.
38. 60 minutes.
A, 6 mi.; B, 5 mi.; C, 4 mi.

Page 50.

8. $\frac{2923}{9}$.
9. $\frac{988}{15}$.
10. $\frac{1080}{20}$; $\frac{4061}{30}$.
11. $\frac{763}{12}$.
12. $\frac{1121}{15}$.
13. $\frac{6187}{30}$.
14. $\frac{5803}{40}$.
15. $\frac{3433}{25}$.
16. $\frac{20409}{50}$.
17. $\frac{24613}{41}$.
18. $\frac{8767}{24}$.
19. $\frac{7291}{35}$.
20. $\frac{7289}{12}$.

Page 51.

28. $16\frac{7}{16}$.
29. 27.
30. $17\frac{10}{15}$.
31. $39\frac{3}{18}$.
32. $19\frac{28}{32}$.
33. 9.
34. $17\frac{40}{64}$.
35. $38\frac{10}{35}$.
36. $46\frac{4}{50}$.
37. $109\frac{9}{39}$.
38. $12\frac{4}{333}$.
39. $53\frac{3}{45}$.
40. $2016\frac{15}{21}$.

Page 53.

51. $\frac{3}{7}$.
52. $\frac{13}{14}$.
53. $\frac{12}{23}$.
54. $\frac{7}{11}$.
55. $\frac{13}{14}$.

56. $\frac{6}{7}$.
57. $\frac{12}{25}$.
58. $\frac{7}{11}$.
59. $\frac{11}{20}$.
60. $\frac{5}{8}$.
61. $\frac{21}{29}$.
62. $\frac{41}{61}$.
63. $\frac{13}{14}$.
64. $\frac{17}{29}$.
65. $\frac{6}{7}$.
66. $\frac{7}{11}$.
67. $\frac{7}{8}$.
68. $\frac{16}{25}$.
69. $\frac{1}{6}$.
70. $\frac{116}{165}$.
71. $\frac{11}{13}$.
72. $\frac{27}{182}$.
73. $\frac{3}{4}$.
74. $\frac{7}{12}$.
75. $\frac{5}{13}$.
76. $\frac{3}{5}$.
77. $\frac{5}{7}$.
78. $\frac{7}{8}$.
79. $\frac{18}{23}$.
80. $\frac{10}{11}$.
81. $\frac{199}{392}$.
82. $\frac{4}{7}$.
84. $\frac{1}{2}$.
85. $\frac{4}{5}$.

Page 54.

97. $\frac{30}{36}, \frac{28}{36}, \frac{15}{36}, \frac{22}{36}$.
98. $\frac{18}{60}, \frac{28}{60}, \frac{27}{60}, \frac{14}{60}$.
99. $\frac{30}{45}, \frac{27}{45}, \frac{25}{45}, \frac{12}{45}$.
100. $\frac{42}{48}, \frac{20}{48}, \frac{27}{48}, \frac{22}{48}$.
101. $\frac{36}{60}, \frac{50}{60}, \frac{28}{60}, \frac{26}{60}$.

Page 55.

104. $\frac{36}{48}, \frac{30}{48}, \frac{21}{48}, \frac{28}{48}$.

105. $\frac{54}{72}, \frac{9}{72}, \frac{60}{72}, \frac{56}{72}$.

106. $\frac{12}{24}, \frac{18}{24}, \frac{21}{24}, \frac{10}{24}$.

107. $\frac{18}{30}, \frac{25}{30}, \frac{14}{30}, \frac{11}{30}$.

108. $\frac{32}{40}, \frac{36}{40}, \frac{26}{40}, \frac{11}{40}$.

109. $\frac{28}{42}, \frac{18}{42}, \frac{35}{42}, \frac{8}{42}$.

110. $\frac{32}{72}, \frac{66}{72}, \frac{84}{72}, \frac{69}{72}$.

111. $\frac{80}{120}, \frac{72}{120}, \frac{100}{120}, \frac{105}{120}$.

112. $\frac{42}{60}, \frac{32}{60}, \frac{33}{60}, \frac{26}{60}$.

113. $\frac{49}{84}, \frac{32}{84}, \frac{33}{84}, \frac{34}{84}$.

114. $\frac{24}{60}, \frac{55}{60}, \frac{33}{60}, \frac{58}{60}, \frac{31}{60}$.

115. $\frac{4025}{7245}, \frac{2898}{7245}, \frac{3542}{7245}, \frac{1380}{7245}, \frac{6363}{7245}$.

Page 56.

125. $\frac{2}{5}$.

126. $\frac{3}{7}$.

127. $1\frac{1}{4}$.

128. $1\frac{3}{5}$.

129. $\frac{20}{21}$.

130. $\frac{4}{5}$.

131. $1\frac{1}{2}$.

132. $1\frac{9}{40}$.

133. $2\frac{2}{3}$.

134. $1\frac{19}{25}$.

Page 57.

135. $\frac{128}{8}$.

136. $\frac{500}{15}$.

137. $12\frac{2}{3}$.

138. $6; 5\frac{1}{25}, 8\frac{1}{12}, 63\frac{7}{11}$.

139. $\frac{150}{12}, \frac{225}{12}, \frac{400}{12}$.

140. $\frac{36}{65}$.

141. $\frac{7}{12}; 2; 5\frac{5}{8}$.

142. $\frac{15}{24}, \frac{20}{24}, \frac{14}{24}$.

143. $\frac{60}{72}, \frac{56}{72}, \frac{66}{72}, \frac{153}{72}$ (or $2\frac{9}{72}$).

144. $\frac{5}{6}, \frac{33}{6}, \frac{2}{6}$.

145. $\frac{28}{63}, \frac{36}{63}, \frac{336}{63}$.

146. $\frac{15}{12}, \frac{30}{12}, \frac{25}{12}$.

147. $\frac{8}{40}, \frac{60}{40}, \frac{35}{40}$.

Page 58.

12. $2\frac{2}{3}$.

13. $2\frac{14}{45}$.

14. $2\frac{71}{160}$.

Page 59.

16. $1\frac{41}{70}$.

17. $1\frac{25}{48}$.

18. $2\frac{17}{36}$.

19. $2\frac{1}{6}$.

20. $2\frac{1}{3}$.

21. $2\frac{37}{80}$.

22. $2\frac{31}{45}$.

23. $2\frac{91}{162}$.

24. $2\frac{5}{36}$.

25. $\frac{7}{30}$.

27. $1\frac{5}{8}$.

28. $3\frac{5}{6}$.

29. $1\frac{17}{42}$.

30. $4\frac{3}{10}$.

32. $288\frac{2}{3}$.

33. $274\frac{11}{12}$.

34. 174.

35. $65\frac{14}{15}$.

36. $2037\frac{1}{2}$.

37. $68\frac{71}{84}$.

38. $3\frac{17}{40}$.

Page 61.

13. $\frac{3}{11}$.

15. $\frac{17}{45}$.

16. $\frac{5}{36}$.

17. $\frac{17}{54}$.

18. $\frac{11}{100}$.

19. $\frac{5}{42}$.

20. $\frac{19}{60}$.

21. $\frac{13}{132}$.

22. $\frac{35}{108}$.

23. $\frac{7}{36}$.

25. $\frac{7}{36}$.

26. $2\frac{39}{40}$.

27. $\frac{5}{72}$.

28. $1\frac{2}{77}$.

Page 62.

30. $2\frac{1}{4}$.

31. $2\frac{1}{6}$.

32. $2\frac{5}{12}$.

33. $46\frac{7}{8}$.

34. $19\frac{1}{10}$.

35. $17\frac{13}{21}$.

36. $88\frac{11}{24}$.

37. $70\frac{5}{6}$.

38. $63\frac{3}{4}$.

39. $\frac{13}{24}$.

40. $9\frac{11}{12}$.

41. $\frac{4}{35}$.

42. $\frac{9}{35}$.

43. $10\frac{5}{12}$.

44. $1\frac{1}{2}$.

45. $1\frac{19}{120}$.

Page 63.

46. $1\frac{7}{15}$.

47. $1\frac{3}{36}$.

48. $7\frac{9}{40}$.

49. $7\frac{31}{66}$.

50. $7\frac{3}{8}$.

51. $\frac{17}{60}$.

52. $\frac{2}{5}$.

53. $\frac{31}{63}$.

Page 64.

12. $4\frac{4}{5}$.

13. $5\frac{5}{12}$.

14. $5\frac{5}{7}$.

15. $7\frac{6}{7}$.

16. $19\frac{1}{5}$.

17. $2\frac{1}{12}$.

18. $2\frac{15}{16}$.

19. $5\frac{1}{6}$.

20. $4\frac{11}{25}$.

21. $40\frac{80}{133}$.

22. 2250.

23. 3648.

24. $16600.

25. $34466\frac{2}{3}$.

26. 4200 feet.

Page 65.

38. $51\frac{1}{3}$.

39. $50\frac{4}{15}$.

40. $29\frac{3}{11}$.

41. $50\frac{10}{11}$.

42. $254\frac{4}{5}$.

43. $623\frac{1}{13}$.

44. $465\frac{3}{10}$.

45. 248.

46. $432\frac{4}{7}$.

47. $1702\frac{1}{2}$.

48. $522\frac{2}{3}$.

49. 2520.

Page 66.

51. 572.

52. 693.

53. 808.

54. $8223\frac{3}{4}$.

55. 8649.

56. $135533\frac{1}{3}$.

57. $45196\frac{2}{3}$.

58. $17427\frac{2}{3}$.

59. $427745\frac{1}{2}$.

60. 29125.

61. 19482.

62. 48702.

63. $48235\frac{5}{7}$.

64. $47521\frac{3}{11}$.

65. 81648.

Page 67.

75. $\frac{11}{16}$.

76. $\frac{20}{27}$.

77. $\frac{3}{10}$.

78. $\frac{3}{4}$.

79. $\frac{2}{7}$.

80. $\frac{1}{20}$.

81. $\frac{35}{64}$.

82. $\frac{1}{2}$.

83. $8\frac{1}{3}$.

84. $24\frac{3}{4}$.

85. $22\frac{11}{12}$.

86. 28.

Page 68.

89. $\frac{14}{15}$.

90. $\frac{2}{9}$.

91. $2\frac{259}{480}$.

92. $\frac{35}{144}$.

93. $5\frac{5}{8}$ acres.

94. 35 cents.

95. $\$\frac{35}{48}$.

96. $34\frac{3}{8}$ cents.

97. $\$3\frac{1}{3}$.

98. $266.

99. $\$4\frac{1}{6}$.

100. $343\frac{3}{4}$ cents.

101. $\$142\frac{5}{8}$.

102. $\$7729\frac{1}{6}$.

Page 70.

14. $\frac{2}{21}$.

15. $\frac{2}{23}$.

16. $\frac{3}{40}$.

17. $\frac{4}{35}$.

18. $\frac{3}{47}$.

19. $\frac{3}{61}$.

20. $\frac{3}{77}$.

21. $\frac{1}{27}$.

22. $\frac{7}{24}$.

23. $\frac{11}{24}$.

24. $\frac{2}{3}$.

25. $\frac{5}{6}$.

28. $14\frac{61}{100}$.

29. $37\frac{1}{3}$.

Page 71.

40. 36.

41. 45.

42. 25.

43. $123\frac{1}{3}$.

44. $169\frac{7}{17}$.

45. $297\frac{13}{21}$.

46. $160\frac{5}{7}$.

47. 300.

48. 12.

49. 36.

50. $40\frac{10}{11}$.

51. 20.

Page 73.

62. $\frac{3}{4}$.

63. $1\frac{7}{26}$.

64. $\frac{5}{8}$.

65. $\frac{4}{5}$.

66. $1\frac{1}{2}$.

67. $1\frac{9}{13}$.

68. $\frac{8}{15}$.

69. 5.

70. $\frac{7}{9}$.

71. $\frac{1}{2}$.

72. $4\frac{2}{3}$.

73. $2\frac{10}{13}$.

76. $10\frac{3}{4}$.

77. $1\frac{7}{45}$.

78. $25\frac{55}{81}$.

Page 74.

1. $\frac{5}{12}$.

2. $\frac{1}{28}$.

3. 27.

4. $\frac{2}{3}$.

5. $\frac{2}{3}$.

6. $1\frac{1}{2}$.

7. 20.

8. $\frac{1}{20}$.

9. $2\frac{6}{7}$.

10. $\frac{4}{33}$.

11. $\frac{2}{5}$.

12. $2\frac{1}{4}$.

13. 9.

14. $\frac{96}{413}$.

15. $3\frac{8}{9}$.

16. $\frac{160}{729}$.

17. 24.

18. $3\frac{3}{20}$.

19. $44\frac{4}{9}$.

20. 21 months.

Page 75.

21. $15\frac{3}{5}$ bushels.

22. $46\frac{7}{8}$ yards.

23. $9\frac{7}{33}$ hours.

24. $126\frac{1}{4}$ acres.

Page 80.

51. 5.

52. $\frac{1}{12}$.

53. $41\frac{1}{3}$.

54. $8\frac{1}{6}$.

55. $1\frac{13}{32}$.

56. $1\frac{27}{28}$.

57. $504\frac{1}{6}$.

58. $1\frac{1}{6}$.

59. $188\frac{5}{8}$ acres.

60. 33 sq. rods.

61. $13\frac{11}{69}$ hours.

62. $12\frac{1}{2}$ tons.

63. $5270.

64. $68\frac{4}{5}$ yd.

65. 105.

66. $115\frac{1}{5}$ miles.

67. $1375.

68. $14175.

69. 390.

Page 81.

70. $14616.

71. $2555\frac{5}{9}$.

72. $\frac{7}{16}$.

73. $\frac{4}{35}$.

74. A, 220 acres; B, 176 acres.

75. A's, $2310; B's, $2800; C's, $1050.

76. $35200.

77. $4875.

78. 8 of each.

79. $9000.

Page 88.

60. .0205

61. .040034

62. .02004

63. .0000615

64. 600.0015

65. 15.015.

66. .00300313

67. .5000085

68. .00012

69. 400.000465

70. 25.025

71. 5000.005

72. 375.000000375

73. 30000.00046

74. .001000045

75. 80040.0306

Page 89.

76. 15000.0015

77. 75.005043

78. 1000000.000001

79. 15000000.000015

7. .0674000

8. .075000

9. 62.70000

10. 5.3300000

11. 3.0000

12. 45.000000

14. 5.240

Page 90.

19. $\frac{9}{40}$.

20. $\frac{3}{4}$.

21. $\frac{3}{40}$.

22. $\frac{1}{16}$.

23. $\frac{13}{80}$.

24. $\frac{9}{40}$.

25. $\frac{1}{250}$.

26. $\frac{9}{16}$.

27. $\frac{1}{80}$.

28. $\frac{141}{400}$.

29. $3\frac{21}{40}$.

30. $37\frac{3}{4}$.

31. $62\frac{1}{40}$.

32. $37\frac{5}{8}$.

33. $56\frac{3}{8}$.

34. $247\frac{1}{3}$.

35. $16\frac{2}{3}$.

36. $214\frac{1}{400}$.

Page 91.

42. .625

43. .5625

44. .04

45. .78125

46. .512

47. .64

48. 1.28

49. 3.625

50. .096

51. .075

52. .0875

53. .095

54. .325

55. .0175

56. .092

57. .0032

58. $.0013\frac{1}{3}$

59. .04375

60. $.0083\frac{1}{3}$

61. $.076\frac{2}{3}$

62. $.126\frac{14}{111}$

63. 12.15

64. 26.032

65. 37.1625

Page 92.

2. 210.08595

3. 111.0188

4. $267.322\frac{2}{3}$

5. $120.0905\frac{1}{3}$

6. .28065444

7. .0252077

8. $148.58\frac{1}{3}$ rods.

9. $5.00\frac{1}{3}$ pounds.

10. 22.84 inches.

Page 93.

3. 2.0425

4. .61625

5. 11.9995

6. .594

7. .043956

8. .026095

9. .005005193

Page 94.

10. .0066744

11. .079984

12. 4.95 miles.

13. 2.55 inches.

14. .22 inch.

Page 95.

9. 4.875

10. .2795

11. .23328

12. 1.152

13. .3136

14. 1.1772

15. 2.048

16. .5454

17. 1.344

18. 4.

19. 2.55

20. 640.

21. 1.08

22. 49.45

23. .75375

24. 256.

25. .00000943

28. 34060.

29. 48.

30. 25.6

31. 6.48

32. .9054

Page 98.

12. 18.
13. 4.
14. 8.
15. 30.
16. 2500.
17. 20.
18. 150.
19. 24.
20. .05
21. .08
22. 2.07
23. .27
24. .0066
25. 790.
26. 900.
27. .009
28. .009
29. 3413.3⅓
30. .001024
31. .00005
32. 20000.
33. .00001
34. 100000.
35. .00005
36. 36.
37. 192.
40. 1500.
41. 2294.11 13/17
42. .00025
44. .048375
45. .0545
46. .000005
47. .0025
48. .0192

Page 99.

1. .024
2. .0028
3. 1 3/40.
4. 9/2000.

Page 100.

5. 1.08
6. 63.5475
7. 39.056875
8. 320.
9. 399.514
10. $177.66⅔
11. 1031.25
12. 105.
13. .000064
14. 50000000000.
15. .014

Page 101.

5. $10.50
6. $40.605
7. $100.374
8. $.508
9. $.010
10. 35000 cents.
11. 625 mills.
12. 4008 cents.
13. 1010 mills.
14. $15.
15. $15.
16. $.45; 25080 mills.
17. 10001 cents; 10100 mills.

Page 102.

7. $952.08
8. $37.775
9. $617.20
10. $3361.25
11. $1053.10
12. $1423.

Page 103.

13. $225.
14. $378.60
15. $83.50

Page 104.

16. $229.01
17. $393.86
18. $4575.15
19. $53449.68

Page 105.

20. $293.42
21. $329.45
22. $24564.22
23. $33460.61
8. $1010.25
9. $9.22 +
10. $86666⅔.

Page 106.

11. $40.75
12. 80 chairs.
13. 94 tons.
14. $68.55
15. $527.05
16. $163.20

Page 108.

26. $1000.
27. $4004.

28. $2343.75

29. $480.

30. 420 dozens.

31. 360 yards.

33. $1.9625

34. $27.21875

Page 109.

35. $35.4375

1. $50.76

Page 110.

2. 14.14\frac{7}{12}$

3. 39.80\frac{5}{6}$

4. 52.50\frac{1}{2}$

5. $70.09

Page 125.

24. 778 pt.; 12 bu. 5 qt.

25. 160 bu. 4 qt.

26. 1530 pt.

27. 35 bu. 3 pk.

28. 23983 yd.

29. 1902 sq. rods.

30. 10 gal. 1 pt.; 47 gal. 2 qt.

31. $\left\{\begin{array}{l}\text{1 mi. 302 rd.}\\\text{5 yd. 2 ft.}\\\text{2 mi. 80 rd.}\end{array}\right.$

32. 7 mi. 94 rd. 3 yd.

33. 867240 in.

34. 1 mi. 252 rd. 4 yd. 1 ft. 8 in.

35. 3° 27′ 40″; 7° 30′.

36. 8 hr. 31 min. 24 sec.

37. 15200 sq. rd.; 51320 sq. rd.

38. $\left\{\begin{array}{l}\text{2 cwt. 55 lb.}\\\text{232 cwt. 53 lb.}\\\text{3 oz.}\end{array}\right.$

39. 127 cu. yd. 21 cu. ft.

40. 140160 hr.

41. 5 yr. 51 days 16 hr.

42. $\left\{\begin{array}{l}\text{31622400 sec.}\\\text{31536000 sec.}\end{array}\right.$

43. 2167200 min.

44. 236.8 pt; 18 bu. 2 pk.

45. 74.25 ft., .96$\frac{2}{33}$ rd.

46. 43.8 oz.; 1.8 lb.

47. 56436″; 163° 28′ 7″.

48. 64944 ft.; .0041

49. 52 w. 1$\frac{1}{4}$ da.

50. 8064 A.

51. 832 sq. rd.

Page 127.

22. $\frac{13}{200}$ oz.

Page 128

23. 19$\frac{1}{2}$ in.

24. 220 pwt.

25. 1.092 hr.

26. .04 lb.

27. .02 rd.

28. .09625 mi.

29. 6.144 pt.

30. $\frac{1}{1584}$ league.

31. $\frac{1}{1620}$ da.

32. .07 A.

33. 326160 grains.

34. 1$\frac{1}{15}$ pt.

35. 12830.4 ft.

36. .000026$\frac{2}{3}$ mi.

37. .00365 + sq. rd

Page 129.

14. 248 rd. 4 yd. 2 ft. 8 in.

15. 2 da. 22 hr.

16. 5 oz. 12 pwt.

17. 4 yd. 1 ft. 4$\frac{7}{8}$ in.

18. 146$\frac{2}{3}$ sq. rd.

19. 3 pk. 4 qt.

20. 13 oz. 9.6 dr.

21. 6 cwt. 50 lb.

22. 3 in.

23. 3 qt. 1 pt. 2 gi.

24. 56 lb. 4 oz.

25. 19 min. 26.4 sec.

Page 130.

11. $\frac{1}{3}$ rd.

12. $\frac{53}{160}$ bu.

13. .001$\frac{7}{73}$ c. yr.

14. .6125 bu.

15. .7 lb.

16. .0568$\frac{2}{11}$ mi.

17. $\frac{23}{28}$.

18. $\frac{2}{15}$.

19. $\frac{1}{8}$.

20. $\frac{3}{16}$.

21. $\frac{1}{3}$.

Page 133.

14. 1127 in.; 8 rd. 2 yd.

15. 368 pwt.

16. 46845″; 4° 15′.

17. 9 cu. yd. 9 cu. ft.; 900 cu. ft.

18. 979$\frac{1}{5}$ min.

19. 128 hr.

20. $\frac{7}{360}$ day.

21. 21.12 yd.

22. .00045$\frac{5}{11}$ mi.

23. $\frac{20}{99}$.

24. $\frac{1}{16}$.

25. $\frac{1}{26}$.

26. 145 ft.

27. 95 rings, with 15 gr. rem.

Page 134.

28. 12 kegs.

29. 264 rotations.

30. 48 bbl.

31. 627 axes, with 1 lb. 7 oz. rem.

32. 154.78\frac{2}{3}$

33. .84375 T.

34. 18 doses, with 16 gr. rem.

35. 128 pills.

36. 6 ℥.

37. $3150.

38. $52.50

39. 2$\frac{2}{9}$ oz.

40. $7.77

41. $1.278 +

Page 135.

2. 58 mi. 129 rd. 2 ft. 3$\frac{7}{12}$ in.

3. 101 lb. 7 oz. 12 pwt. 12 gr.

4. 131 bu. 1 pk. 1 qt. 1 pt.

5. 1 c. 11 s. 15° 54′ 24″.

Page 136.

7. 51° 22′ 6″.

8. 10° 58′.

9. 34° 11′.

11. 65 yr. 4 mo. 1 da.

12. 49 yr. 10 mo.

13. 5 yr. 3 mo. 23 da

Page 137.

15. 4 mi. 297 rd. 4 yd.

16. 16 rd. 3 yd. 9 in.

17. 7 rd. 4 yd. 1 ft. 8.2 in.

19. 203 bu. 2 pk. 5 qt. 1 pt.

Page 138.

20. 115 rd. 2 yd. 1 ft. 6 in.

21. 2248 bu. 1 pk. 2 qt.

22. 60 T. 16 cwt. 28 lb.

23. 2 lb. 8 oz. 3 pwt.

25. 2 mi. 82 rd. 2 ft. 5 in.

26. 1° 52′ 1$\frac{19}{21}$″.

27. 1 lb. 7 oz. 15 pwt. 17$\frac{9}{15}$ gr.

28. 35 bu. 3 pk. 4 qt.

29. 3 da. 2 hr. 51 min. 40 sec.

30. 161 rd. 4 yd. 1 ft. 3$\frac{6}{11}$ in.

31. 10 lb. 10$\frac{4}{9}$ oz.

32. 213 da. 1 hr. 23 min. 28 sec.

Page 141.

12. 42 min. 20 sec.

13. 37 min. 20 sec.

14. 1 hr. 4 min. 56 sec.

15. 5 hr. 8 min. 4 sec.

16. 1 hr. 13 min. 42 sec.

17. 3 hr. 46 min. 24$\frac{4}{5}$ sec.

18. 1 hr. 10 min. 21 sec.

19. 1 hr. 16 min. 3 sec.

21. 20°.

22. 32° 30'.

23. 49° 33'.

24. 75° 10'.

25. 11° 27' 30".

26. 93° 6'.

27. 46° 3'.

28. 11° 42' 30".

29. 22 min. 4 sec.

Page 142.

30. 12 hr. 37 min. P. M.; 2 hr. 23 min. P. M.

31. { 3 hr. 6 min. 35 sec. P. M. 10 hr. 53 min. 25 sec. A. M.

32. { 5 hr. 50. min. 59 sec. A. M. 4 hr. 9 min. 1 sec. P. M.

33. 8 o'clock; 3 o'clock.

34. 10 o'c. 1 min.; 7 o'clk. 57 min.

35. 11 o'c. 32 min.; 1 o'clk. 7 min.

36. 5 hr. 37 min. 52$\frac{2}{15}$ sec. P. M.

Page 143.

37. 2 hr. 58 min. $\frac{2}{15}$ sec. P. M.

38. 33° 47' 30".

39. 15° 35'.

40. 15° 45' E.

41. 37° 30'.

42. 40° 15' W.

43. 97° 2' 30" W.

44. 87° 36' 15" W.

45. { (a) 12 o'clk. 31 m. 16 s. P.M. (b) 11 o'clk. 47 m. 24 s. A.M. (c) 9 o'clk. 27 m. 59 s. A.M.

Page 147.

10. 7063.47^m

11. 507.064^m

Page 148.

13. 482^m

14. 5865^{Dm}

15. 265^{mm}

16. 529^m

17. 1460^{dm}

19. 3.075^m

20. 4.876^{Dm}

21. .307624^{Hm}

Page 149.

10. 6.0704$^{sq. m}$

11. 904.06^a

Page 150.

13. 2250000$^{sq. m}$

14. 20050$^{sq. cm}$

16. 4.05^{ha}; 40500^{ca}

Page 152.

9. 74.56^l

10. 9065.039^l

12. 37.5^l; 3750^{cl}

13. 5290^{dl}

15. .0405^{Hl}; .00405^{Kl}

16. 456^{Hl}; 4560^{cl}

Page 153.

9. 5068.09^g

10. 970.56^g

12. 74580^{Dg}; 745800^g

14. 74.635^g; .074635^{Kg}

Page 154.

2. 27.6523 mi.

3. 9.4488 in.

4. 710 bu.

5. 9.9065 gal.

6. 330.9 lb.

7. 33.1205^l

8. 72.48 sters.

9. 30.3525^a

10. 536.448^m

Page 155.

1. 133.4^m

2. 1649.986^l

3. 8.4501^{Kg}

4. 54^{Kg}

5. 94.5

6. 1500$^{sq. dm}$

7. 16.20 ª

8. 62.9 ˢ𐞥·ᵐ ;
107.07 ˢ𐞥·ᵐ

9. $305.876 +

10. 3.924 ᴴˡ ;
94.176 ᴴˡ

11. .605 ˡ

12. 200 pills.

13. 11 rings.

14. 17.16 ᴷᵍ

15. $1.53

16. $92.00

Page 156.

17. $3821.10

18. $362.04

19. $8.10

20. 2000 times.

21. 99.294 ᴷᵍ

22. 17.52 ᴴˡ

23. 1066⅔ hr.

24. $18.70

25. $1032.

26. $162.50

27. $17.34

28. $11108.13 +

29. $241.878 +

30. $1109.618

Page 159.

12. 1128.27 sq. yd.

13. 149.75 sq. yd.

14. 7035 sq. rd. ;
43 31/32 A.

15. 13000 sq. ft. ;
1444 sq. yd. 4
sq. ft.

16. 66 yd. long.

17. 3⅓ rd. wide

19. 904.7 sq. yd.

20. 12½ A.

21. 15 in.

Page 160.

23. 188.496 yd.

25. 1256.64 sq. ft.

26. 201.06 + sq. in.

27. 314.16 sq. ft.

28. 5026.56 sq. ft.

Page 162.

1. 49 yd. ; 9 in. ;
6 in.

2. 48 yd.

3. 43 17/18 yd.

4. 62¼ yd. ; $99.60

5. Across.

6. { 228¾ yd. ;
7/9 of strip ;
$371.718 +

7. 10¼ yd. ;
$23.06¼

Page 163.

8. $31.587 +

9. $54.405 +

10. $99.316⅔.

11. $7.606⅔.

12. $25.20

13. $11.25 (1 1/12 roll
rem.).

Page 164.

14. $29.36⅔

15. 13⅓ sq. ft.

Page 165.

16. 7 7/12 bd. ft.

17. 140 bd. ft.

18. 144 bd. ft.

19. 70 bd. ft.

20. 333⅓ bd. ft.

21. $18.312

22. $6.912

23. $7.392

24. 3212.5 bd. ft.

25. $58.50

Page 167.

27. $3480; $5800.

29. 12.6 A.; 32.8 A.

30. 7.254 A.

31. 14.1 A.; $514.65

32. 6 A. ; 16⅔ A.

33. ½ sect. ; $7200.

Page 169.

10. 1102½ cu. ft.

11. 140 cu. yd.

12. 1953.125 cu. ft.

13. 5040 cu. ft.

14. 8 ft.

15. 76545 bricks.

Page 170.

17. 15.708 cu. ft.

18. 166.8975 cu. ft.

19. 376.992 cu. ft.

Page 171.

1. $7\frac{7}{8}$ cd.
2. $18\frac{27}{64}$ cd.
3. $6\frac{3}{4}$ cd.
4. $10\frac{9}{16}$ cd.
5. $4\frac{1}{2}$ cd.
6. $4.05
7. $95.185 +
8. 300 perches.

Page 172.

9. 21.21 + P.
10. 110.653 + P.
11. 103.7037 + cu. yd.
13. 22.098 + bu.
14. 30.1339 + bu.

Page 173.

16. 498.701+ gal.; 16.087 + bbl.
17. 311.688+ gal.; 10.054 + bbl.
18. 1175.04 gal.
19. 30.323 + bbl.
20. 21.42 gal.
21. 23.5 + gal.

Page 174.

22. $8\frac{1}{3}$ lb.; $8.58\frac{1}{3}$ lb.
23. 57.5 lb.;$165\frac{5}{8}$ lb.
24. 32.98 + lb.
25. 24.305 + lb.
26. No; 25.75 ^{Kg}
1. $241920.
2. 128 rd.
3. 4.417875 A.

Page 175.

4. 3442.5 bricks.
5. $82\frac{1}{2}$ yd.(9 strips)
6. $44\frac{1}{3}$ yd.
7. $29.50
8. 90 bu.
9. $174.5\frac{1}{8}$ cu. ft.
10. 930.24 gal.
11. 17.057 + bbl.
12. 216 blocks.
13. $35.91
14. $70.938
15. 77.21463 $^{cu. m}$
16. 156.25 ^{HI}; 4127.75 + gal.

Page 176.

11. .09
12. .45
13. 2.20

Page 177.

15. .3025
16. $.00\frac{7}{15}$
17. .2025
19. 4 hr.; 8 hr.
20. $15;$37.50;$50.

Page 179.

9. 12.25
10. 31.5
11. 180.
12. 9.375
13. $49.50
14. $3.
15. $5.4075
16. 14 lb.

17. 1.52 lb.
18. 70 days.
19. $2.70
20. $4.
21. 93 ft.
22. $.36375
23. $321\frac{2}{3}$ days.
24. $.09
25. .135
26. $1\frac{7}{8}$.
27. .054
28. .046875
29. 200.25 mi.
30. 2618 lb.
31. $28\frac{3}{4}$ T.

Page 181.

7. 6%.
8. 20%.
9. $33\frac{1}{3}$%.
10. 20%.
11. $16\frac{2}{3}$%.
12. $2\frac{1}{2}$%.
13. $\frac{1}{2}$%.
14. $7\frac{1}{2}$%.
15. 22%.
16. 6%.
17. $13\frac{1}{3}$%.
18. 20%.
19. 75%.
20. 40%.
21. $83\frac{1}{3}$%.
22. 30%.
23. 15%.
24. 75%; $66\frac{2}{3}$%.
25. $55\frac{5}{9}$%.

Page 182.

15. $731\frac{3}{4}$.
16. $716\frac{2}{3}$.
17. 297.
18. $66\frac{2}{3}$ lb.
19. 156.25
20. $416\frac{2}{3}$.
21. $35\frac{3}{4}$.
22. $10\frac{2}{3}$.
23. 1920 men.
24. $780.
25. 3.
26. 1500 sheep.
27. 7920 lb.
28. $182.50

Page 183.

30. 24.0566 +
31. 240.
32. 12.5
33. 46.5 yd.
34. $520.
35. $39.4285 +
36. $46.1379 +
37. 500.
38. 125.
39. 2430.

Page 184.

1. 9.96
2. $5\frac{1}{3}$.
3. $482.75
4. 42.125 ft.
5. 253.8
6. 44.
7. 5259 days.
8. $57.26\frac{2}{3}$
9. $480.60

Page 185.

26. $206.25
27. $78\frac{2}{3}\%$.
28. 525 pupils.
29. 14500.
30. $50.
31. $14400.
32. 375 bbl.

Page 186.

33. $40000.
34. 150000000 sq. mi.
35. 80000.
36. $5680.
37. $\begin{cases} 21937.5 \text{ bu. by steamer,} \\ 19500 \text{ bu. by schooner,} \\ 17062.5 \text{ bu. by rail.} \end{cases}$
38. 74422.
39. 450 A.
40. $120.
41. $.83\frac{1}{3}$
42. 600 pupils.
43. 800 pupils.
44. 145400.
45. $\begin{cases} 144 \text{ acres meadow.} \\ 122.4 \text{ acres pasture.} \\ 80 \text{ acres grain land.} \\ 133.6 \text{ acres woodland.} \end{cases}$

Page 187.

46. 60%.
47. $36\frac{6}{19}\%$.
48. $700.
49. $6480.
50. $9500.
51. $14175.
52. $\begin{cases} 540 \text{ apple,} \\ 264 \text{ peach,} \\ 150 \text{ cherry,} \\ 246 \text{ pear.} \end{cases}$
53. A's, $14875 ; B's, $12950 ; C's, $7175.
54. $24570 ; $30\frac{70}{91}\%$.
55. 37760.
56. 60000.

Page 190.

23. $7593.75
24. $29.70
25. 20%.
26. 30%.
27. $12\frac{59}{68}\%$.
28. $16\frac{2}{3}\%$.
29. $65280.
30. $2.50
31. $216.
32. $6750.
33. $36375.

Page 191.

34. $360.
35. $4.735
36. $1401.33\frac{1}{3}$

Page 193.

11. $103.275
12. $199.06¼
13. $88.136 +
14. $38.59 + ;
    $578.90 +
15. $76312.50

Page 194.

16. $1950.
17. 12.
18. 6⅔.
19. $30000.
20. $4170.
21. $5948.25
22. $3460;
    $69.20
23. $11600;
    $174.
24. $113.012 +
25. $1357.886 +
26. 4434.58 + bu.

Page 197.

11. $6937.50
12. $507.50
13. $300.

Page 198.

14. $456.
15. $270.
16. 8 shares.
17. 80 shares.
18. $7200 worth.
19. 100 shares.

---

20. $252.
21. 50 shares.
22. 3⅓%.
23. $585.
24. $8500.
25. $22000;
    $24500.

Page 199.

26. 10 37⁄66%;
    $469.36 +

Page 201.

7. $625.
8. $120.875
9. $36.93 +
10. $64.25
11. $840.
12. { 1st, $20000;
    2d, $24000;
    3d, $16000.
13. ½%.
14. 2⅕%.

Page 202.

15. ⅘.
16. $12000.
17. $15600.
18. $35000.
19. $32000.
20. $22500.
21. $12040.
22. $12000.
23. $34650.
24. $141.60
25. $2225.

Page 204.

2. 1⅕% ;
   12 mills.
3. $18530.20;
   1.3%, or
   13 mills.

Page 205.

5. $12845.487, or
   $12861.368
6. $130280.51 +
7. $478747.83

Page 206.

1. $390.

Page 207.

2. $375.
3. $488.75
4. $423.36
5. $2000.
6. $3589.525 .
7. $2.20 ; $3.696
8. $5850.
9. $4415.85

Page 208.

2. { 1st, $2219.60 ;
   2d, $2873.70 ;
   3d, $3286.00 ;
   4th, $1385.70.
3. { A, $1925.00 ;
   B, $687.50 ;
   C, $2062.50 ;
   D, $550.00 ;
   E, $1375.00

Page 209.

4. $.646
1. $10 ;
$2.50
2. $200.
3. $4.80
4. $39 (on face).
5. $18\frac{3}{4}\%$.
6. 800 T.

Page 210.

7. $8\frac{188}{339}\%$.
8. 4%.
9. $120.
10. $495.
11. $2600.
12. $3290.
13. $20000. .
14. $48636.
15. $791131.5635
16. $1743.75

Page 211.

17. $3.997 + \%$.
18. 5.3%.
19. $346.875
20. 25%.
21. $12857.14 +
22. $2077.82 + ;
$174.975
23. $25256.9 +$ lb. ;
$403.06+com.

Page 213.

16. $225.596 ;
$180.4768
N· C. A.—30.

17. $6.53
18. $314.951 +
19. $79.08\frac{1}{3}
20. $13.706 +
21. $21.431 +

Page 214.

23. $80.336
24. $126.289 +
25. $18.48
26. $55.654
28. $23.869
29. $1955.
30. $90.782
31. $155.564
32. $238.565
33. $187.716
34. $88.16\frac{2}{3}
35. $87.285 +
36. $807.202
37. $2.237
38. $166.31
39. $93.634 +
40. $424.5806
41. $297.498 +
42. $242.804
43. $263.04
44. $208.84
45. $144.718 +

Page 215.

46. $132.396 +
47. $241.9899
48. $158.093 +

Page 217.

17. $15.597 + ;
$21.466 +
18. $100.347 + ;
$49.284 +

Page 218.

20. $38.88
21. $41.483\frac{1}{3}
22. $13.105
23. $1120.759 +
24. $25.846 +
25. $891.377
26. $119.523
27. $2238.944
28. $8.206
29. $19.188
30. $58.49 +
31. $286.888
32. $31.711
33. $4.933 +
34. $783.082 +
35. $66.54
36. $53.946

Page 219.

37. $410.84
38. $169.928
39. $1440.555
40. $101.767
41. $76.611

Page 220.

2. $3.075
3. $25.744
4. $67.207 +

Page 256.

9. $980.
10. $1250.
11. $4740.506 +
13. $800.
14. $360.
15. $4654.04 +

Page 258.

2. $1078.111
3. $974.1136
4. $1465.952
5. $1216.518 +
7. £451 2s. 6d.
8. £240.

Page 259.

10. $1250.
11. $1040.
13. $12565\frac{1}{3}$ fr.

Page 260.

14. $1250.
15. $3347\frac{1}{2}$ fr.
17. $405.30
18. $769.

Page 261.

20. $1371\frac{3}{7}$ marks.
21. $229.20
22. 2160 marks.
23. 997.4+ marks.

Page 262.

2. 7 mo.
3. 8 mo.
4. 4 mo.
5. 7 mo.
6. $5\frac{1}{11}$ mo.

Page 263.

7. 4 mo.
9. 49 da. (48.9).
10. 68 da.
11. 46 da.

Page 264.

12. July 4, 1880.
13. July 29, 1880.
14. July 6, 1880.

Page 265.

17. 6 mo. after maturity.
18. 3 mo. after maturity.
19. $400.
20. $9\frac{2}{3}$ mo. after maturity.
21. 83 days (83.5) after matu'y, Oct. 1st, 1880.

Page 267.

23. Oct. 14, 1879.
24. Oct. 9, 1880; $1244.30\frac{1}{4}$.
25. Aug. 30, 1883; $949.49

Page 275.

13. $2\frac{2}{3}$.
14. $\frac{3}{5}$.
15. 2.2
16. .45
17. $\frac{2}{5}$.
18. 9.
19. $\frac{50}{121}$.
20. 6.
21. $\frac{1}{4}$.
22. $\frac{1}{3}$.
23. $\frac{1}{5}$.
24. $\frac{3}{10}$.

Page 276.

25. 3 : 4.
26. 9 : 12.
27. .3 : .8
28. $\frac{1}{2} : \frac{2}{3}$.
29. The same.
30. The same.
31. 9 oz. : 6 oz.
32. $\frac{3}{5}$ yr. : $\frac{2}{3}$ yr.
34. $\frac{5}{6}$.
35. $\frac{8}{35}$.
36. $\frac{8}{15}$.
38. 2 : 3.

Page 278.

11. 12.
12. 48.
13. 6.
14. 30.
15. 36.
16. .13
17. 14.4

18. .75

19. $\frac{15}{16}$.

20. $\frac{63}{80}$.

21. $1\frac{13}{36}$.

22. $\frac{5}{18}$.

23. 54 lb.

24. 14 oz.

25. 240 days.

26. 1.

Page 281.

28. $824.44 +

29. $17142.85 +

30. 180 A.

31. $6.90

32. 36000.

33. 66600.

34. 52°.

35. 54 bbl.

36. 200 ft.

37. 150 ft.

Page 282.

38. $5400.

39. $80.

40. $18\frac{1}{2}$ T.

41. 208 bbl.

42. $41\frac{2}{3}$ A.

Page 283.

44. $14\frac{2}{5}$ days.

45. 36 men.

46. 40 and 50.

47. 140 and 500.

48. $4500; $5100.

49. 60 mi.; 90 mi.

Page 284.

2. 10.

3. $33\frac{1}{3}$.

4. 81.

5. 49.

7. 18 men.

Page 285.

8. $60.

9. 960 cu. ft.

10. 63 bu.

11. 256 mi.

12. 125 slabs.

13. $99.

14. 15 days.

15. $675.

16. 8 men.

17. 10 days.

18. 6 men.

Page 287.

2. $\begin{cases} \text{A's, } \$2500; \\ \text{B's, } \$2000. \end{cases}$

Page 288.

3. $\begin{cases} \text{A's, } \$1600; \\ \text{B's, } \$900; \\ \text{C's, } \$700. \end{cases}$

4. $\begin{cases} \text{A's, } \$4400; \\ \text{B's, } \$3300. \end{cases}$

5. $\begin{cases} \text{A's, } \$5000; \\ \text{B's, } \$8000; \\ \text{C's, } \$7000. \end{cases}$

6. $\begin{cases} \text{A's, } \$5005; \\ \text{B's, } \$5915. \end{cases}$

Page 289.

8. $\begin{cases} \text{A's, } \$1350; \\ \text{B's, } \$1200; \\ \text{C's, } \$1050. \end{cases}$

Page 293.

3. 4096.

4. 3136.

5. 5625.

6. 6724.

7. 1444.

8. 6889.

9. 8649.

10. 1521.

11. 6084.

12. 7225.

Page 294.

14. 3.

15. 3.

16. 3.

17. 4.

18. 4.

19. 5.

21. 6; 4.

22. 8; 6.

Page 295.

24. 25.

25. 26.

26. 24.

27. 28.

28. 29.

29. 23.

30. 31.

31. 38.

55. 130 sacks; 1 bu. 1 pk., rem.
56. $60.25
57. $6415\frac{1}{5}$.
58. 11 h. 28 min. 44 sec. A. M.
59. 5 P. M.
60. 4 h. 42 min. 51$\frac{2}{5}$ sec. P. M.
61. $\frac{1}{6}$.
62. .65
63. $\frac{1}{7744}$.
64. $\frac{97}{120}$ lb.
65. $\frac{3}{256}$ bu.

Page 315.

66. 900 men.
67. $11\frac{2}{3}\%$.
68. $4.50
69. $6\frac{1}{4}\%$ gain.
70. 4% loss.
71. $20 loss.
72. $100.
73. $986; 17% gain.
74. $6 per yd.
75. 60%.
76. 0%.
77. 25%.

Page 316.

78. $141.382
79. $16\frac{71}{80}\%$.
80. $369.322 +
81. $16.20
82. $2048.

83. $609.758 +; 487804.87 lb.
84. 400 yd.
85. $5.368
86. $688.882 +
87. $6.511
88. $4\frac{1}{2}\%$
89. $6\frac{21}{89}\%$.
90. $466\frac{2}{3}$.
91. $600; $8\frac{1}{3}\%$.

Page 317.

92. $289.532
93. $2.583 +; $122.417
94. $7.429\frac{2}{3}$
95. $310.61
96. $1100; $220.
97. $620.
98. $212.50
99. $289.20
100. $1225.
101. 12396 fr.
102. $4680.281 +
103. 9 mo.
104. 6 mo.

Page 318.

105. $6\frac{2}{3}$ mo.
106. $75.
107. $11 and $16.
108. 24 men.
109. 126 bu.
110. $216.
111. $375\frac{2}{3}$.
112. $4800.
113. $2400.

114. { A's, $555\frac{5}{8}$; B's, $333\frac{3}{8}$.
115. 20.5
116. 3.5
117. 40 feet.

Page 319.

118. 65 miles.
119. 50 feet.
120. 160 rods.
121. 28.3 + feet.
122. 28.28 + feet.
123. 154 cu. ft.
124. 78 sq. ft.
125. 7.854 A. area.
126. 24.4 + in.
127. 64 balls.
128. 1728 blocks.
129. 120 blocks
130. 60 bars.
131. 128.57 + bu.
132. 1480.55 + gal.; 47.75 + bbl.

Page 320.

133. 61.405 + bbl.
134. $55\frac{23}{31}$ bbl.
135. 564.019 gal.
136. 9.5 in.
137. 35.014 + ft.
138. 70688.827 cu. ft.
139. 65512.7 + mi.
140. 105434.8 + mi.
141. $4\frac{1}{8}$ mi.
142. 50 feet.
143. 3 hours.